DESIGN
AND THE PRODUCTION OF HOUSES

SERIES IN HOUSING AND
COMMUNITY DEVELOPMENT
Directed and Edited by Martin Meyerson

DESIGN AND THE PRODUCTION OF HOUSES

Burnham Kelly
Associate Professor of City Planning,
Massachusetts Institute of Technology

IN ASSOCIATION WITH

Castle N. Day   *Albert G. H. Dietz*   *John T. Dunlop*
Carl Koch   *James A. Murray*   *Hideo Sasaki*
Bernard P. Spring

McGRAW-HILL BOOK COMPANY, INC. 1959
New York Toronto London

Design and the Production of Houses

ACTION *ad hoc* Committee on the Producer

Roy W. Johnson,* *Chairman*
Director, Advanced Research Projects Agency, Department of Defense; past Executive Vice-President of General Electric Company; past President of ACTION

C. J. BACKSTRAND *
President, Armstrong Cork Company

MARTIN L. BARTLING, JR.
Chairman of Research Institute; Secretary of National Association of Home Builders

REEVE K. BIGGERS
National Account Executive, Owens-Corning Fiberglas Corporation

(MRS.) ELEANOR S. CLARKE *
Member of the Corporation, American Friends Service Committee

DONALD D. COUCH
Vice-President, Marketing and Commercial Development, American Radiator and Standard Sanitary Corporation

PETER F. DRUCKER
Management Consultant

RICHARD J. GRAY
President, Building and Construction Trades Department, AFL-CIO

RICHARD HUGHES *
Builder; past President of National Association of Home Builders

JOSEPH D. KEENAN *
Secretary, International Brotherhood of Electrical Workers

FRANKLIN A. LINDSAY
McKinsey and Company, Inc.

MONTAGU MILLER
Vice-President, Young and Rubicam, Inc.

GEORGE NELSON
George Nelson and Company, Industrial Designers

ROGER SCHAFER
Secretary, United Housing Foundation

CLARENCE A. THOMPSON
Chairman, Lumber Dealers Research Council

RALPH WALKER *
Voorhees, Walker, Smith, Smith and Haines

BROWN L. WHATLEY *
President, Stockton, Whatley, Davin and Company

WILLIAM ZECKENDORF *
President, Webb and Knapp

Ex officio
ANDREW HEISKELL *
Publisher, Life Magazine

FERD KRAMER *
President, Draper and Kramer, Inc.

* Members of ACTION's Board of Directors.

This volume is one in the ACTION Series in Housing and Community Development made possible by a grant from the Ford Foundation to the American Council To Improve Our Neighborhoods. Some of the contributors to the Series are members of ACTION's staff; others are at universities or in private practice. The findings they present here are the product of their own selective process. The conclusions they reach have had the benefit of advice and comment from a wide variety of persons, including members of ACTION's *ad hoc* committees for the Series. Neither individually nor collectively, however, has ACTION's Board of Directors attempted to limit the authors in the facts they present, the conclusions they reach, or the recommendations they propose to solve or mitigate a particular problem. Whether prepared by staff or consultants, the volumes in the Series are uniquely the product of their authors. To say here that the authors' findings and views do not necessarily reflect the knowledge and attitude of ACTION or of any or all of the ACTION Board of Directors is also to underline the Board's intention that the Series should provide fresh points of view to some of the most complex and controversial problems of housing and urban development in America.

ACTION hopes that both the expert and the student will find the volumes useful additions to the literature on housing and community development. The principal purpose of the Series, however, is to inform and stimulate the growing body of influential businessmen, professionals, and citizen leaders whose opinions on many facets of urban life are having a profound effect upon the kinds of policy and actions required for the provision of adequate housing.

Andrew Heiskell, Chairman, ACTION Board of Directors

Ferd Kramer, Chairman, ACTION Research Committee

Joseph W. Lund, Chairman, *ad hoc* Committee on the Investor

Roy W. Johnson, Chairman, *ad hoc* Committee on the Producer

Ben Fischer, Chairman, *ad hoc* Committee on the Consumer

Philip L. Graham, Chairman, *ad hoc* Committee on the Government

Guy T. O. Hollyday, Chairman, *ad hoc* Committee on the Community

Foreword

The ACTION Series in Housing and Community Development is the published part of a two-pronged effort of the American Council To Improve Our Neighborhoods (ACTION) to help bring about a higher level of living in this country's urban areas. It has been made possible by a grant from the Ford Foundation. These volumes analyze many of the facts about the present condition of American communities, particularly with respect to housing, and offer new conclusions about the problems and potentialities implied by the facts. The other part of this ACTION effort is made up of many activities through which ACTION and other groups are aiding communities and their citizens to meet present local problems and to realize future potentialities for sound urban growth. These activities put to the test the proposals of the authors and the members of the *ad hoc* committees for improving the nation's urban life.

Specifically, ACTION aims through this Series and its related program efforts to create a climate within which the choices available to the American people for improved urban living can be expanded in terms of a larger supply of housing, of better quality and at lesser cost. At the least, this means the realization of the following objectives:

1. The elimination of slums that cannot be economically rehabilitated.

2. The improvement of properties that can be economically rehabilitated.

3. The preservation of currently sound housing and neighborhoods by slowing down their rates of obsolescence.

4. The provision of new housing on both cleared and vacant land in sufficient quantity and in satisfactory quality to

meet current requirements and the requirements of the huge urban growth foreseen in the years ahead.

5. The accomplishment of the foregoing objectives in conjunction with a high level of coordinated community services and in such a manner that all income, racial, and other groups in the population will be served.

6. The effective planning and distribution of urban functions in order to correct the costly imbalances which now exist among them both within the central city and between it and its surrounding metropolitan area.

These objectives cannot be accomplished without intensive effort to organize pertinent knowledge systematically and to clarify the aims of urban policy. Obviously, this Series cannot furnish all the information necessary to solve all the problems. But the authors of the volumes do provide a basis for policy. They do so by analyzing the current problems and indicating possible future changes. The summary volume, the over-all view, takes the major findings of each of these specific studies and presents them along with the suggestions which the AC-TION *ad hoc* committees believe to be most promising for solving a number of critical current problems.

The framework of the Series is based on the primacy of the consumer in the housing market and in housing policy. Because the largest number of Americans live in urban communities, the studies deal only with cities and urban housing.

Most of the wealth of America is in its cities. And most of the wealth of cities is in residential structures and their related utilities and facilities. The value of dwellings alone stands at over $300 billion, a figure twice as large as the assets of the country's 500 biggest manufacturing companies. Not only is housing the largest single item in our national wealth, but that part of it which is newly constructed amounts on the average to more than a fifth of all our capital expenditures each year. New housing uses one-third of the lumber produced in the country, two-thirds of the bricks, at least half of most plumbing items, and three-fourths of all gypsum products. Yet new housing in any given year is only 3 per cent of all housing. These statistics prove that housing is among the most important commodities in our economy, but they do not prove that our supply of housing meets the requirements of all consumers nor that it is produced as efficiently as possible.

For housing, as for other commodities, the market place tends to govern the quantity, quality, cost, and distribution of the product. America is properly famous for what it produces. It is equally admired for the methods of production and distribution which its industries have developed. Particularly in the past 25 years, accomplishments in housing have been considerable, but either they are not considerable enough or the dissatisfied observers of, and participants in, the housing market argue their case more eloquently than people do about other commodities and services.

The very nature of housing makes almost inevitable that both the product of the housing industry and the mechanism of the housing market should come under criticism. Unlike most other economic commodities, housing is also a social commodity. As such, it is overlaid with all kinds of attributes that blur the lines between supply and demand, need and preference. In our system of values as well as in our vernacular, the house is the home. So long as it stands as the symbol of the family, satisfaction with it will take as many forms as the traditional sentiments which people attach to it.

But putting aside its social values, housing is still very different from other economic commodities. Its scale of cost, for one thing, is not matched by any other commodity. For most householders, monthly housing outlays represent their largest current expenditure after food and—if they buy a house—their largest single expenditure in a lifetime. Another of its distinguishing attributes is immobility. A pair of shoes or an automobile can be shipped from one part of the country to another as demand varies regionally. Most housing, on the other hand, is immobile; it is tied to its land. Still another example of difference is the fact that the market for housing is essentially one for an existing stockpile; even in years of highest new housing production, the stockpile still meets 97 per cent of the demand for housing. Coupled with the high level of expenditure always required for housing, it makes the market respond disproportionately to sudden declines in the economy and in consumer income. The Depression of the thirties, for example, while it greatly reduced the production of automobiles and other consumer goods, cut down the number of new housing starts proportionately very much more. Because housing is so vulnerable to economic fluctuations, it has rarely attracted large amounts of risk capital from individual firms.

Relatively few of housing's small businessmen have introduced technological advances into their operations. Where they have, the results have been remarkable, but the small scale at which most of them operate has generally precluded their investing in much more than an occasional market analysis or research in design. Their scale of operation also tends to foster labor practices which, while protecting the otherwise precarious position of workers in a seasonal and fluctuating trade, nevertheless contribute to production inefficiencies. But if the small businessman in housing sometimes operates at a disadvantage, he has nonetheless been remarkably successful in Washington. Since the 1930s he has persuaded the Federal government to underwrite the housing market with credit mechanisms and other benefits which eliminate much of his risk.

It is important to remember, however, that Federal policies which reduce risk in home building have not been adopted simply because housing has extraordinary persuasive spokesmen. Inducements to the construction industry and to the manufacturers of materials have become traditional compensatory measures when the economy slumps.

There is considerable irony in the fact that the very protective devices which surround the production and marketing of housing inhibit its industrial rationalization. As the risk goes down, so does competition, and competition is one of the essential ingredients for successful production and merchan

dising in America. Piece by piece, the whole setting for housing tends to magnify the inability of private enterprise to
merchandise housing in the extraordinary way that the American economy merchandises its soup and soap, aspirins and
automobiles. It is hardly surprising, therefore, that the consumer has come to place less and less attention on his dwelling
and more and more attention on nationally advertised commodities to go into his dwelling or to use outside it.

This widespread shift in consumer values hits hard at every
city's struggle to stay viable, for the state of our dwellings and
the state of our cities are inseparable. Relatively minor deterioration and obsolescence in a city's residential parts can have
major economic repercussions on the whole urbanized area.
So can inappropriate locations of housing types and levels of
density. If housing types determine the pattern of social organization and activity in the city, density determines the
city's size and circulation. In different combinations they add
up to a greater or lesser public investment in schools, parks,
playgrounds, streets, and utilities and to a greater or lesser
economic return to the private entrepreneurs who invest in,
build, own, and manage housing or provide a range of services
and commodities for its occupants. Next to their employment,
where people live and the way they live constitute the most
important feature of urban policy.

Within this general setting, the ACTION Series in Housing
and Community Development deliberately combines research
and policy-making activities to help clear away obstacles that
stand in the way of the kinds of communities that will meet
the requirements of new quantities and qualities—aesthetic as
well as economic and social—in American life. Throughout
the preparation of the volumes there has been unique interplay
between the researcher and representatives of the key groups
which make public and private policy for the housing market
and for urban development.

For all the studies, I sought to associate with the Series the
ablest persons I could find. Some of the authors, although in-

formed on housing matters, had not previously written about them. Their points of view, I felt, were likely to be uncluttered by old attachments. I asked other persons to participate in the Series, however, because they so clearly were experts in the field.

My method of organization for the Series was this: The primary agents whose decisions determine how effectively housing and community services respond at any point in time to the often conflicting demands and requirements that are made upon them were identified as the investor, the producer, the consumer, the government, and the community. For each of these major areas of housing involvement and interest, ACTION'S directors set up an *ad hoc* committee whose responsibility was to suggest feasible courses of action which stemmed from the subject matter dealt with by the researchers for the separate volumes.

Thus, within the broad category of investment, the *ad hoc* Committee on the Investor considered the problems of rental housing and rehabilitation. In his study, *Rental Housing: Opportunities for Private Investment,* Louis Winnick uncovers many of the deep-seated forces which have produced a significant decline in apartment construction. He sets forth reasons why life insurance companies have abandoned their rental-housing programs and why apartment developers have become so dependent on government mortgage aids. But he also outlines an impressive list of factors which point to a broader demand for urban apartments in the future. The committee's second area of interest, the economic feasibility of rehabilitation, had its inception in the great stress on rehabilitation expressed in the urban-renewal provisions of the Housing Act of 1954. In *Residential Rehabilitation: Private Profits and Public Purposes,* William W. Nash and Miles L. Colean present a comprehensive examination of the rehabilitation market and the individuals who operate successfully in it. Based on intensive field investigation and factual accounts of operations by well-known rehabilitators in a number of cities, the study explores investment opportunities in housing rehabilitation and discusses the role local government can play in stimulating rehabilitation either inside or outside official urban-renewal areas.

The Committee on the Producer accepted the challenge of proposing ways to achieve the potential opportunities for technological change in the design and production of housing. As a basis for these proposals, Burnham Kelly and a team of associated experts at the Massachusetts Institute of Technology analyze the blocks which prevent the housing industry from taking advantage of a new way of life and cost-saving features offered by new design and technology. Their book, *Design and the Production of Houses*, explores the roles of the builder, the labor union, the manufacturer of building materials, the architect, and the public official and points out ways in which their combined efforts can introduce many forms of improved design and technological innovation into future home-building operations.

Problems with which the Committee on the Consumer dealt are interrelated with all the other studies in the Series, as the committee faced the issue of whether the behavior of the consumer can be altered to induce him to place a higher value on housing and the neighborhood amenities which complement it. Nelson Foote, Janet Abu-Lughod, Mary Mix Foley, and Louis Winnick collaborated in the research and writing of *Housing Choices and Housing Constraints*, which brings together knowledge about the values people attach to their housing and the degree to which they appear to be realizing or sacrificing those values. In his chapters, Foote presents some original and thought-provoking material on the organization of the dwelling unit for the kind of urban life now developing in most American cities.

Because housing is a commodity whose social value makes it a matter of national interest, it was necessary to explore the role the Federal government plays in its production and consumption. The Committee on the Government, therefore, was concerned largely with how housing credit policies of the

Federal government impede or stimulate desirable competitive practices in the housing market and provide necessary protective devices for consumers who for reasons of age, income, discrimination, or incapacity cannot compete successfully in the market. Charles M. Haar, in *Federal Credit and Private Housing: The Mass Financing Dilemma*, gives a comprehensive account of the twenty-year evolution of Federal housing credit programs and provides a stimulating reappraisal of their impact on the housing market.

Finally, the studies which came under the view of the Committee on the Community explore both the responsibility and the limitations of local government in the achievement of a higher standard of urban life. Here the principal issues were ones of governmental structure as it affects the standard of housing in metropolitan areas, and of levels of expenditure for housing and related facilities required to reach a set of tentative goals throughout an urban area. Edward C. Banfield and Morton Grodzins are deliberately quizzical and provocative as they explore the first issue in *Government and Housing in Metropolitan Areas*. They look carefully at the political impediments to large-scale structural changes in metropolitan governments; examine the lack of logic underlying many current schemes for reorganization; point up some values of the "chaos of governments" in metropolitan areas; and offer a "model for action" looking to governmental change on a scale needed in terms of improved housing and possible in terms of political realities. In the second study prepared for the Committee on the Community, John W. Dyckman and Reginald R. Isaacs explore the questions of our ability to pay for required investment in cities and the organization of our economy necessary to realize urban goals. In *Capital Requirements for Urban Development and Renewal*, they translate national expenditure totals into specific changes in the urban environment and convert specific local programs into a national bill of goods.

The final volume—the over-all view of the ACTION Series

—brings together the principal points in each of the other volumes and puts them in the setting of the total housing market and public policy. The consolidated suggestions of the five *ad hoc* committees, which appear in the over-all view, thus become the preface for action.

As the committees reviewed the research materials presented to them, they sought to suggest policies and activities which if implemented by public agencies, private groups, or institutions under the stimulus of ACTION might reasonably help achieve the major objectives for the Series. The steps the committees recommend are an attempt to establish a level of aspiration for housing and urban development against which private and public decision makers can formulate policies and programs that with more ingenuity and flexibility than has been shown in the past will enable the housing market to function to its limit in satisfying the value we place upon its product. The combined report of the committees, which appears in the last volume of the Series, includes a plea for the empirical testing in many communities of a wide variety of new practices.

In a field such as housing and urban development, in which only a small amount of research has or is being done, any effort is a pioneering one. Those who make it do so not only with the expectation that it will provide a fresh outlook for scholars and policy makers, but with the intention that it will provoke the next push forward. This Series, whose preparation began in February of 1956, is heavily indebted to several important predecessors: The Twentieth Century Fund's comprehensive analysis by Miles L. Colean, *American Housing: Problems and Prospects;* the scholarly research of Ernest M. Fisher and his associates at Columbia University's Institute for Urban Land Use and Housing Studies; and Coleman Woodbury's collection of perceptive essays for *The Future of Cities* and *Urban Redevelopment.* Moreover, this ACTION Series looks forward to being complemented by one which the Commission on Race and Housing is sponsoring.

Barbara Terrett, Deputy Director of Research at ACTION, shared the responsibility of administration, criticism and editing. Among many other persons whose knowledge and experience I called on frequently were Neal J. Hardy, director of the National Housing Center, and Arthur S. Goldman, director of marketing for *House & Home* magazine. Both of them were endlessly generous with their time and counsel. William L. C. Wheaton, a collaborator on the final volume, gave constructive review to several of the other volumes, as did Herrymon Maurer, the editorial consultant for the Series. Most of all, I am indebted to the authors of the separate volumes for the excellence of their contribution, and to the understanding and wisdom of the ACTION directors and *ad hoc* committee members. In particular, Ferd Kramer, ACTION Vice Chairman, who heads the Research Committee, Andrew Heiskell, Chairman of ACTION's Board of Directors, and James E. Lash, ACTION Executive Vice President, provided helpful criticism without which the Series would never have been developed.

Martin Meyerson
ACTION Vice President

Preface

From the start, the authors of this book have agreed on over-all aims. The first requirement for improved production of houses in the future is an understanding and pursuit of quality in living. This truism is often overlooked in discussions of the housing problem, possibly because there is no easy definition of living quality nor any sure direction in which to seek it, and because the practical considerations of staying in business press hard upon all producers. Yet the housebuilding industry must seek to upgrade family life by providing better housing values for all income groups.

Living quality is an attribute not merely of the house, but also of its environment. Indeed, social science indicates that the character of family life may be more strongly affected by the nature of the family's adjustment to its social surroundings than by the quality of the physical house itself. In the future, therefore, producers of housing will have to take an increasing interest in community planning.

Our second purpose is to open the door to new ideas, new systems of production, and new organizations, for we are confident that this will lead to a maximum availability of good housing. Under such conditions, there may emerge an industry of considerable strength and stability, able to override temporary or localized difficulties without sharp fluctuations, and ready both to stimulate and to respond to a housing demand that seems sure to expand rapidly in the next decade.

Our major concern is new single-family houses. Conventional rental, apartment, and public housing are all important elements of supply, and there are indications that they may become more so in the future. Yet they are typically built by a significantly different kind of producer—the building con-

tractor who may bid also on commercial, industrial, or institutional buildings. It is important to add the qualification,
however, that small-scale multifamily houses—row houses,
garden apartments, and the like—might be given a great deal
of flexibility in design and construction in the course of the
advances that we foresee; they might come to be considered
by the industry as just another type of single-family house,
sited contiguously. The existing stock of 55 million housing
units is also an important element of housing supply and offers
a tremendous market for remodeling and renewal. This work,
however, like multifamily construction, is done by a different
type of builder.

To a much greater degree than any of these, the builders
of new single houses are using up our land resources and giving form to our expanding urban society. To balance the
concern for deteriorating central urban areas expressed in
other ACTION programs, it is appropriate to consider those
who are spreading housing developments for miles into the
open countryside.

Such a concentration carries with it a reduced concern for
many aspects of broad housing policy. Only as they may call
for significant differences in the way that housing units may
be designed and produced does this book deal with such subjects as public housing, cooperatives, middle-income housing,
and old-age housing. Broad fiscal and credit factors and detailed money manipulations have an essential bearing on who
will be in business and how much production will be undertaken, but only an indirect effect on design and method of
production. Other ACTION books in this series deal with
interest and premium rates, down payments and closing costs,
mortgage terms and conditions, and the complex operations
of the Federal Reserve System, the Home Loan Bank System,
the Federal National Mortgage Association, and the other
agencies that guide the flow of money into this area. These
subjects are mentioned here only in passing.

We claim no panacea for the ills of the industry. If the

problem were that simple, it would have been solved long since. Yet, certain assumptions underlying this book may be made explicit at the start.

First, the consumer—the house buyer—tends to feel that he receives poor value for his money, that he pays too much for what he gets, particularly in contrast to other types of consumption. The average consumer finds his demands and living patterns changing in broad general ways, and he senses that the housing industry is not able easily to adapt its operations to emerging design and production potentials.

Next, value to the consumer and health for the industry would be improved if innovation were freed to a degree comparable to that of other industries. Creative and forward-looking spirits have tended to turn away from housing in favor of other fields where the hurdles between the generation of a new idea and its profitable application are relatively few and obvious.

Innovation is needed not only in dwelling design and production, but also in distribution, financing, and over-all entrepreneurial methods. We are satisfied to leave it to the market to determine what forms of organization, systems of production, and designs of house and community will finally emerge. We have no fear that a better-organized production process will inevitably bring a sterile and uniform house. We believe that if the creative energies and the production tools that should and could be brought to bear on housing were freed from artificial and unnecessary impediments, the product would be improved in every quality, including variety and versatility.

Reasoning thus, we seek to identify, understand, and explain factors impeding the full realization of potentials: the small and weak producing units; the localism and vested interests of the conventional approach; the relatively minor importance of the housing market as compared with that of most other large producers of materials and equipment; and the complexities of a production process that carries thousands of products from raw materials to a final home. The crux of our assignment is to spread our conviction that these impediments are real and significant and to suggest ways of removing them which promise reasonable hope of success without postulating a revolution.

At its present stage of development, the housebuilding industry is not well suited to either of the most convenient methods of industrial analysis: the manipulation of statistical data and the "horse's-mouth" survey. Statistical analysis can make an important contribution to our understanding of the over-all economic importance of housing and of the structure and scale of its current production enterprises, but it is unlikely to give a sense of emerging potentials. By comparison with some sectors of the national economy, statistical material on housing may be abundant, but its quality is highly variable and there are yawning gaps. A necessary oversimplification of assumptions and conditions tends to screen out the factors that become most important to those concerned with expanding the over-all output. Furthermore, as we shall see, the very definition of the product and of those who produce it tends to be unsatisfactory. The housing industry is narrower than the construction industry, on the one hand, and broader than the group known as home builders, on the other. Broad statistical analysis rarely reveals, therefore, the prospects of getting houses built for people.

Surveying the builders themselves to get the "real picture" has undoubted value, too. But in a field as loosely organized and complex as that of housing, the final yield tends to be either a few isolated pools of specialized insight or a meandering stream of sparkling but superficial commentary. Normal difficulties of this approach are multiplied by the circumstances of housebuilding, which compel most builders to become expert in the art, not just of the possible, but of the *immediately* possible. The "horse's-mouth" approach, therefore, rarely gives a sense of the larger reality in which, given time, reasonable changes are possible nor of the long-term shifts in background conditions which may be seen to be undermining and destroying current basic assumptions. The implications for the future are as likely to be missed in this approach as in a broad statistical analysis.

We have focused our attention on the potentials of innovation. The power and value of these potentials are often brought out in discussions of the housing problem, but a balanced consideration of them is hard to find. We hope to suggest the directions that offer most hope to the innovating entrepreneur and to deal with the difficulties that stand in his way. Such an analysis may help impatient executives in other fields understand why the field merits study, and why the turn of a screw here and the adjustment of a knob there will not immediately result in masses of fine new houses at vastly reduced prices. Such an analysis may also persuade those whose long experience with the frustrations and complexities of housebuilding has led them to abandon all real hope for significant innovation (or to abandon the field entirely). The old ways cannot prevail much longer. Thus the question is not whether there will be changes, but only when and how. In the broad sense given the word by the design professions, therefore, this becomes a *design* analysis.

One might caricature the current situation by showing a group of men moving backward into the future while raising their voices in lip service to the past. Progress under such conditions is understandably uncertain, but when any one of the group tries to turn around and walk forward, the others hasten to bring pressure to keep him "conventional." Yet it is essential to develop an understanding of the operating point of view. The production of houses is a tremendously complex business, and no single aspect of it can be mastered without taking into account its relationship to the rest of the process. A factory operation that might at first glance seem entirely illogical often may be rationally explained by the demands of transportation, finance, local controls, or final-site labor.

It would be easy to make sensational allegations, attacks, and oversimplifications, and thus win the plaudits of the many producers and consumers long frustrated in their hopes. The broad and considered view is often less exciting, and to the degree that it yields clear statements, it runs the risk of seeming painfully obvious. Yet, in seeking to gain our objective of increased freedom for innovation throughout the field, it would be worse than foolish to allow attention to be diverted by aimless bickering about details and the pinning of "blame." If we can stimulate understanding, hope, and possibly action on a broad front, the opportunity for creative activity should be more than enough to keep all hands productively occupied. And the consumer should be the principal beneficiary.

The organization and planning of this book has been very much a group project. Chapters were assigned to individuals to draft, but several have had such substantial alteration and addition that it is hard to attribute final authorship. To make the credits clear, a headnote has been added to each chapter. I accept the responsibility for a good deal of editing throughout, some of it of major dimensions.

Many people have helped our efforts toward the completion of the book. I should like particularly to acknowledge the assistance of the ACTION *ad hoc* Committee on the Producer; of Robin Boyd, Richard W. Hamilton, Werner H. Gumpertz, and Arthur N. BecVar; and, to a degree far beyond the normal call of duty, of Martin Meyerson and his able staff. Invaluable expediting and editing services were performed by Harriet Crain Blume and Mary Elliott.

Burnham Kelly

Contents

Chapter 1

PROBLEMS AND POTENTIALS — THE HOUSING INDUSTRY TODAY

In this chapter, Burnham Kelly gives a broad view of the current housing industry, starting with some common impressions and a brief statistical description, and proceeding to survey the tremendous range and complication of the problems and opportunities now facing the industry. After introducing many of the issues that are discussed in detail in later chapters, the chapter emphasizes the fact that there has been significant change in recent years in the fundamental character of both the industry and the house itself.

To begin with, we need a general view of the housing industry both to introduce more detailed discussions and to serve as a framework within which to illustrate the meaning here given to the term "design." For this will be no mere study of decoration, of builder cosmetics to make houses more salable, or of so-called architectural styles. As used here, "design" means the creative process by which—on the basis of insight into the way of life of those who will live in the house and understanding of the entire process by which houses are produced—one visualizes patterns and forms that have not previously existed. Only when he succeeds in achieving both a high level of satisfaction and a high degree of economy of total resources does a designer serve his function.

Necessarily this implies the right if not the duty to innovate.[1] The main hope of the designer for the housing industry is that his new ideas may be given a fair trial in competition with the old. When this is possible, it will be far less disturbing to leave the choice among many alternative possibilities to the decision of the public, expressed in the market place. Under present conditions in the industry, it is rarely possible.

The small house to be built in quantity offers one of the toughest design problems, for houses are not simple, finite products but complex summations of space and service, individual satisfactions and social relationships, tangibles and intangibles, technology and art. And the processes by which they are currently produced provide a fascinating example of the flowering of absurdities which can occur when a field has for too long a time been hemmed in by tradition and convention.

To start on a happy note, however, we may call attention at this point to a not inconsiderable victory already won by the producers of housing: their success in avoiding the very term "housing," the connotations of which Frank Lloyd Wright considered inhuman, unpleasantly like those of "stabling." Somehow, the producers have managed to take over for themselves the friendly term "home," so that today "housing" is commonly and inescapably associated with government programs, professorial studies, and a difficult cultural problem, whereas houses are the product of "home builders." This is a tribute to an ingenuity that will be taxed in solving the broader complexities which this chapter attempts to summarize.

[1] *Architectural Forum*, vol. 106, no. 1, January, 1957, pp. 93ff., in an issue devoted to technology in the building field, summarized the whole tenor of developments in housing in the single term "control": chemical control of the properties of materials, mechanical control of all aspects of human environment, engineering control of utilities and community services, operational control of output to introduce variety while retaining the advantages of the production line, and finally, control of the land itself through the tremendous power and versatility of earth-shaping machinery. In this application of the word, its sense closely approximates what is here meant by design.

Character of the Industry

The housing industry must be understood in the very broadest terms if the future potentials of design and production are to be made clear. For our purposes, moreover, interrelationships and insights about the various aspects of the industry, as they suggest future housing potentials, are more important than the detailed and definitive analysis of each aspect. Accordingly, the following discussion proceeds freely, rating inferences and impressions fully as highly as statistics.

Common Impressions. Everyone has opinions on housing. The shortage of houses has held a prominent position in the news for some years now; during two periods of crisis—a depression and a postwar boom—it became a major political issue. Through this time, expert propagandists and journalists have crystallized in the public mind a number of judgments and opinions about the industry and its problems. Often these judgments conflict; quite as often, they spring from biases which are unconscious but emerge clearly under provocation.

Many an economist and policy planner has proclaimed a connection between the fluctuations of construction and the onset of general economic depressions and booms. The first government programs in housing were aimed at restoring building volume, employment, and income and the security of mortgage investment, and the importance to the nation's general economy of high production and full employment in the building industry is frequently asserted.[2]

It has been widely asserted that the housing industry is obsolete or, to put it in the terms once used by *Fortune*, that housing is "The Industry Capitalism Forgot."[3] Ever since the

[2] Some doubt that construction is well suited to manipulation as a means of preserving economic stability. Miles L. Colean and Robinson Newcomb, *Stabilizing Construction*, McGraw-Hill Book Company, Inc., New York, 1952.

[3] *Fortune*, vol. 36, no. 2, August, 1947, p. 61. For higher hopes, see "The Insatiable Market for Housing," *Fortune*, vol. 49, no. 2, February, 1954, p. 102; for a renewed sense of depression, see "Housing: The Stalled Revolution," *Fortune*, vol. 55, no. 4, April, 1957, p. 120.

findings of the Temporary National Economic Committee in 1940,[4] unflattering contrasts with other industries have been sounding in the press, frequently citing that presumed paragon of productive know-how, the automobile industry.[5] Low opinion of the industrial IQ of the industry during the period of housing boom immediately following World War II was typified by an influential series of newspaper articles entitled: "Housing: Puny Giant." [6] More recently, John Keats has subjected the industry and much of modern Suburbia to a very cynical look in his widely discussed book, *The Crack in the Picture Window.*[7]

These attacks all had much to justify them; the facts are not good. On the other hand, how do we reconcile them with the judgment of a series of European productivity and building teams who, after visiting this country and observing in detail the methods and productivity of our housing industry, have uniformly expressed admiration? More is involved here than the polite compliments of a grateful guest. We may conclude that the production of houses has nowhere turned out to be a simple problem. Considering the nature of the impediments with which the housing industry is surrounded and the strength and subtlety of the individual and social attitudes that have produced and perpetuated them, it may be doing a reasonably good job—in some instances a very good job indeed.

Some in the business community charge that the industry has abandoned industrial independence and integrity and turned itself into a fawning parasite on the Federal purse. An outstanding example of this appeared in an article in the "Review

---

[4] "Toward More Housing," U.S. Temporary National Economic Committee, Investigation of Concentration of Economic Power, Monograph no. 8, 1940, p. xv.

[5] Distinctions between automobiles and houses as industrial products have been sharply drawn for some time. A list of distinguishing features appears in Burnham Kelly, *The Prefabrication of Houses,* Technology Press and John Wiley & Sons, Inc., New York, 1951, pp. 51–55.

[6] *Wall Street Journal,* October 9–21, 1947.

[7] Houghton Mifflin Company, Boston, 1956.

and Outlook" column of the *Wall Street Journal* for May, 1957, which began:

Suppose the automakers were now screaming to the Government to "do something" because sales are not as good as they would like, certainly not nearly on a par with record 1955. They would be laughed off the streets.

Yet the home-building industry has no hesitation—or pride, apparently—about yelping for government help because housing starts are off. . . .

In its own interest it is time the housing industry came to its senses. And it would be salutary if other businessmen would begin to see just who it is [the taxpayer] that's gambling when they implore the Government to "help" them.

To this charge, spokesmen for the industry have replied [8] that the troubles of the housing industry in the tight money market then prevailing were specifically the result of governmental refusal to let interest rates rise for housing mortgages, while stimulating the vast increase in corporate borrowing that tightened the money market. To quote:

The home building industry is not asking the Federal Government for help to sell more houses; it is not asking for help of any kind.

It is asking for *relief* from Federal actions which have indeed brought many builders to the brink of bankruptcy.[9]

George F. Price of National Homes put this story in different terms:

The depressing effect of uneven credit grows. Home builders must watch not only an increasing number of their potential customers eliminated from the market by credit restrictions, but a growing share of the consumer dollar going to automobile dealers, appliance stores, soft goods merchants, and others with whom we are in competition.[10]

---

[8] In *House & Home*, vol. 11, no. 6, June, 1957, p. 120; prepared with the help of Miles L. Colean.

[9] *Ibid.*, p. 121.

[10] In his talk as president at the fall meeting of the Prefabricated Home Manufacturers' Institute, held at St. Petersburg, Florida, on November 12, 1956, entitled "The Depressing Effect of Uneven Credit on the Housing Market."

Indeed, the industrialist in other fields rarely hesitates to use government favors. One ardent proponent of a new over-all housing system, who tried in turn to interest airplane companies, shipyards, and metals manufacturers in producing basic housing units, found that a high degree of early enthusiasm quickly waned when it became clear that in the housing field there was no government program against which the costs of tooling up for production could be written off. The mighty automobile industry is hardly indifferent to the large expenditures for public roads. It seems no more accurate to conclude that the housing industry is a parasite on government than that it is obsolete.

Many believe, however, that the government has never really had a housing policy worthy of the name, and that its own activities and inactivities are much to blame for the complex problems faced by the industry. In testimony on the urban-renewal program, for example, Leo Grebler [11] expressed such views when he called for stable United States policy and an end to the annual enactment of omnibus housing legislation. He pointed out that too frequent change in the basic rules could produce only confusion, and stated that the numerous special-purpose programs created within the Federal Housing Administration (for example: housing for those displaced by slum clearance, housing for the aged, and trailer parks) were disrupting normal housing markets and Balkanizing the government insurance program. In testimony before the Senate, Joseph P. McMurray pointed out that the Federal Home Loan Bank System, far from serving as a central bank for mortgage credit, as had originally been expected, had actually had a negative total effect in regard to mortgage expansion.[12] Aside from the gains to be made by playing one against the other, it is hard to see why both the FHA and the

---

[11] *Housing Amendments of 1957. Hearings before a Subcommittee of the Senate Committee on Banking and Currency*, 85th Cong., 1st Sess., November, 1957.

[12] *Ibid.*, p. 870.

VA need to be engaged in mortgage guaranteeing. It is certainly fair to conclude that one may question the over-all aims and consistency of the Federal programs in the housing field.

Perhaps the most pervading notion, and inherently one of the most dangerous, is the assumption that the basic objective and the most effective measure of success in industrializing the production of houses is the reduction of final cost to the purchaser—this despite the fact that on all sides the consumer appears to be clamoring for more space and a wider range of services and equipment. Reduction in elements of cost surely may be expected with quantity production and simplified distribution and erection, particularly if a significant reduction can be made in labor hours per unit of housing. And in the absence of improvement elsewhere, final cost is an essential market determinant; a common saying is that each $100 cut from the price of housing adds 15,000 units to the market. But the experience of other industrial operations is that the consumer will usually want an improved product for the same money in preference to the same one at lower cost. And there is reason to believe that his community tax officials, bankers, and taxpaying neighbors will find reasons to encourage him in this preference. The main benefit from rationalized production is not likely, therefore, to be reduction in over-all price.

Basic Facts.[13] Housing is perhaps the second largest industry

[13] Useful sources of statistics on housing are Housing and Home Finance Agency, *Housing Statistics* (monthly), U.S. Bureau of the Census, *Statistical Abstracts* (annual), publications of the Federal Reserve Board, and publications of private groups such as E. H. Boeckh & Associates, Roy Wenzlick & Company, and the F. W. Dodge Corporation. *Construction Review*, published monthly by the Departments of Labor and Commerce, and *Housing in the Economy*, published annually by the HHFA, summarize basic data derived from the housing census, the Bureau of Labor Statistics, and the HHFA.

This chapter seeks to give a quick impression of the housing industry today, an effort much simplified by a group of studies of the industry from different viewpoints to which one may refer those who wish to go into these matters more deeply. Perhaps the most informative picture of housebuilding in recent years is Sherman J. Maisel, *Housebuilding in Transition,* in the United States, after food and food processing, and it operates in practically every community in the country. The largest user of long-term credit, it is periodically plagued by a shortage in that essential commodity. The value of new residences exclusive of land has been running at about $16 billion per year,[14] or about 4 per cent of the gross national product, with the total representing almost one-quarter of the national wealth.[15] Future estimates have been optimistic.

The long-range forecasts for the growth of our economy indicate that the dollar volume of housing will rise from its 1956 level of fifteen billion dollars to approximately twenty-three billion in 1970—an increase of fifty per cent. I think this is very conservative. If something is done to inject the same intelligence, professional skill, and attention to

---

University of California Press, Berkeley, Calif., 1953, which concentrates on the San Francisco Bay area just after World War II. The general summary study of the industry with the best over-all balance is Miles L. Colean, *American Housing*, The Twentieth Century Fund, Inc., New York, 1944. Although more than a quarter of a century old, William Haber, *Industrial Relations in the Building Industry*, Harvard University Press, Cambridge, Mass., 1930, still gives an outstanding picture of the detailed building operations on a typical project. The broadest analysis of the prefabrication industry is Burnham Kelly, *The Prefabrication of Houses*, Technology Press and John Wiley & Sons, Inc., New York, 1951. Those concerned with the production of houses in terms of industrial economics will find a general view in Leo Grebler's monograph, *Production of New Housing*, Social Science Research Council, New York, 1950. Excellent sections on the industry are contained in J. Frederick Dewhurst and Associates, *America's Needs and Resources: A New Survey*, The Twentieth Century Fund, Inc., New York, 1955. Finally, for an insight into the roles of many different participants in the building process, one may recommend the slim, well-written volume, *Building, U.S.A.*, by the editors of *Architectural Forum*, McGraw-Hill Book Company, Inc., New York, 1957.

[14] In 1957, the value of new private, nonfarm dwellings was just over $12 billion, a drop of 10 per cent from 1956. By comparison, the value of all public construction was just under $14 billion, an increase of 9 per cent from 1956. Private construction other than nonfarm dwellings amounted to well over $16 billion. Additions and alterations to private, nonfarm dwellings came to almost $4 billion. *Construction Review*, vol. 4, no. 2, February, 1958, p. 17.

[15] Estimated by Raymond W. Goldsmith of the National Bureau of Economic Research.

marketing, financing, and research in the housing field as is customary in most other major industries, we may see housing advance faster within the next few decades than comparable programs in other fields.[16]

The industry has provided about 2½ million jobs in recent years, half of them at the building site and half in the off-site work of producing and distributing materials and equipment. Materials demands of all types of residential construction take about one-third of the annual production of lumber, two-thirds of that of brick, and four-fifths of that of gypsum products. And it has been estimated that each new house sale generates $1,500 worth of retail sales in furnishings and equipment.[17]

An essentially local character has long typified the entire structure of the housing industry, in which about three-quarters of the builders put up fewer than five houses per year (see Charts 1 and 2). This pattern has prevailed even though the larger builders have rapidly increased their domination over the output of houses. Between 1938 and 1955, builders of five or more houses rose from 14 to 27 per cent of the total; the number of houses they produced rose from 64 to 92 per cent of the total (see Chart 3).

It has been estimated that 1 per cent of the builders now build one-third of the houses; the top 10 per cent build more than two-thirds.[18] Many of those who erected only one house were owner-builders. Maisel [19] estimates that in 1949, owners built 33 per cent of the total houses in the United States and that these "nonprofessionals" constructed 18 per cent of the

[16] Leon Chatelain, Jr., "President's Address, Centennial Celebration Convention, American Institute of Architects, May 14, 1957," The Producers Council, Technical Bulletin no. 80, Washington, D.C., June, 1957.

[17] Based on information from Nathaniel Rogg, Economist, National Association of Home Builders.

[18] "The Round Table on Selling," *House & Home,* vol. 11, no. 4, April, 1957, p. 156.

[19] Sherman J. Maisel, *op. cit.,* p. 344. Detailed breakdowns for later than 1949 are not available.

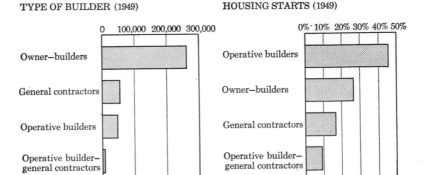

Chart 1. Who builds houses? (*Housing and Home Finance Agency, Housing in the United States, 1956, p. 55.*)

new houses in metropolitan areas. If owner-builders are excluded from the housing statistics, in 1949 the top 1 per cent of the builders erected 31 per cent of the new homes in metropolitan areas and the top 13 per cent accounted for nearly 60 per cent. There can be no doubt that the size of housing

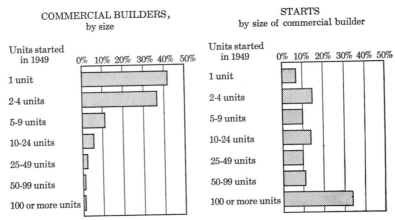

Chart 2. Most commercial home builders are small. Percentages are based by commercial builders on commercial building starts only. (*Housing and Home Finance Agency, Housing in the United States, 1956, p. 57.*)

firms has increased sharply and continues to increase at the present time; nothing indicates a reversal of this trend in the near future.

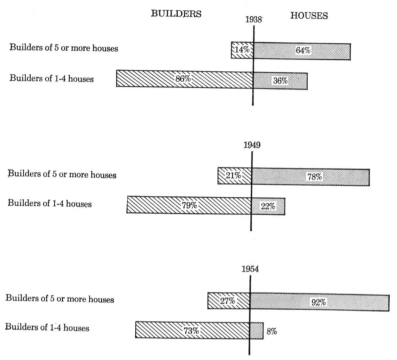

Chart 3. Percentages of large and small builders, and of total houses built by each type. (Sources: 1938, *Monthly Labor Review, vol. 51, pp. 732–739, September, 1946;* 1949, *Bulletin no. 1170, Bureau of Labor Statistics;* 1954, *F. W. Dodge Corp.*)

Production figures covering a number of years have been gathered in Tables 1 and 2, from which a few conclusions may be noted.

1. Public housing is a small element in total production, rising briefly in the early 1940s to a peak of 15 per cent and staying well under 5 per cent in recent years.

2. Houses financed by Federal mortgage guarantees rose briefly in the early 1940s to 75 per cent of the total and then

TABLE 1.   Total Permanent Nonfarm Dwelling Units Started
(in thousands of dwelling units)

		Private ownership			Public owner-ship total	As a percentage of total starts	
Year	Starts	Total	FHA	VA		FHA and VA starts	Public owner-ship
1935	221	215.7	14.0	....	5.3	6.3	2.4
1936	319	304.2	49.4	....	14.8	15.5	4.6
1937	336	332.4	60.0	....	3.6	17.9	1.1
1938	406	399.3	118.7	....	6.7	29.2	1.6
1939	515	458.5	158.1	....	56.5	30.7	11.0
1940	602.6	529.6	180.1	....	73.0	30.0	12.1
1941	706.1	619.5	220.4	....	86.6	31.2	12.3
1942	356	301.2	165.7	....	54.8	46.6	15.4
1943	191	183.7	146.1	....	7.3	76.5	3.8
1944	141.8	138.7	93.2	....	3.1	65.8	2.2
1945	209.3	208.1	41.1	a	1.2	a	.6
1946	670.5	662.5	69.0	a	8.0	a	1.2
1947	849.0	845.6	229.0	a	3.4	a	.4
1948	931.6	913.5	294.0	a	18.1	a	1.9
1949	1,025.1	988.8	363.8	a	36.3	a	3.5
1950	1,396.0	1,352.2	486.7	200.0	43.8	51	3.1
1951	1,091.3	1,020.1	263.5	148.7	71.2	41	6.5
1952	1,127.0	1,068.5	279.9	141.3	58.5	39	5.2
1953	1,103.8	1,068.3	252.0	156.6	35.5	49	3.2
1954	1,220.4	1,201.7	276.3	307.0	18.7	49	1.5
1955	1,328.9	1,309.5	276.7	392.9	19.4	51	1.5
1956	1,118.2	1,093.9	189.3	270.7	24.2	42	2.2
1957	1,039.2	989.7	168.4	128.3	49.5	30	4.8

a Not available.

Source: U.S. Department of Commerce, National Production Authority, *Construction and Building Materials, Statistical Supplement,* May, 1951, p. 56; Housing and Home Finance Agency, *Annual Reports; Construction Review,* vol. 4, no. 2, February, 1958, pp. 22, 26.

declined, but they remain a significant element in the industry, running about 40 per cent of the total.

3. Single-family houses have grown steadily in proportion since the 1920s, when as much as 20 per cent of the total were

two-family houses and as much as 36 per cent were multi-family houses. In the late 1950s, close to 90 per cent of the total were single-family houses.

4. Over 1,000,000 total new dwelling units have been started every year since 1948. The total starts for 1957 were 1,039,000, the lowest figure since 1949.

Production figures for manufacturers of prefabricated houses and trailers are given in Chapter 5, where these specialized branches of the housing industry are discussed at

TABLE 2. Permanent Nonfarm Dwelling Units Started
         (by type of structure)

Year	Number of dwelling units (in thousands)			As a percentage of total dwelling units started		
	One-family structures	Two-family structures	Multi-family structures	One-family structures	Two-family structures	Multi-family structures
1920	202	24	21	82	10	8
1921	316	70	63	70	16	14
1922	437	146	133	61	20	19
1923	513	175	183	59	20	21
1924	534	173	186	60	19	21
1925	572	157	208	61	17	22
1926	491	117	241	58	14	28
1927	454	99	257	56	12	32
1928	436	78	239	58	10	36
1929	316	51	142	62	10	28
1930	227	29	74	69	9	22
1931	187	22	45	73	9	18
1932	118	7	9	88	5	7
1933	76	5	12	82	5	13
1934	109	5	12	86	4	10
1935	183	8	30	83	4	13
1936	244	14	61	77	4	19
1937	267	16	53	79	5	16
1938	317	18	71	78	5	17
1939	399	29	87	77	6	17

TABLE 2. Permanent Nonfarm Dwelling Units Started
(by type of structure) (*Continued*)

	Number of dwelling units (*in thousands*)			As a percentage of total dwelling units started		
Year	One-family structures	Two-family structures	Multi-family structures	One-family structures	Two-family structures	Multi-family structures
1940	485.7	37.3	79.6	81	6	13
1941	603.5	34.3	68.3	85	5	10
1942	292.8	20.1	43.1	82	6	12
1943	143.6	17.8	29.6	75	9	16
1944	117.7	10.6	13.5	83	7	10
1945	184.6	8.8	15.9	88	4	8
1946	590.0	24.3	56.2	88	4	8
1947	740.2	33.9	74.9	87	4	9
1948	766.6	46.9	118.1	82	5	13
1949	794.3	36.5	194.3	77	4	19
1950	1,154.1	44.8	197.1	83	3	14
1951	900.1	40.4	150.8	82	4	14
1952	942.5	45.9	138.6	84	4	12
1953	937.8	41.5	124.5	85	4	11
1954	1,077.9	34.2	108.3	88	3	9
1955	1,194.4	32.8	101.7	90	2	8
1956	989.7	a	a	88.4	a	a

[a] Not available.
Source: U.S. Department of Commerce, National Production Authority, *Construction and Building Materials, Statistical Supplement*, May, 1953, p. 47; HHFA, *Annual Reports*.

length, and estimates of demand are contained in Appendix A. Demolitions in the current stock of 55 million houses have been estimated at half a million units per year and conversions (creating added units within existing buildings) at one-third of a million units per year.[20]

[20] Charles E. Silberman and Sanford S. Parker, "Housing's Crucial Decade," *Fortune*, vol. 56, no. 4, April, 1958, p. 124.

TABLE 3. Building Materials Industry (by size of firm)

Industry group	Number of firms	Number of employees	Average number of employees per firm
Lumber and wood products	26,231	635,708	24.2
Heating and cooking apparatus	841	110,475	130.3
Metal plumbing fixtures and fittings	247	34,089	138.0
Vitreous plumbing fixtures	33	7,831	237.3
Roofing felts and coatings	174	16,579	95.2
Paints and varnishes	1,291	53,412	41.4
Brick and hollow tile	674	29,617	43.9
Floor and wall tile	37	6,828	184.5
Cement, hydraulic	155	35,662	230.1
Gypsum products	73	7,472	102.4
Construction	270,950	1,734,500	6.4

Source: U.S. Department of Commerce, 1947.

Just as no single company dominates the house-producing industry, so no single company dominates materials production. There are large producers primarily concerned with building materials, like Johns-Manville, U.S. Gypsum, and Weyerhaeuser, but none ranks among the very largest United States companies, and none even dominates completely the production of any one of the important building materials. Many material and equipment items, however, are produced by industrial giants like General Electric, Westinghouse, and U.S. Steel, for whom housing is not a primary market. New materials like plastics come in relatively raw form from large chemical producers like du Pont, Dow, and Monsanto, but the actual building products are fabricated by a large number of shops, most of them very small. Further details on the building materials producers are supplied in Tables 3 and 4. Table 3 also shows the average number of employees per firm in the building materials firms.

TABLE 4. 1957 Sales and Earnings for Sixty-four Producers

Company	Sales	Percentage change in sales 1956–1957	Percentage change in net 1956–1957
Appliances:			
Worthington	$ 191,727,439	12.0	7.2
Whirlpool	402,322,212	− 2.9	−24.0
Trane	80,648,000	8.3	8.8
Maytag	98,613,291	−12.7	−21.6
Westinghouse	2,009,043,000	31.7	95 a
Carrier	263,426,097	10.5	−33.5
General Electric	4,335,664,061	6.0	16.0
Cement:			
Penn-Dixie	40,753,792	−28.2	−16.2
Lehigh Portland	70,407,706	− 7.3	−32.0
Ideal	78,254,763	0.8	− 3.0
General Portland	37,762,700	−16.7	−26.7
Marquette	46,615,860	9.6	− 0.9
Lone Star	94,676,587	− 3.7	− 3.4
Alpha Portland	30,958,384	−12.6	−22.8
North American	17,079,341	− 2.6	− 2.8
Glass:			
Owens Corning	163,327,463	1.4	− 9.0
Pittsburgh Plate	620,803,296	4.0	4.2
Thatcher	42,019,715	33.0	7.6
American Window	17,595,477	−24.0	−91.5
Libbey Owens	237,199,069	− 8.5	− 4.0
Lumber and plywood:			
Roddis	53,344,456	− 3.4	−78.2
E. L. Bruce	12,678,713 g	−15.7	− 8.4
Georgia Pacific	147,649,368 h	−21.7	12.2
Weyerhaeuser	427,000,000	− 4.4	−17.4
U.S. Plywood	154,416,000 h	2.8	−24.1
General Plywood	7,025,446	−12.0	b
International Paper Co.	940,427,571	− 3.0	− 9.5
Prefabbers:			
Harnischfeger	87,548,369	7.9	17
National Homes	45,382,042	− 3.6	−19
Scholz Holmes	6,149,914 g	−12.4	28.7

TABLE 4. 1957 Sales and Earnings for Sixty-four Producers
(*Continued*)

Company	Sales	Percentage change in sales 1956–1957	Percentage change in net 1956–1957
Paints:			
Sherwin-Williams	257,807,442	5.9	7.9
National Lead	417,300,000	− 2.4	2.9
Glidden	225,537,290	− 0.3	−10.8
	52,800,715	− 9.4	−40.4 c
Plumbing and heating:			
Rheem	188,580,607 h	8.0	d
Coleman	30,953,057 i	−11.9	−82.6
A.O. Smith	140,515,665 g	17.1	24.1
Universal Rundle	12,963,157 g	−12.7	−58.4
Bell & Gossett	11,495,443 g	1.9	8.7
Briggs	13,432,935 h	−27.3	e
Crane	268,902,000 h	− 1.8	−28.1
American Standard	368,783,000	− 8.1	−35.8
Minneapolis Honeywell	324,886,719	12.8	− 5.0
Metals:			
Alcoa	869,378,093	0.6	−15.4
Kaiser Aluminum	400,000,000	16.4	−32.9
Revere	199,625,549	−20.3	−11.4
Anaconda	96,145,526 h	−52.3	−59.9
Bridgeport Brass	150,868,526	− 9.8	18.7
Jones & Laughlin	837,568,000	21.0	0.7
U.S. Steel	4,413,824,266	5.1	20.4
Wallboard, roofing, tile:			
Celotex	66,629,231	−12.9	−34.2
	13,314,667	− 5.5	−99.8 f
Masonite	58,861,372	− 4.1	−29.3
	15,827,194	14.9	1.9 c
Johns-Manville	308,293,000	− 0.7	−29.0
Armstrong	246,528,518	− 0.4	−17.0
Ruberoid	81,073,947	6.2	14.4
U.S. Gypsum	249,646,019	− 5.8	− 4.6
Philip Carey	69,889,864	0.7	2.4
National Gypsum	141,472,944	− 6.8	−11.0
Bestwall Gypsum	29,401,797	− 6.9	−17.3
Certain-teed	83,633,776	− 9.2	− 6.5
Flintkote	116,249,878	2.3	− 1.2

TABLE 4. 1957 Sales and Earnings for Sixty-four Producers
(*Continued*)

Company	Sales	Percentage change in sales 1956–1957	Percentage change in net 1956–1957
Miscellaneous:			
American Hardware	35,624,097	16.7	29.9
Yale & Towne	128,558,408	4.9	−22.1
Monsanto	708,005,000	8.3	6.8
Minnesota Mining & Mfg	370,106,838	11.9	2.6

a 1956 profit affected by five-months strike.
b Loss of $506,291, up $310,700 from 1956 loss of $195,591.
c Three months to November 30.
d 1957 net of $1,968,916 following 1956 loss of $9,163,134.
e Loss of $131,029, showed $1,333,428 net in 1956.
f Three months to January 31.
g Nine-month report.
h Six-month report.
i Ten-month report.
Source: *House & Home*, vol. 13, no. 4, April, 1958, p. 72.

Average wage for all building construction trades in January, 1958, was $3.23 per hour, which is 5 per cent (15 cents) higher than a year earlier. An analysis by the Bureau of Labor Statistics in 1957 [21] indicated that for contract construction workers as a whole, both hourly and weekly pay are significantly higher than for workers in manufacturing industry as a group. These data may help to explain the concern among producers of housing for the reduction of on-site labor costs and the motive for many attempts at industrializing house production. Table 5 puts together some details from official sources regarding employment numbers and wages, tending to support the notions that both are steadily rising, with the wages of specialists such as electricians rising the most rapidly, and that there is great regional variation. Newark has the highest rates in most categories, but many other cities in the

21 *U.S. Monthly Labor Review*, vol. 80, no. 2, February, 1957, pp. 170, 187.

TABLE 5. Employment and Wages

1957 hourly pay	Newark, N.J.	Cleveland	Los Angeles	Raleigh, N.C.	Estimated average		
					1953	1955	1957*
Bricklayer	4.25	3.715	3.80	2.75		3.79	
Carpenter	4.00	3.75	3.225	2.00		3.34	
Electrician	4.25	3.765	3.75	2.625		3.53	
Painter	3.60	3.415	3.26	1.9		3.20	
Plasterer	4.25	3.74	3.937	2.75		3.66	
Plumber	4.00	3.64	3.7	2.75		3.60	
Laborer	3.20	3.00	2.5	1.15		2.39	

1957 employment	Total (in thousands)			Average weekly earnings			Average weekly hours		
	1953	1955	1957*	1953	1955	1957*	1953	1955	1957*
All building construction	2,109	2,243	2,567	91.76	96.29	110.48	37.0	36.9	37.2
All specialty trades	1,175.1	1,320	1,537	94.79	100.83	115.63	36.6	36.2	37.3
Plumbing and heating	288.9	317	344	98.30	106.40	120.74	38.1	38.0	38.7
Painting and decorating	148.1	162.3	226.6	87.10	94.38	107.76	34.7	34.7	35.8
Electrical	159.7	168.4	242.7	111.61	116.52	132.50	39.3	39.1	39.2
Other	578.4	637.1	723.5	91.04	96.21	110.60	35.7	35.8	36.8

* August.
Source: *Construction Review*, vol. 4, no. 2, February, 1958, E-5 pp. 40–41; G-1 p. 51; G-6 p. 56.

Northeast are comparable. Cleveland and Los Angeles typify the middle range of rates; Raleigh shows how low the rates may go in the Southeast.

The housebuilding industry is subject to wide seasonal variations, which have an adverse effect on production efficiency and costs. In 1957, total starts were at the figure of 63,000 for the month of January and rose to a peak of 103,000 by April, after which they fluttered down to 95,000 in October before plummeting to the low of 62,000 in December. By comparison, in 1950 the peak of 150,000 was reached in May and the low point in January was just under 80,000. Private nonfarm single houses followed about the same curve. As might be expected, the North Central area had the largest seasonal fluctuations, varying from 14,000 units in February to 27,800 units in June, and the West had the least, 17,500 units in February and 22,700 in May. This may explain some part of the large cost differential found between these two areas.

The production volume and many of the characteristics of houses vary from region to region. For example, the 7 per cent drop in total housing starts between 1956 and 1957 took place almost entirely in metropolitan areas (699,300 units in 1957 versus 779,800 in 1956) and in housing financed under FHA and VA. Regionally, the decline was more than 15 per cent in the Northeast and North Central regions and about 7 per cent in the Far West, whereas the South actually made a slight gain.[22] Characteristics of houses in these regions have been selected for presentation in Table 6, where some factual support is given to the general opinion that houses in the North tend to be more expensive and to require better heating systems, whereas those in the South and West tend to do without basements and to experiment somewhat more in materials and construction.

Largest volumes of home building occur in the metropolitan areas (nonmetropolitan areas have only one-third of the

[22] *Construction Review,* vol. 4, no. 2, February, 1958.

TABLE 6. Regional Trends in Selected Characteristics by Per Cent of New Nonfarm Single Houses

	All areas			North-east			North Central			South			West		
	1954	1955	1956	1954	1955	1956	1954	1955	1956	1954	1955	1956	1954	1955	1956
Selling price (selected ranges):															
Less than $7,000	11	7	4	8	1	..	12	3	2	15	17	9	4	2	1
$12,000–14,999	24	29	27	26	36	34	27	23	21	17	22	25	30	39	33
More than $20,000	10	10	18	13	8	25	11	19	26	8	9	12	6	6	15
Exterior wall:															
Masonry	13	20	16	8	9	9	12	14	15	19	36	19	12	13	18
Frame	82	77	83	89	87	90	82	81	84	76	62	78	83	85	82
All other	3	1	..	2	1	..	4	3	..	2	1	..	3	1	..
No basement	58	55	55	21	9	18	44	39	30	73	79	79	79	71	72
Window frame:															
Wood	63	57	57	67	73	72	68	72	67	68	57	54	47	34	44
Steel	18	16	11	17	13	8	20	9	7	10	10	7	29	30	23
Aluminum	17	24	29	15	10	19	10	16	25	20	28	36	21	33	29
Number of stories:															
1		87			59			91			89			97	
2		4			10			2			5			1	
Split-level		6			25			4			3			1	
Other		2			4			2			1			..	
Heating system:															
Hot-water furnace		8			41			3			1			..	
Warm-air furnace		73			56			94			60			81	
Space heater		13			..			1			26			17	
Garage		50			60			44			32			75	
Carport		17			9			6			33			10	
Plaster wall		43			38			57			28			54	
Dry wall		55			61			41			69			45	
Air-conditioner		7			2			5			10			7	

Source: *Construction Review*, vol. 3, no. 4, April, 1957, pp. 5, 7.

total), concentrating in areas with the largest population and in those in the rapidly growing regions of the South and West. Table 7 presents the figures for the twelve leading home-building areas for the years 1954, 1955, and 1956 and shows that, in most such areas, a large majority of the new houses are built in the suburbs.

These figures indicate the degree to which production volume in the housing industry is tending to concentrate, and a clear correlation exists between them and the emergence of the large operative builders.

Far more important to the housing industry than usually realized is the growing appliance industry, which is able to offer the consumer a fairly specific service with little conventional complication and has made startling inroads into house design as a result. Table 4 gave figures on the 1957 earnings of some of the industry leaders, and the importance of housing generally to the appliance makers may be illustrated by the reminder of Roy W. Johnson, then executive vice-president of General Electric,[23] that if only 10 per cent of the renewal program urged by ACTION should be carried out, there would be $2 billion increased sales for the appliance industry and $300 million increased annual income for the utility industry.

So great has been success in certain areas that the index of saturation (houses having electricity that have obtained the appliance) exceeds 95 per cent for refrigerators and radios and 85 per cent for electric washers, television sets, and irons. Refrigerator sales alone yearly exceed $1 billion in retail value, and the industry as a whole, starting from almost nothing in 1920, did annual retail business in excess of $6 billion in 1957 and expects to pass $10 billion in the next decade.[24]

[23] In "The Bigger Piece of Pie," an address before the International Association of Electric Leagues, Detroit, Michigan, October 5, 1956.

[24] Information on appliance industry gathered by Arthur N. BecVar, manager, industrial design operation, General Electric Company, Appliance Park, Louisville, Kentucky.

TABLE 7. Leading Home-building Areas

Rank 1956	1955	1954	Metropolitan area	Number of units 1956	1955	1954	Per cent change 1955–56	1954–55
1	1	1	Los Angeles	89,300	103,700	104,000	−14	. .
2	2	2	New York–New Jersey	77,700	97,400	94,300	−20	+ 3
3	3	3	Chicago	51,500	60,100	49,000	−14	+23
4	4	4	Detroit	31,400	40,600	41,000	−23	− 1
5	5	5	Philadelphia	23,900	36,500	30,500	−35	+20
6	6	6	San Francisco–Oakland	22,000	32,100	28,400	−31	+13
7	8	12	San Bernardino–Riverside–Ontario	17,200	18,900	15,500	− 9	+22
8	11	9	Miami	17,100	16,400	16,200	+ 4	+ 1
9	7	7	Washington, D.C.	15,900	22,600	23,900	−30	− 5
10	18	19	Tampa–St. Petersburg	13,800	12,900	11,800	+ 7	+ 9
11	22	23	San Diego	13,300	11,400	10,200	+17	+12
12	10	8	Houston	13,100	17,000	17,800	−23	− 4

Per cent in suburbs 1956	1955	1954	Metropolitan area	Per cent change 1955–56 Center	Suburbs	1954–55 Center	Suburbs
70	77	73	Los Angeles	+11	−22	−14	+ 5
68	68	70	New York–New Jersey	−18	−21	+ 7	+ 2
76	71	75	Chicago	−29	− 8	+43	+16
92	91	89	Detroit	−28	−22	−22	+ 2
80	84	84	Philadelphia	−17	−38	+17	+20
87	89	86	San Francisco–Oakland	−20	−33	− 8	+16
80	80	78	San Bernardino–Riverside–Ontario	−10	− 9	+12	+25
84	84	78	Miami	+ 3	+ 4	−26	+ 9
86	88	88	Washington, D.C.	−22	−31	− 6	− 5
52	47	44	Tampa–St. Petersburg	− 3	+18	+ 3	+17
48	47	47	San Diego	+14	+20	+11	+12
64	60	51	Houston	−31	−17	−21	+11

Source: *Construction Review,* vol. 3, no. 9, September, 1957, pp. 5, 7.

These gains have been the result of aggressive research, development, and merchandising. In the case of its garbage grinder, for example, General Electric spent four years and $90,000 before the design was accepted for volume production, at which time an education campaign was undertaken to persuade both the general public and the municipal authorities that this new idea was both a real advantage and perfectly compatible with public and private sewage disposal systems. The key to success was the marked total environmental improvement when an entire town had turned garbage disposal over to such appliances. Nineteen years and well over $1 million after the idea was first explored, the company was finally able to declare a profit on the unit. Where in the housing industry would this have been possible?

Greatest limitations to further advances are not consumer conventions or fiscal problems, but the code and labor requirements regarding installation and connection to electricity and water lines, and the electricity problems (mainly of labor) are simple compared with the water problems; urgently desired by the industry is public awareness of the need for national acceptance of a standard code for plumbing.

Weakness of Statistics. From the evidence that has been given, one might conclude that the statistical background of the housing industry is exceedingly strong. It is true that the government has made an effort in this field, as it should, and that in terms of sheer volume of statistics and of broad summaries, the industry does well by comparison with many others. Yet there can be no doubt whatever that those who must work with them find the government effort in many respects exceedingly and unnecessarily incomplete. Only in 1950 was the Census Bureau granted funds to make the first detailed census of housing, covering such vital pieces of information as family (as opposed to individual) income. The latest general information regarding output of houses per builder is dated 1949. And the Council of Economic Advisers voices a representative opinion when it terms our basic economic statistics on construction and real estate "very weak" and quotes the often-repeated remark of Ernest Fisher of Columbia University that "more facts are known, literally, about a single agricultural product, peanuts, than about urban real estate." [25] The three items needing top priority according to the Council are better dollar-volume estimates of new construction put in place (now considered unreliable even for long-range movements); reliable data on maintenance and repair (a tremendous housing market and one that will grow with the success of the urban renewal program); and better figures on materials and labor (currently derived from estimates the basis for which is much in need of change to recognize advances in technology). Noted as also ripe for consideration are the composite construction-cost index of the Department of Commerce and additional information on mortgage activity, figures on the backlog of planned construction, facts on conversions and demolitions, and government price series for real estate. Those who work with producers urge that information be gathered on the distribution and consumption of building products in the industry. And particular criticism is leveled at the highly publicized statistics on housing starts, which tend to underestimate figures by 50 per cent or more in areas that do not require building permits and which, it is claimed, could be made significantly more accurate for very little added cost. [26]

General Problems

Although the growth of large builders has been rapid in recent years, the essential character of the housebuilding in-

[25] Reported in "Hard to Get Statistics," *Architectural Forum*, vol. 106, no. 6, June, 1957, p. 132.

[26] Some consternation resulted from the finding of the 1956 National Housing Inventory that 2.7 million more dwelling units had been added since 1950 than were tabulated in the periodical reports of the Bureau of Labor Statistics. Even allowing for its inclusion of trailers and farm dwellings, the Census figures were nearly two million units higher than was expected, and it is even possible that gross national product during the period was underestimated. Vacancies also were higher than had been indicated by BLS, 9.9 per cent instead of 8.6 per cent. The total housing stock was estimated to be 55.3 million units. See *Construction Review*, vol. 4, no. 4, April, 1958, p. 4. Collection of this information has since been consolidated in the Bureau of the Census.

dustry has been determined by the still diffuse and localized picture that emerged in the review of basic industry facts. Ease of entry for new building organizations remains unusually great and so does competition among builders. To the typical builder, a wide availability of general and specialty subcontract facilities and local materials outlets for almost every aspect of building has meant that there is no need to maintain staff, equipment, or inventory. The chief skill demanded has tended to be the ability to improvise organizations, hire labor and equipment, and schedule the arrival of materials so as to gain maximum efficiency in the use of the building trades at the site; supplies are purchased from local distributors, whose margin of profit has to reflect the fact that they stock a tremendous variety of building materials and supplies over long periods of fluctuation in the local demand for new housing, during which the local builders may expand 1,000 per cent or shrink to the hard core of a few relatives waiting for an upturn next year.

The system of construction and mortgage finance, the basis of building regulation and inspection, even the organization of the design profession itself, all derive their basic form from the premise that houses are and will continue to be assembled at the site by skilled craftsmen under the direction of contractors who have estimated what it will cost them to buy materials from local distributors and have them put into place according to drawings and specifications.

The labor force is mobile and flexible, unattached to any single employing organization, with individuals shifting status from employee to employer when the situation warrants. Building craft unions have set up standards for craft performance on a highly localized basis varying from place to place and trade to trade, and they wield powerful tools in their ability to block or delay construction progress on the job, where time is of the essence for builder and buyer alike. Only about half the workers in housing have joined unions, however; those that have find difficulties in carrying on effective collective bargaining, maintaining job security, agreeing on reasonable performance and pacing standards, and resisting the temptation to take on specialized subcontracts on a piecework basis where large numbers of houses are to be built by an aggressive builder.

Innovation of all sorts is hampered by the fact that few companies dare to bring new channels of distribution and new building teams into play unaided, and none likes to risk being the first to make a major change in manner of doing business, either during a period when business is flourishing or during a period when business is generally bad and management is focusing its attention on retrenchment. As a result, most builders have come to assume that present housebuilding conditions cannot change, and that the only way to deal with inefficiencies is through the liberalizing of financial terms and government supports.

Builders have generally complained that improvement in the production of houses is blocked by external restrictions, and they are quick to cite lists of restrictive practices carried on by building labor, instances of outrageous treatment under local codes, and evidences of inflexible conservatism or anti-industry prejudice on the part of those manipulating money rates and approving the allocation of mortgage funds. In his careful study of the industry in the San Francisco Bay area, Maisel attempted to summarize the effect of external restrictions upon the final production cost of houses. He concluded:

> Summing up these restrictions, we find that by making the estimate purposely high so as to show the outside limits of the problem, perhaps as much as 7 per cent of the cost of the house, or $650, was due to restrictive forces outside the firm. This estimate, if anything, over-states the problem for the housebuilding industry. Most industries have similar problems.[27]

This may be true for a producer who wishes to build rapidly for a seller's market and can accommodate his operations to

[27] Sherman J. Maisel, *Housebuilding in Transition*, University of California Press, Berkeley, Calif., 1953, p. 255.

the restrictions. Should he wish to introduce a significant innovation, however, whether of material, method of construction, manner of distribution, or pattern of labor, the effect of the restrictions would be much greater. Since it is essential to the improvement of design to stimulate innovation throughout the entire production operation in housing, artificial limitations anywhere in the operation may not be regarded as external. These limitations are in the main stream of the problem of production.

In view of all these complicating elements, builders are by no means agreed on the economies of scale. On the one hand, the argument runs that larger companies, with volume production, mass distribution and sales, and accompanying improvements in management and fiscal status, are the main hope for significant improvement in the house. Maisel indicates [28] that in the San Francisco Bay area, assuming identical land costs, the sum of expenditures for the composite house dropped from $9,500 to $8,750 as builder size rose from small to large, while overhead and profit rose from $741 to $1,608. Others claim that the largest producers, like Levitt among the site fabricators and National Homes among the prefabricators, give the most value for the money in their houses. Yet size as such will not solve all problems.

Grebler's monograph on production efficiency [29] indicates that costs often *rise* with volume, although he concedes that this conclusion may be illusory, for even the largest builders at the time of his study may not have been large enough to realize full economies of scale. Yet he points out that many typical housing producers have very low or no fixed costs, so that little reduction on that score may be expected through increased production volume. Grebler's summary breakdown of the claims for and against economies of scale is a good

---

[28] *Ibid.*, p. 190. Savings allocated to subcontractor were over $700; those allocated to direct labor and direct materials were about $400 each.

[29] Leo Grebler, *The Production of New Housing*, Social Science Research Council, New York, 1950, p. 83.

listing of the general contradictions to be encountered. (See Table 8.)

In addition to the increase in the size and strength of builders, there are also trends in the direction of higher performance at higher cost, of an increased per cent of value added away from the site, of an increasing amount devoted to equipment and services within the house, and of increasing size and complexity in the design both of the house itself and of the

TABLE 8. Economies of Scale in Housing Production

Claims for large scale	Claims for small scale
Savings from bulk purchase of materials	Savings from avoidance of inventorying, handling, and processing of materials
Greater efficiency of labor crews performing large numbers of identical operations	Direct and more efficient supervision of labor by builders, particularly where builder is "on the job"
Greater use of mechanical equipment	
Planning, research, scientific work organization, cost and performance control	Greater use of unorganized labor, at least in certain areas
More effective promotion and use of own sales organization	Greater flexibility in adjusting to changed market conditions

Source: Leo Grebler, *The Production of New Housing*, Social Science Research Council, New York, 1950, p. 83.

development of which it is a part. Groups of houses are larger, better planned, and more completely served by schools, shopping centers, and other community facilities than was the case just after World War II. And a continually larger share of total cost goes to producers not ordinarily thought of as part of the housing industry—large and aggressive companies, well capitalized and with extensive research and development facilities. These companies are not committed to existing channels of distribution nor do they have any vested interest in maintaining conventional code and labor arrangements.

On the other hand, the small builders, the local labor force, the local banker, the materials-supply yard, the code officials, the FHA inspectors, and the producers of many of the conventional building materials are all working parts of the great conventional house production system, and none of them is anxious to have that system as they know it be changed. Furthermore, they and their customers are firm in the knowledge that their methods have stood up for many years to the tests of actual performance in place. Staying within the confines of a conventional system, they can count on a sound and reliable job, whereas the experimental house that seemed so wonderful may fail under the impact of many unexpected and unsolved problems.

Important changes are already under way in the industry, however, and even larger changes are inevitable in the future, so that the problem of the producers is not *whether* but *how* and *when* to adjust to the emerging situation. The industry should aim to free the channels for innovation, with restrictions and controls reduced to the minimum actually required for the safety of the public and the health of the industry itself, counting on the market place to decide which innovations merit full development.

Management

Even for the average local builder, the problems of management can be great. One can sympathize with those who, in the recent period of housing boom when demand was strong and all-out production was encouraged by public policy, were content to have governmental fiscal manipulations bail out even large degrees of inefficiency. Even more, one feels for those who, alarmed at the fly-by-night tactics of some of the new entrants into the field, withdrew until a future time when productive ability might have more to do with profit. The nature of conventional management problems may be indicated by summarizing the benefits which George Price of

National Homes claims will accrue to builders who abandon the struggle and become dealers for prefabricated houses: [30]

1. Better cost control in a price squeeze
2. Simplified purchasing:

> about 7 invoices instead of 50 to 200
> no materials expediters or checkers
> no warehousing cost
> no need to maintain an inventory
> no need to speculate on the market

3. Faster completion of units, and so more profit on the same capital
4. More flexible operations:

> small staff
> quick adjustment to changed conditions
> elimination of needless overhead

5. Broad-based merchandising, superior techniques, and salesmanship
6. Better design:

> able to retain best-qualified man
> able to offer a good variety of house styles
> able to shift fast with market shifts in price and taste

7. Steady financing, even in tight money periods, with no need to resort to second and third mortgages

Prefabrication is not the only choice, however. Industry leaders argue that any group of builders with a combined production volume in the order of 250 houses per year should be able to reap enough benefits to beat out the prefabricator for a share of the market. Prefabrication, these leaders suggest, is for lazy builders or high-cost or labor-shortage areas. To reach large volumes, builders may prefer to band together to buy and develop land, arrange for utilities and services, and clear

[30] From *PF, The Magazine of Prefabrication,* vol. 6, no. 1, January, 1958, p. 8.

administrative and regulatory approvals, thus leaving the actual construction operations at the old familiar scale. Or a builder may attempt to build an organization large enough and sufficiently well integrated to cope with the whole range of problems, although it must operate at a higher volume, overhead, and break-even point.

If materials and equipment producers continue to bring out larger and more complete components, including whole units of the kitchen, bath, and mechanical services that can be put in place with only a connection or two at the site, perhaps the builder should redesign his operations to use such components. If he prefers to remain small and independent, he may well wonder what form custom building will take. Will it be confined largely to the growing repair [31] or do-it-yourself business?

The large builder must give management attention to all the steps in the production process, for, as the late Lustron Corporation learned, production savings in the plant may only too easily be outweighed by increased costs in distribution and erection.[32] Upon careful study, rapid assembly or high precision may prove less effective than simplified assembly, using designs and dimensions suited to rough-and-ready handling and able to absorb common errors in foundation preparation and the erection process. Design for rough construction of fine houses is thus a key objective, and it is especially important to the degree that it can reduce the expense of skilled workmen who perform specialized operations like plastering and duct making at specific stages in construction, and then only for a short time. Important site-cost savings can be made by select-

[31] Estimated by the Department of Commerce to have risen, for residential nonfarm construction, from a volume of $4.6 billion in 1950 to $7 billion in 1956. *Construction Review*, vol. 3, no. 10, October, 1957, p. 6.

[32] Exterior wall panels 2 feet square were produced by fully automatic machinery and porcelain-enameled on a continuous line, but fabrication savings were lost because these panels had to be hand loaded into a special-body trailer in which they sat at the site until workers laboriously put them in place and fitted Koroseal gaskets to seal the four-way joints thus created.

ing materials and methods and planning construction operations from the start to reduce to a minimum the number of construction trades and processes. Setting up the repetitive use of special tools may bring savings that will more than justify the failure to design each housing element for maximum efficiency in its own terms. Thus a simple and strong system of concrete forms may amply justify in speed and operating cost savings the waste of materials involved in overdesigning certain areas of a standardized foundation.

In the larger scales of production, an important management role is that of averting problems. Management must consider not only regional differences in requirements but also seasonal variations (sure to persist even with full factory-fabrication techniques in operation), family mobility, changes over the years in average family composition, and stages of growth and development in the individual family. Until recently, producers have been preoccupied with new houses, but it seems likely that in the future the establishment of a second-hand market, the rehabilitation and resale of existing houses, and the design of new houses for simplified servicing and repair (and eventual replacement) of major mechanical and other services will be equally important. One significant benefit of a mechanical core, for example, is the fact that it permits the builder, once he has provided a small access opening, to take care of his mechanical work at the site at any time in the erection schedule without holding up other trades or operations.

Labor is often blamed for the inefficiencies of the housing industry. Such claims are largely unfair or irrelevant, for the industry has generally been too disordered to enjoy the privileges and responsibilities of long-term capitalization, of broad research and development, or of stable labor relations. Also the labor problem tends to rest on dead center, with just about half of the producers unionized, nobody anxious to rock the boat, and the views of both sides archaic.

The union craft structure developed with the subcontract

structure in conventional building operations, and it is likely to continue its dominant role in home building, even though craftsmanship itself seems to be disappearing. In the future, there may be labor shortages rather than technological unemployment, as the middle-aged groups increase more slowly than the young and the old, and the man-hours available to the labor market are reduced by longer education, earlier marriage, and the shorter work week.[33] By comparison with the working conditions and trends in collateral benefits increasingly awarded elsewhere in industry, conditions for site labor in housing production may become so inherently unattractive to the young man that continually rising rates of pay must be offered. Furthermore, there are heavy demands for labor on other types of building. It has been estimated, for example, that the Federal highway program alone might take as many as 1,400,000 of the total supply of 3,000,000 building craftsmen. We may conclude that our standard of living will continue to improve only to the degree that we succeed in improving productivity, which under these conditions in the housing field will require the encouragement of innovation.[34]

Management and labor have found difficulty in reaching an adequate bargaining status in a situation where the builders are often more Balkanized and unstable than their labor organizations, and where such structure as is given to wages and working conditions tends to be worked out by the general construction industry, with home builders left to go along or not. In this situation, many home builders have hoped to group themselves into a bargaining unit separate from the general contractors, who have found them unreliable and have no use

[33] See Peter Drucker, "America's Next Twenty Years: I. The Coming Labor Shortage," *Harper's Magazine*, vol. 210, no. 1258, March, 1955.

[34] There is evidence that labor productivity in the building field has not risen as rapidly as industrial labor productivity generally, and construction cost indices have risen more rapidly than the consumer price index. Labor productivity clearly needs a boost, but management must share the blame, for it generally has not been able to use labor effectively enough to warrant the rates that the unions believe should be paid.

for them, but only too often members of home builders' groups cannot resist the pressures of delay, and will reach a separate peace in order to plunge ahead after the market. Sooner or later a way of bargaining jointly with the general contractors may have to be found.

The labor unions have sought a stable basis of negotiation and planning, more so among those intimately concerned with the fate of the housing industry, like the carpenters, than among those supplying a relatively brief specialty service, like the electricians and especially the plumbers.[35] National union leaders have taken the initiative to weed out artificial restraints on building labor productivity and internal difficulties between craft and industrial unions, but these problems remain primarily in the hands of the locals, whose views tend to be less broad. Eventually, as the industry changes character, the craft unions will have to work out special systems for the performance of high-volume site work and the incorporation of new materials and methods of construction. They will also have to face the question of who will organize the emerging off-site production operations, particularly those involving nonwood technology. There seems no need to fear unemployment in the coming boom periods, hence the unions have everything to gain through intelligent organization of the whole industry.

Distribution and Marketing

The typical stock turnover of a local building materials supplier is slow, perhaps two or three times a year, and the markup

---

[35] The latter unions are essentially subcontractor unions and the builders cannot touch them. Small in percentage of work, they are large in percentage of trouble caused, counting on the fact that it is usually better to meet an unreasonable demand for their brief but crucial services than to have a strike over small cost increments. In some degree, their actions have stimulated innovations to dispense with their services, reinforcing the trend on the part of appliance makers to develop whole kitchen and service components complete in themselves, which may be installed merely by plugging them in.

is high. A key market is the remodeling of existing units, fifty-five times as numerous as the new houses built each year. Largest profit to the supplier comes from the tried and true materials and methods of conventional construction. The typical builder hesitates to try out new materials and faces resistance from every quarter when he does, and so the system of distribution itself tends to become an impediment to innovation. When a company engaged in the production of traditional building products considers bringing out something new —perhaps a panel using its basic material as a facing—it must decide whether to distribute the new product through existing channels, where it is not likely to fit conventional needs and so will not be pushed very hard, or to find or build new channels which might put it into competition with the company's own best customers. Unless the case for the new product line is overwhelmingly clear and secure, a company in such a position is likely to abandon development "for the present."

For a company outside of the traditional housing industry, the choice of channels of distribution is also important. Should the company use its established, nonhousing, channels? Should it place its products in traditional distribution channels in competition with traditional lines? Can it afford to find or develop other channels? Doubts raised by questions like these have been the reason for quietly dropping product ideas which, had they been developed further, might have made a substantial contribution to the housing industry.

Another consideration in distribution is the growth of component systems, which seek to combine process economy with final product variety through the individual selection and site assembly of standard parts. Many large site builders have worked out component systems, to improve construction efficiency rather than design potential of the final product. Recently many of the prefabricators have begun to market a line of building components in addition to their regular house "packages," but these are only parts and not a complete component system, in which the whole range of housing components is available, like large-scale building materials, to be combined into highly individual houses. Holding up the development of such a system is a lack of effective operational pattern. Who would be the entrepreneur? How far would he have to go in land development and final house assembly to assure a reasonable market and profit? Managerial innovation is needed as much as technical.

An understanding of the role of distribution is also required for the producer's evaluation of dimensional coordination.[36] The benefits of this idea are usually presented in terms of avoiding waste of materials at the site and reducing the range of sizes to be produced. At least as great advantages for standardizing the dimensions of building products, however, lie in the area of distribution. To illustrate, sheet materials could be produced, shipped, and stocked in a few large sizes; yet when the sheets were cut for local use the leftover pieces would remain standard and salable items. Furthermore, many complex items such as panels and trusses, if they had to fit relatively few standard dimensions, could more readily be produced to stock.

Until recently, standardization has made little impact on the average builder, because it has offered him no special price advantage. However, the benefits of the idea tend to be clearer to larger producers. Makers of appliances, for example, are using coordinated dimensions on their kitchen and bathroom products, where much marketing emphasis has been given to the feature of ability to combine units easily and in a variety of forms in the final house.

How is the average builder to deal with the problem of middlemen in the distribution channels? So long as he is small and his future production plans are uncertain, they are his valued allies. But when he is larger and more efficient, middlemen become a needless complication. Charles Abrams puts the usual complaint this way:

[36] Discussed in more detail in Chap. 6.

Producers, moreover, are removed from the home buyer by a wall of middlemen—sales agencies who buy the products at wholesale; subcontractors who buy from the sales agencies; contractors who hire the subcontractors; etc. . . .

Any attempt to eliminate middlemen meets with opposition from all those who are engaged in the handling of supplies. . . .[37]

Large builders tend to meet the problem by setting up their own materials-purchasing subsidiary, which acts as a regular distributor but sells only to the builder and at a vastly reduced markup. With large enough orders, such a subsidiary can demand and obtain from the supplier special designs or simplifications. Thus Levitt's North Shore Supply Company with an order of 200 units had the drain in the kitchen sink moved to one side, thereby shortening plumbing attachments and giving the housewife a better sink surface in which to set or clean dishes and pans. For an order of 2,000 units, the waste disposal and drain combination both could be redesigned and moved to the side, adding to the previous advantages a considerable improvement in the usefulness of the storage space under the sink.

The marketing process contains its own complications. In the first stages of any new housing product development, producers try to give the impression that big strides have been taken and that something really new and different has become available. Soon, however, attention must be directed to combining with other products, increasing compactness, and easing problems of repairs and replacement, and this means making an over-all organizational and dimensional plan in advance.

In considering the problems of marketing, also, a good deal of importance attaches to the probability that much of the new housing to be built in the next decades will be in the form of well-organized projects of good size on outlying undeveloped land. For experience indicates that conventional

[37] "The Residential Construction Industry," in Walter Adams (ed.), *The Structure of American Industry*, The Macmillan Company, New York, 1950, p. 125.

design resistances tend to disappear when people are moved out of conventional surroundings.

Another new element in marketing is the growing importance of the second-time buyer, and the possibility of working out what was only a few years ago regarded as unworkable: an effective "filtering down" to lower-income groups at second hand of houses built originally for higher-income groups. Not many years ago, housing experts attacked this concept on the grounds that those able to build new houses were so few that the impact of their secondhand houses would be insignificant, and that in any case differences in requirements and tastes would lead to so extensive remodeling in order to meet the needs of the lower-income groups as to leave little if any economic advantage. Today, variations in family housing requirements and tastes are sharply reduced as between income levels: the wealthy are little inclined to build palaces, servants are rare, and all families tend to have similar compositions and requirements. Principal differences between the income levels are in standards of equipment and service and in locational and community advantages. Thus the "filtering-down" theory stands a significantly better chance today of working effectively, and indeed such students of the economics of housing as Louis Winnick believe that it is only by such a development that the industry can serve the expected future demand.

Finance and Controls

Financial problems are among the most complex faced by producers of housing, and the health and future of the industry sometimes depend more upon money rates, tax depreciation, and terms of government aid than upon any factor of design, fabrication, or erection. Yet the attempt to stimulate production by making fiscal terms more attractive has often resulted primarily in the inflation of costs to the ultimate consumer. This has led some thoughtful analysts to suggest that the production capacity of the housing field may be limited and so unable to handle the predicted demands for the near future.

Cost increases may also mean, however, that it is easier during a boom period for producers to take care of difficulties by putting pressure on the government for easier fiscal terms than by dealing directly with the mass of impediments that stand between them and the increase of productivity. But manipulating fiscal terms brings other complexities. Such trusted friends of the industry as economist Miles L. Colean have pointed out that the sum total of investment funds can never be enough to finance all the needs of all industries, and that housing must therefore make an increasing effort to hold the line, even to make reductions, in unit production costs. Indeed Colean adds that increasingly long-term mortgage loans, with a reduced flow back into use for new construction, may in the long run shorten the supply of capital available to the industry. Yet one of the chief financial objectives of producers today is to reduce down payments and monthly costs for a consumer who typically has a good job but no accumulated savings.

FHA has recently changed its income formula to authorize mortgage guarantee when families with above-average incomes spend considerably more on their houses than had been permitted under the old formula, and it has also announced that it will encourage the creation of long-term value in the form of reduced maintenance or improved performance by reflecting the increased initial costs in its valuations. Thus the industry is encouraged to raise its sights on quality. The public in many areas is able to do likewise, but volume production requires a mass market, and the largest market will always be found in the area of the lowest costs.

One possible means of combining high quality with low cost would be a substantial increase in the amount of labor and care supplied by the owner himself—the "sweat equity," or in more modern terms, do-it-yourself housing. Remodeling, repair, and renovation work is increasingly done in this way, particularly where small repairs, painting, or the simple assembly of small units is involved; the cost of using trained crafts-men for this sort of work has become too great. The building industry has found a lucrative market for materials, equipment, and kits that have been specially designed for the do-it-yourself market.

It is doubtful, however, whether there will ever be a sizable market for housing to which a large amount of owner labor must be added, for the typical buyer wants his house as complete as possible. When do-it-yourself house construction succeeds in an advanced technology, it may be considered an indication of the degree to which artificial impediments stand in the way of normal progress. Even for remodeling, renovation, and repair work, a strong and creative housing industry should be able to work out building systems that would effectively take care of the most common conditions, reducing to a minimum the work supplied by the owner himself.

One financial need of the housing industry is fairly clear: a form of production finance that is not based upon the financing of individual consumers, and that can, when related to sound design and production decisions, make it possible to produce to stock. Often suggested as a step in this direction is the creation of a central mortgage bank to increase the liquidity of mortgage financing as a production finance device and give a high degree of predictability regarding over-all terms and commitments.

Financial aids are also used as control devices, and mortgage guarantees play a very important role in this respect. Builders find that, even where there are no community restrictions to limit their freedom, FHA and VA still exercise substantial control over their operations. Leaders in the field have asked very seriously whether in the long run it is not a mistake to have a government fiscal agency thus involved with design control, and whether, if provision could be made for the health, safety, and welfare of the consumer through effective local controls, it would not be better for the fiscal agencies to limit themselves entirely to fiscal matters.

At present, FHA is undergoing a careful review of its own role, and it has taken steps to extend its operations in small communities and still to reduce the detail, complexity, and local variability of its regulations—to the applause of most of the housing industry. Yet many builders hesitate to exchange a familiar local friend for a set of general principles set up in Washington, and not a few doubt that FHA can ever move at an industrial pace. A merchant builder whose average time for completion of his houses has been just two weeks has pointed out [38] that in addition to the careful planning required to make such speed possible, it was also necessary to abandon the use of FHA financing because time was simply not available for the number and timing of inspections required by that agency.

Financing is a vastly larger and more troublesome problem to large-scale builders than to small ones who deal in local areas and attempt little in the way of new methods. The latter have few difficulties on this score, whereas a significant part of the cost of each unit of a large housing project must be allocated to the administrative costs of getting ready to start, before any real building operation as such is put in motion.

As for community controls, local governments are rapidly expanding systems of control over the use and development of land, often without understanding the operational requirements of the industry which they seek thus to regulate. Evidence and enlightenment are needed from those who can explain the importance of innovation for the creation of significant advances in housing.

Materials and Production

Technological advance in housing has been pretty much limited to the making of minor improvements within the conventional framework, with cost increases or materials shortages spurring the search for substitutes or the use of wastes.

[38] See *House & Home*, vol. 13, no. 2, February, 1958, p. 141.

Typically, the National Association of Home Builders [39] predicts that the changes to be expected in the immediate future will be less in the shape, size, and basic design of housing than in the techniques and materials used.

The builder who looks ahead, however, must take additional factors into account. The very scale of future demand calls for new methods and for the application to housing of advances made in other fields. Continuing increase may be expected in the nature and extent of household services, utilities, and mechanical equipment; already these represent at least as large a share of the large-project house costs as do the structural and space-enclosing elements conventionally regarded as the house. Significant to the average builder is the tendency for appliances to become components, for components to become unitized sections of kitchens or baths, and for manufacturers of these sections to set up special design teams and to offer financing for full-dress remodeling of houses.

Also to be expected are higher-quality and more easily maintained finishes, lighter and simpler connectors (a great deal of attention is being given to the building possibilities of the new adhesives and the fasteners applied by explosive charges), refinements of both old (post and beam) and new (supported entirely by low-pressure air, for example) structural systems, and new kinds of roofing (rolls of metal so designed that they simply snap in place, plastics).

Despite all these advances and potential advances, the average builder does not support and is not adequately supported by research, although this is deplored by spokesmen for the industry. More important than surveying research in progress and finding means of coordinating it, is recognizing the broad potentials of research which is never undertaken because of the old impediments of distribution bottlenecks, code problems, labor resistances, and the inertia of tradition.

Producers cannot solve this dilemma alone, but must seek

[39] *Journal of Homebuilding*, vol. 12, no. 1, January, 1958.

out some form of industry cooperation on a broad front: in one situation, developing joint distribution channels for a group of new product lines; in another, creating the facilities for comprehensive accelerated-weathering and long-range performance tests that will resolve all doubts of financiers and code officials; and in general, supporting a searching inquiry into the nature of housing as a whole—structure, function, environment, and community. In a strongly conventionalized field, significant advances are less often breakthroughs than "end runs," based on insights from over-all analysis of the production of houses. It is not enough to urge that more research be done; there must be a careful study of the conditions that must be satisfied before any far-reaching research can hope to have results in terms of the actual production of houses.

Land Development

Second only to the supply and cost of money as a builder problem in recent years has been the supply and cost of land. Magazines and newspapers are full of it, and the natural trend toward the strict control of suburban land development by local government brings the issue to white heat.

In recent years, the ratio between cost of land and cost of typical house has risen from 10 per cent to 20 per cent, with required improvements running close to $2,000 per lot. Experience with FHA housing under Title 203 has been a rise in land cost per housing unit from $750 to $1,850 in ten years.

Subject to increases of this sort, many a prospective project builder has failed under the burden of required initial outlays. However much income may be expected to exceed expense in the final accounting, the builder will face nothing but outlays during the period of planning, installation of services, and land development, which often extends more than a year before construction of houses can start—let alone before any money begins to come in again.

Project developers must also cope with the urge of citizens

of this country to own large amounts of land as a matter of pride as much as privacy, and with an automobile fixation which, spawning the two-car family, may close off every means of escape from the detached single-family dwelling, since only detached house lots appear to provide the direct access, visitor parking, and on-the-lot storage that appear to be general requirements of typical purchasers.

Long-range problems are raised by the emergence of residential "scatteration" along new highway channels, with balanced new developments controlling all the surrounding land at the most favorable locations. Subsequent developers, therefore, tend to move along the access road system to another large piece of land, equally subject to over-all entrepreneurial control, rather than to build nearby. The result: instead of the constant filling in of development and land values that has been assumed by economists, there may emerge a general pattern in which top locations are developed to the hilt and protected on all sides, leaving the remaining land undeveloped because it offers only slim possibilities of profit. Implied: a significant change in metropolitan growth patterns, in living habits, and in development-value relationships.

Granting the dimensions of the suburban boom, a critical problem for the future production of housing is the control of needless speculation in housing land. This is not a matter of individual communities deciding whether or not to limit or exclude housing developers, but one of finding a basis of understanding of the dimensions of the problem at a metropolitan scale, and tools with which to cope with it. An important tool is comprehensive community planning. What will be the appropriate land-development characteristics for the community of the future? Producers have only the sketchiest examples in current experience from which to draw, because it has been so rarely possible to carry out a genuine innovation in land development. And there is no way of knowing what will work without an actual illustration. Studies of consumer opinion regarding the desirability of entirely theoretical living patterns are sure to be misleading; indeed, the history of land development has been one of resistance to new ideas. Current practices and regulations have stamped monotonous, and in the long run questionable, patterns on residential neighborhoods, segregating not only by use, category, and number of dwellings per acre, but also by income, social, and family composition groups. Far better development planning is needed if we are to provide the kind of total living environment which we technically can provide and for which we are currently paying without getting it.

Design

It is fair to say that the major innovations in the housing field have come from the leaders in the design professions, and thus to remind the producers that it is important to keep an eye on them. However far ahead of the current market they may seem to be, when a substantial consensus exists among top designers regarding some improvement of housing design, sooner or later this improvement will take place. It will come to the attention of opinion leaders and be reported in key magazines; a few top builders will try it; and bit by bit it will be modified and adapted until it appears widely throughout the industry. By such a process of adaptation, the basic design of the house has been substantially changed during the years following World War II, until the new house is conventional in the same sense as the modern young lady, who may appear scandalous to her grandmother. In its open plan, low elevation, large windows, simplified heating, drywall construction, and extensive use of mechanical facilities, the conventional house of today represents radical changes over the house of the 1920s.

Characteristics of the new houses are summarized each year by government agencies. In general it may be said that since World War II trends continue upward all along the line—in number of rooms, in number of baths, in size, in facilities, and in total cost. The upward trend in cost is sharp everywhere, reflecting not only the other factors noted above, but also the rising cost of materials and construction, of raw land, and of land development. Excluding land and improvement costs and all other nonconstruction expense, but reflecting changing characteristics, the average cost of new private single houses was estimated to be $12,225 in 1956, or 7.7 per cent more than in 1955 and a resounding 40.9 per cent more than in 1950. Government experts call this a significant gain in housing quality, by which they mean more space and facilities rather than better design and construction.[40] Obviously the cost of the house is getting higher and the market for new houses is demanding more space and services all the time. Unless a greater value for the dollar is offered in the future, the continuing rise in costs may price more and more housing out of the market. Conversely, the possibilities inherent in cost reduction through better design and the stripping down of nonessentials require far more consideration, if only for special groups and situations.

One difficulty is that most good designers tend to be ahead of the current market, and only a few can be said to be market oriented. They are fairly accused of being too fancy and of having little access to real cost information or essential production facts, and the majority do not understand or like the idea of designing for statistical neutrality. The combination of genuine design ability and a sensitive understanding of the housing industry is rare, and almost nowhere is it being taught.

Nor are the consumer's fears of advanced design always groundless. Sometimes he senses a designer's lack of produc-

---

[40] Houses averaged 1,230 square feet of floor area in 1956, or 25 per cent more than in 1950. In 1956, 78 per cent had three or more bedrooms and 28 per cent had two or more full bathrooms, as compared with 34 per cent and 4 per cent respectively in 1950. Other characteristics of the 1956 houses included frame construction (83 per cent) and absence of basement (55 per cent); the median price was $14,500 as compared with $13,700 the year before. HHFA, Office of the Administrator, *Housing in the Economy, 1956,* p. 8.

tion sense, and often he is convinced that he dislikes advanced design anyway. Judging by most of the houses that are identified by builders as modern—the word typically used is "modernistic"—one can sympathize with him.

How is the designer to assess the true desires of the consumer? Asking him will not get very useful answers. In the first place, his desires are infinite, and he makes real choices only when forced to in the market. Secondly, the measurement of tastes is unbelievably complex, although marketing agencies have no alternative but to attempt it. Some of the common mistakes are technical, such as disregarding the reduction in intensity of color that must accompany reduction in scale when small models of houses are shown to find consumer color preferences. Others occur in the use of complex social science procedures for identifying attitudes.

A good design must express intangibles—qualities that are almost impossible to measure or to assess scientifically, but are still strong factors in the final judgment of the consumer. Richard Neutra gives a fine illustration of this point in a recent book [41] when he notes that a sliding exterior wall, although hard to defend on any analysis of construction cost, operating expense, or heat loss, will be more than justified in the owner's mind on every early April morning when, with the birds singing about him and the sun drawing warmth from the ground, he slides open the wall and has his coffee out in the yard. Thus the designer tackles problems that are not subject to rational calculation. He deals with a wide range of qualities affecting human environment, and for him the challenge of industrial production of houses is not economy so much as it is opportunity.

Basically, the consumer is conservative, and it is reasonable for him to be so. Increased mobility means that he is buying for later sale, and long experience has conditioned him not to

[41] *Survival through Design,* Oxford University Press, New York, 1954.

accept innovation for its own sake, but only when it represents a real advance. Yet it is important to recognize that the attitudes of the consumer are subject to change, with the rate of change much influenced by the character of the problem involved. Men alter their work patterns rapidly, learning to operate a fluid transmission, a television set, or an electric kitchen with equal alacrity. Changes in living habits are accepted more slowly, taking years in most cases. The open plan, the large window, and the backyard barbecue reflect the emergence of new living habits since World War II. When changes affect man's fundamental personality, however—privacy balanced with sociability, for example, or self-expression balanced with conformity—the time scale may be that of the glacier.

Human attitudes also relate to the nature of the specific judgment involved. Relatively few problems occur in incorporating a new truss design or improved insulating material, because the consumer expects that all necessary questions are settled by experienced engineers and covered under a group of codes. When the over-all design of the house is concerned, the situation changes. Here the consumer has both consciously and emotionally become deeply involved. This explains why the majority of developments in the design of houses in recent years have been obvious simplifications of tasks or improvements of services, whereas those who have tried to put across more fundamental architectural improvements have met real difficulties.

The "typical" consumer enjoys his home, and if given fair value for his money, would become even more involved in the total domestic operation than at present. On the other hand, an increasing number of consumers prefer minimum involvement. The childless professional couple living near the city center tends to like simplified meals, fully automatic cleaning and washing, and any other means of saving time and simplifying work about the house, as contrasted with the large family in the outer suburbs, which believes in maximum creativity for everyone, and a staggering range of machines and gadgets with which to create. The housewife in such a house obtains every possible aid in routine housekeeping and child care, but rejoices in the ability to entertain a dozen friends at a dinner worthy of the best restaurants. Hence if the producer were to ask such a family whether it preferred minimum involvement or maximum creativity, the answer might be: both! If the typical consumer cannot directly tell the producer all about this, he has revealed many of his wishes by his actions and by the choices he makes in living facilities.

With a rising standard of living, the consumer could afford to spend a good deal more on a house, and he might like to do so. If so, will he want more space or more complex domestic equipment and services? Or will he prefer a second house, farther in the country, for family relaxation? Will he have a larger family? Some predictions may be made on these points, but to a large degree his decision to invest in housing will depend on his sense of value received in performance as well as in cost. This in turn tends to depend on the degree to which the producers of housing are free to try out new ideas and methods, and to seek both efficiency and excellence.

Emerging Role of the House

There seems to be general agreement that the production of houses is likely neither to rise nor to fall radically in the immediate future, but after that the scope of agreement diminishes rapidly. Some economists regard housing as a growth area, others consider it likely to fall behind in the face of increasing competition from all other sectors of the economy, and some think it entirely possible that the end of the postwar boom will mean a real pinch for housebuilders and destroy the prospect of significant production advances during the next few years. Perhaps the most accurate generalization would be that the industry will level off for a few years, and then, as the war babies of World War II form families in the early 1960s, find itself participating in another boom. This gives the industry a little time in which to carry out a program of reconsideration, regrouping, and retooling with the pressure off.

A major item of debate in this connection is the claim by various experts that the percentage of income allocated by the average consumer to housing has been steadily dropping for half a century, with the implication that this decline will continue in the future. In one report [42] it is stated that consumer expenditures for housing decreased from 19.3 per cent to 12.2 per cent of total consumer expenditures in half a century [43] and that a general downgrading of housing in our system of consumer values is also indicated by a drop in the per capita value of housing inventory of 7 per cent by comparison with the early years of the century and 15 per cent by comparison with the values reached after the housing boom of the 1920s. This fall in capital values is attributed to (1) progressive decline in the size (despite an upswing in recent years) and value of houses (attributed in part to more building in mild climates, the use of less costly materials, and a general lightening of the structure), and (2) the wave of conversions in the 1930s and 1940s. The report goes on to point out that the decline in budget allocation to housing is almost exactly balanced by an increase in budget allocation to transportation-recreation, and that this was what changes in living and commuting patterns might have suggested.

Such an analysis raises the very important and difficult question of what we mean by the terms "house" and "housing industry." There is reason to believe that important changes have occurred in assumptions and in the significance of definitions during the last half-century; perhaps consumer expend-

---

[42] See Nelson N. Foote, Janet Abu-Lughod, Mary Mix Foley, and Louis Winnick, *Housing Choices and Housing Constraints*, Action Series in Housing and Community Development, McGraw-Hill Book Company, Inc. (in press).

[43] From 24 per cent to less than 16 per cent including utilities.

itures for housing have not fallen off nearly so sharply as is indicated in this report.

In 1900, one might reasonably define the house as a structural shell and finished interior components, together with certain elementary facilities for heating, cooking, and toilet, the exact character varying according to convention and state of development in various parts of the country. One might also include sewer, water, gas, and electric lines, when they existed. The family moving into such a house considered it a fairly complete domestic plant. Food preparation, house cleaning, clothing care, and heating-plant operation called for a heavy expenditure of manual labor, and the members of the family, often including three generations, were kept busy at these things. Their "real property" in the legal sense—the physical plant and fixtures attached to the land and passing to the purchaser in a title transfer—was a fairly simple package which could serve as an adequate basis for the definition of the house.

Today the house is considerably less simple. Once, money went into space in which to do the housekeeping; now money goes into equipment with which to do it. How do we now define the house? Presumably the air conditioner is a fixture if it is built in as part of the central heating system, but what if it is simply placed on the window sill of an individual room? In how many states are dishwashers, clothes washers, clothes dryers, dehumidifiers, water softeners, and garbage grinders regarded as part of the real property? Does it depend on the degree to which they are built in, or can they become fixtures under the "intent theory" by which all states but one can make free-standing units part of the real estate if lender and borrower so agree in writing? [44] Is the legal concept of

[44] The degree of variation among local FHA offices in authorizing the financing of such items under a mortgage is presented in an effective chart in *House & Home*, vol. 13, no. 2, February, 1958, p. 125. Commenting on this "Balkanized" situation, *House & Home* notes on p. 124: "Almost all savings and loan associations from coast to coast and many other conven-

fixtures, or the statistician's definition of housing, at all adequate for modern domestic purposes? Under the views that seem to be emerging, what is a house? Does it include a component kitchen, or a unitized bathroom? What if you add a "mechanical core" to a house that has been designed to permit its replacement by a later model? What, for that matter, about a mobile home, which can be removed entirely by disconnecting the plumbing and utilities and which is generally purchased today on a chattel mortgage, like an automobile?

This subject has taken on a lively interest because of the attempt of retail furniture and appliance dealers in 1956 to obtain legislation that would bar from FHA financing items not an integral part of the real estate. Assuming that a clarification of the remaining real estate would exclude a large number of appliances and articles of furnishing, this legislation would strike at the flourishing "package mortgage," under which all such items can be supplied by the original builder and included within the original mortgage loan on terms considerably easier for the purchaser than if he bought them separately. In his letter of January 4, 1957, to Senator Fulbright of the Banking and Currency Committee concerning this legislation, Commissioner Norman P. Mason of FHA said:

> Among the hundreds of people polled, the equipment dealers were the only group in favor of the amendment—there was no question in the minds of this group that the house should be provided with the equipment in order to be a real house. The area of controversy was solely who sold the equipment.[45]

If the economists who call attention to the decline in percentage of consumer expenditure mean only to underline the

---

tional lenders now finance without question not only appliances but many other items like shades, awnings, wall-to-wall carpeting. Ever since 1950 almost all VA offices have included almost all appliances in their certification of reasonable value."

[45] Mimeographed copy made available by HHFA.

falling share of the housing market to be gained by builders of structure and finish, one need not criticize the old definitions, but if the economists intend to cast some light on the inclination of families in the United States to allocate money for domestic purposes, then the conclusion seems both oversimplified and misleading.

Today the typical family plans from the start to put a great deal of money, energy, and equipment into a home that will serve its domestic purposes. These expenditures are not properly chargeable to transportation-recreation, food, or anything but housing. For today, the line between the basic house and its equipment begins to fade. Studies have indicated that, as a builder's production volume rises, the total cost of mechanical equipment and services in each of his houses increases to equal and occasionally to surpass the total cost of structure, shell, and the rest of the conventional items. With the same total expenditure for housing, therefore, such a builder would cut in half the allocation to the conventional aspects of the industry. Does this alter the fact that his total allocation is still for housing within the meaning of the modern industry?

There can be little doubt that the major appliance company has a vital interest in modern houses and sells an important amount of product per house, both before and after the house is finished. And all the indications are that this trend will continue in the future.

Economists, therefore, should go beyond the statistical data on *housing* and include in their consideration expenditures on *household operation,* which covers furniture, appliances, service, maintenance, communication, and miscellaneous expense.[46] It is made clear in Chart 4 that, while the percentage of the consumer budget allocated to housing plus utilities has dropped from 24.0 per cent to 14.0 per cent in forty years,

---

[46] A detailed discussion of these terms and their changing significance appears in J. Frederic Dewhurst and Associates, *America's Needs and Resources: A New Survey,* The Twentieth Century Fund, Inc., New York, 1955, pp. 196–232.

the percentage allocated to household operation climbed during the same period from 11.8 per cent to 14.9 per cent, so that, although at the start of the period housing was twice as important an item as household operation, the latter has re-

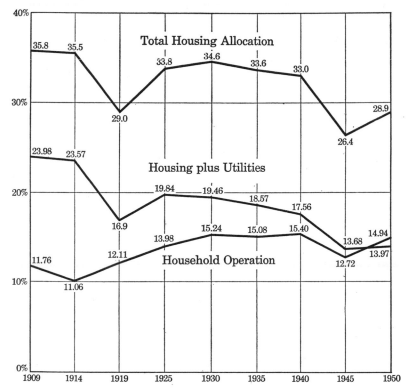

Chart 4. Percentage allocation of consumer budget for housing. (*J. Frederick Dewhurst and Associates, America's Needs and Resources: A New Survey, The Twentieth Century Fund, Inc., New York, 1955, pp. 987–989.*)

cently passed the former in importance. In money terms, each represented in 1950 an outlay per year of slightly under $15 billion. Combining the two, it may be seen that the budget allocation for housing in the modern comprehensive sense fell during the period from 35.8 per cent to 28.9 per cent, a significant drop and one probably accounted for in part by factors of the type noted by Foote, Abu-Lughod, Foley, and Winnick, but a drop of small proportions compared with that to which so great attention has been drawn.

If to this allocation one adds essential landscaping, entertainment, and recreational items that would have no meaning aside from the house, then we might conclude with Drucker [47] that consumer spending for domestic living has *increased* during the first half of this century, and there is no present indication of a change. In short, the field obviously is fast developing and clearly warrants industrial interest. It is in no sense of the word a declining sector of the economy, and it is ripe for good ideas and sound management.

[47] At meeting of ACTION *ad hoc* Committee on the Producer, New York, January 24, 1957.

Chapter 2

ADVANCES IN
HOUSE DESIGN

*This chapter, written by Bernard P. Spring, deals
with the broad influences that affect the design of a
house. It opens with a comment on the influence of
selected design pioneers, continues with a consideration of the effect on house design of changing living
patterns in the typical suburban family and changing methods and forms in the emerging housing
technology, and concludes with a summary check
list of factors to be kept in mind in designing a
house.*

The "House of the Future"—in the Past

Changes in architectural style can often seem perplexingly
arbitrary to the casual observer. Does a shift in the fifteenth
century from Gothic to Classic building, in the present day
from Colonial to Modern, or on a smaller scale from "Cape"
to "Ranch," result from the same forces which yearly change
the neckline and hemline of feminine attire? Is there some
large logic in the progression through the years from one
type of house to another, or is it merely the product of jaded
appetites and a need for accelerating the normal rate of
obsolescence?

There are, of course, some logical reasons behind all the
changes in architectural style. These are made clearer by a
study of history, where we find that every change in style

has been preceded by marked shifts in commonly held values, in command of materials, and in social and economic patterns.

However, in most eras there has been a noticeable time lag between the development of new conditions of life and their expression in terms of design. Our contemporary situation is no exception to this sequence; today, the housing industry stands immobilized in just such a time lag between a cultural change and a corresponding change in its product. That is one reason for an analysis of this kind.

We know that the past fifty years have seen a revolution in our way of life and in technology. We know that the methods of building and the planning and use of houses have changed in that period too, but in their basic form the vast majority of our houses today look essentially the same as they did in the early 1900s.

In the gap between potentialities and realizations that marks the first stage of a cultural development, however, there are invariably prophets, unusually sensitive men, who are the first to appreciate the practical implications of changed techniques and values. The housing field has had its fair share of prophets in the last half-century. They have thundered predictions of decay and collapse of the *status quo* under the weight of its own illogic. In their designs they have shown us what they considered the clear paths to better living conditions. They have been the designers of the "house of the future."

Decay and collapse have not, of course, come to the industry—only discomfort and dislocation. The paths to the house of the future have not been as clear as the pioneers confidently hoped, and today's home builder still finds it easier to build and to sell a house produced without significant regard for advanced techniques. The very same pleas for industrial logic that Albert Farwell Bemis [1] made a generation ago are still being heard today.

True, a fair number of isolated ideas introduced first in

---

[1] Albert Farwell Bemis, *The Evolving House*, vol. III, *Rational Design*, Technology Press, M.I.T., Cambridge, Mass., 1936.

"house-of-the-future" designs have been adopted as standard practice by builders. Large glass areas have been translated into the picture window. From the call for variety in living space has evolved the "family room." Planned outdoor space has fathered the barbecue area. Modular coordination has influenced product sizes, and a larger percentage of factory-finished parts now enters the typical house.

We know that to date the developments in construction technique yielding the greatest economic advantages have been such modifications of the conventional wood frame as the tilt-up wall, plank-and-beam or panelized-stud wall. Through changes of this order, the conventional house type has easily survived, its appearance rarely showing any effect of the considerable advance in mechanical equipment and services that has been going on within the familiar spaces.

Small gains should be encouraging. But it is important to realize that the changes which have been made in house-building are largely incidental to the strong motivating precepts of the design pioneers. The heart of the idea put forth by the most eloquent prophets was that a clear reflection of new materials and technology, combined with a sensitive recognition of new living patterns, would have to lead to building forms and site relationships significantly different from those we now know.

This potent idea has been germinating for fifty years and has developed broad roots among designers. At every major turn in our country's recent history, we have heard confident predictions that revolution in housing was upon us. Periods of stress like the depression of the thirties and the last years of World War II brought forth the largest portion of prophetic proposals for a "house of the future." But the conditions for its flowering have yet to evolve.

First among the difficulties blocking the success of dramatic proposals has been the designer's preoccupation with isolated aspects of either technology or social life, instead of with all the implications of both. Most designers supposed that changes in materials and construction details would be enough to put the industrial production of houses into high gear. On the other hand, designs for greater fulfillment of family goals tended to neglect the effective development of construction techniques.

Many of the proposals for radically new house forms looked awkward to most people, chiefly because the forms were unfamiliar, but also because the earlier prophets failed to consider a wide range of problems in their designs. The dramatic solution of a single aspect of design to the exclusion of other aspects has actually worked to hinder acceptance.

The second difficulty has been the "new look" which may be a great selling point in the automotive and appliance industries but will not sell houses. Men of conviction and courage have brought radical design schemes to a point where enthusiastic publicity would seem to have assured success. In 1932, *Fortune* predicted that Howard T. Fisher's General Houses were ready to start a new trend.[2] In 1946, the same magazine proclaimed that R. Buckminster Fuller's Dymaxion II "has a better than even chance of upsetting the building industry." [3] The opportunities presented themselves but the general demand that could have tipped the scales in their favor did not arise.

Even that small segment of the industry which does successfully produce factory-fabricated houses generally yields to any indication of public favor for traditional design. The prefabricators certainly know better than most the production advantages which would result if the public were prepared to accept a house that looks unconventional. It is a credit to their ingenuity and business acumen that they have developed the ability to prefabricate a structure which in appearance is a perfect replica of the traditional site-built house. The buying public in general has not asked for more rapid progress toward the house of the future.

[2] *Fortune*, vol. 6, no. 1, July, 1932, p. 67.
[3] *Fortune*, vol. 33, no. 4, April, 1946, p. 172.

Yet that very public enjoys hearing about a radically new home life. The eagerness with which the press continues to report basically novel concepts shows that readers enjoy such stories. Nevertheless, they seem unwilling to relate these ideas to the decisions they make about the home they bought yesterday or will buy today.[4] There is momentary stimulation but no sense of active participation in a movement toward making this world of dreams a reality. At the same time, people expect what has never happened; that is, the sudden arrival on the market of a full-blown house of the future, readily available to all. They do not understand the inherent difficulties of organization which prevent the building industry from introducing a new dream house every year with the same inevitability that appliance manufacturers produce a dream kitchen.

Effective design is not so much a fixed set of rules for making a house look beautiful as a way of thinking that, from a consistent point of view, links analyses of all aspects of the production and distribution process to the creation of expressive form.

There have been well over one hundred serious attempts to predict the nature of the "house of the future" since the turn of the century. Illustrations of eighteen such designs appear in the photographic section of this book; Appendix B is a bibliographic review of forty-two of the most significant. Some were merely demonstrations of a principle, never intended to go further than the drawing board; others were actually put into limited production. The attention of the designers of these houses of the future has typically been centered on the potentialities of one product, one structural form, one process of the many in the total industrial complex, one way of organizing life or land. For most of these designers have been convinced that their dramatization of a solution to some one aspect of the problem of home design would

[4] Indeed it sometimes seems that there is an inherent public fear of innovation as likely to injure current investment and future resale values.

break the roadblock that stands in the way of changes needed in the housing industry. But for the most part, they have been unaware of the depth and complexity of the roadblock; hence no individual has been able to integrate the influence of all the relevant elements in the design and production of houses into a single unified design concept.

None of the designs, taken as a total concept, was influential in changing the course of the building industry. A few isolated details which first appeared as a part of such design projections—for example, the generous use of glass, the open plan, the family room—were after a considerable time lag to become common practice in home building.

Clearly, what is needed if the designer's crystal gazing is to have a positive and constructive influence on the future of the industry is an approach which squarely focuses *all* of the myriad factors which contribute to the production of a house. A really useful design for the future would be a creative synthesis of many factors: planning for use and flexibility; visual quality in terms of form, scale, and expression of materials; techniques of structural analysis; materials technology; fabrication processes; handling operations; erection processes; integration of environmental controls; marketing and financing procedures; and legal controls.

A few designers today may command a working knowledge of all these elements. Among them would certainly be some designers of some of the houses listed in Appendix B. In attempting to promote their schemes for the future, they will certainly have learned the hard way that a narrow approach, however brilliant, cannot lead to important changes in a complex industry.

Perhaps the approach most likely to succeed would be made by a design team, each member of which is expert in one or more of the many elements which must be weighted and considered. Such a team, conscious of past errors and understanding the potentialities of the future, could make proposals that might be immediately useful to the building industry in taking the first real steps toward the house of the future.

The building industry must take the initiative in going beyond the necessarily limited proposals of the individual designer, if it wants the clear view ahead which it so badly needs to guide its development. The industry should find some means of assembling qualified teams of experts and give these teams a clear mandate to explore the future, supported in this vital mission by the wealth of experience and knowledge at the command of the industry.

New Factors in House Design

When a civil engineer designs a replacement for an old stone bridge, we expect to see something that looks quite different. We appreciate the fact that changes in materials and construction methods, and the increase in traffic in the years since the original bridge was built, will radically influence the appearance of the new construction. Why should the design of houses not evoke the same kind of fresh response to new conditions?

We look to the house, of course, to provide a refuge, to satisfy complex emotional needs, whereas we expect a bridge to perform a simple service—as gracefully as possible. Yet it appears likely that the building industry's shift from handicraft to machine production and society's even more important shift to fluid informal living patterns will lead gradually to new, unfamiliar forms for our houses.

We can already see a trend toward new forms in certain major public buildings, designed since World War II, where dramatic, thin-shell concrete arches span large spaces, or factory-built modular wall panels shield against the weather. And the increasing attention designers are paying to frankly experimental houses suggests impending changes in the appearance of the typical dwelling.

As a matter of fact some sign of all the innovations discussed in this chapter may already be seen in practice. Examples of a new kind of design expression, though still few and isolated, are springing up in every part of the country. These represent the work of a handful of designers who are peculiarly sensitive to the implications of new elements that have almost imperceptibly crept into standard building practice.

Even the most conservative builder can no longer find or afford the men and materials it would take to build a house exactly as he did before World War II. Changes have come along slowly enough, however, to enable most builders to assimilate them without significantly disturbing the appearance of their product at any given time.

But in retrospect, the substitutions of new materials and methods for old have added up until the typical builder's house, despite all efforts to maintain a *status quo* in design, does indeed look substantially different from the house he built before 1940, although the basic form remains static. This new look has evolved mainly by the agglomeration of makeshift adaptations to new conditions. What many designers hope for is an opportunity to go beyond these accidental changes in character and clearly to express the underlying nature of the technological changes and new patterns of domestic living that have occurred and will continue to occur in home building.

Changing Patterns of Living

Responsible designers have always sought ways of reflecting the nature of changing social patterns and values. In our time and in our country, the probable basic trends affecting housing design are the narrowing range of income levels and the continuing over-all rise in living standards.

The two-generation, servantless family unit, one of the by-products of our emerging social structure, becomes an important factor in design. With only the parents to care for the children and maintain an increasing area of house, mechanized aids to housework are required to sustain family life. Thus, we may expect to find living areas planned around, and perhaps left open to, work areas like the kitchen or workshop.

Wall, floor, and ceiling materials and finishes greatly influence the character of an interior. All of these surfaces are being chosen increasingly on the basis of ease of maintenance. Manufacturers are developing hard, impervious finishes and mottled, dirt-concealing colors and textures. But interior design based only on ease of maintenance is not an entirely attractive prospect; designers, by exercising ingenuity, can bring much of the warmth and variety of a material such as wood to the newer low-maintenance materials.

The child-centered family seems to be an American institution, with adult control gradually loosening under the sheer weight of what might be labeled "adolescent nationalism." A way to avoid the many battles that could come out of such a conflict of interests is to provide parallel living spaces for children and adults. With constantly rising standards of living, our definition of decent housing may soon have to include a separate play space, quiet study area, and greatly expanded storage space.

Under the pressure of new needs, familiar plan relationships must certainly change. The central role of children in the family life combined with their characteristically changing needs as they grow will prompt the use of flexible plan arrangements. Initially a good design might have an open plan that permits easy supervision of younger children by the parents. But then it should be possible, when the children reach the age at which privacy is all-important to them, easily to convert the plan, by means of movable partitions or the like, into segregated rooms.

Modern hobbies, with their usual complement of equipment, can turn the interior of the conventional house into a scene of confusion. Changes in interior planning must be made if the equipment required for these important pastimes is to live harmoniously in the same space with the more conventional easy chair, fireplace, and coffee table. So intimately have the latter objects been bound up with the activities of the family that they virtually symbolize the idea of "home." The pursuit of hobbies, however, begins to supplant the quiet evening by the fire as the principal family activity. Is it not natural that the objects used in this new kind of activity should begin to share an important symbolic and visual role in the home of the future?

The increased leisure people have today has already affected house design in the form of the family room, the inclusion of which is now fairly standard practice among builders. And the outdoor space around the house is being used more and more intensively for family activities. This, in turn, leads to a desire for privacy, for screening outdoor activities from public view.

Most of our current site-planning and landscaping practice allows neighbors and passers-by to see such activities. This is no more satisfactory than having the indoor living areas on display. Rational site design, in which screening achieved by landscaping and walls plays as important a part in the total picture as the house itself, may eventually give an entirely new appearance to our neighborhoods.

Besides the active, free-flowing space needed for hobbies, entertaining, and the like, rising levels of education and a friendlier attitude toward intellectual pursuits will make places for reading, study, and quiet contemplation desirable if not necessary. Everything points to an increase in the amount of communication—education and information as well as entertainment—that will be pumped directly into the home in the future. The design of an effective communications center in the house will be no easy task if the programing becomes an even more essential part of the family's life. Here again, children and adults have different needs and require separate facilities.

The fluid, informal way of life at home that we are developing can make for endless group combinations in a single household, equally unsuited to the cramped "efficiency" of a minimum house and to the formal symmetry of some traditional styles. The house of the future is likely, therefore, to be casual, unimposing, and loosely organized in its exterior appearance and interior arrangements.

Though new modes of living seem to call for more space and more differentiated space, it is by no means inevitable that future housing will actually provide it. The kind of house that incorporates all the new planning needs mentioned here could take a substantial part of even the expanded incomes we optimistically predict for the future. Attractions outside the home, such as the automobile, the boat, the drive-in, the country club, and the vacation trip, will compete strenuously for the family's dollar. If we are interested in maintaining the family and the home as our central social institution, then it is essential that we understand the need for better home design which will satisfy the demands of today's more active family at a price it can afford. Larger, better-equipped houses in carefully planned neighborhoods can be afforded only if they are designed and constructed with all the efficiency of modern industrial techniques. If houses are not efficiently made, a good part of the market will be lost to the products of industries which are flexible enough to reflect changing conditions.

It would be fatuous to ignore the fact that certain builders have developed sufficient command of today's practical know-how and popular styles to be able to offer the public comparatively good value in a home.[5] But it is good only in comparison with the even poorer examples of builders' houses which are more commonly found. From the point of view of how well they provide for the fulfillment of family goals, these houses are full of inadequacies. Larger, more luxurious builders' houses in the higher price brackets suffer in most cases from the very same inadequacies. Among the most conspicuous of

[5] "The Low-cost Home Has Come a Long Way, Too," *House & Home*, vol. 11, no. 5, May, 1957, p. 129.

their shortcomings is a standardized form which becomes grotesque when repeated countless times on typical small lots. Such houses do not provide a harmonious neighborhood pattern; they offer neither continuity between house and site, nor privacy inside or out. The planning allows only either a rigid schedule of activities or a constant internal conflict. There is no real control over light or view. The forms and materials provided are unrelated to the way the family uses the house. In short, these houses are spruced-up versions of the very inadequate minimum houses of the past. We must set our sights higher to find the basis on which to begin designing for tomorrow.

Changing Technology

What will be the effect of a changed technology on housing designs? To begin with, the designer's role in the production process itself will be changed. Today most of his time and energy is usually given to detailing and specifying the assembly of the myriad pieces of material and equipment that make up the house. With a shift to factory production of housing components, the details and assemblies will be largely predetermined. If the designer is to maintain any influence on the appearance of our housing, he will want to become involved in the detailed design of units and components before they are produced and assembled at the factory. He may, for example, want to increase the size and the number of functions performed by a single assembly: if factory-made, one unit could provide at once the structure, enclosure, finished wearing surfaces, insulation, and built-in channels for mechanical services.

Inevitably, the design of large assemblies will be standardized to a certain extent, for it will not be possible to offer the buyer an infinite variety of combinations of materials, sizes, or shapes. The prospect of losing any kind of freedom of choice disturbs most people in this country; they are apt to assume that absolute uniformity is on the way. Yet automatic

feedback controls of machine production are already per-
fected to the point where production lines can be made to
provide variations of a basic theme and need not turn out the
same identical object over and over again. Thus it is more
likely that a whole system of construction rather than any
individual building component will be standardized. Within
any system there could be a variety of sizes, models, or finishes. For that small minority of people who insist on genuine
individuality—and can pay for it—there will always remain
the custom-built house. For most families, however, standardization will actually mean increased freedom of choice because
it will bring a greater variety of house designs within their
price range.

Dimensional coordination is needed if factory-produced
parts are to fit together in the final assembly of a house on its
site. The larger and more complete the unit going into a house,
the more important that it mesh with units from other production lines, for it cannot be squeezed, cut, fitted, or justified
like the little bits and pieces and the primarily wood-based
technology we build with today.

The use of a coordinating module or a "preferred measure"
can have a visible influence on design. Units ranging from 2
to 5 feet have proved to be useful devices for organizing a
complex plan or elevation. Rhythm has always been one of the
basic elements of good design. Strong modular rhythms will
no doubt come to play an even more conspicuous role in
tomorrow's designs.

With the coming of standardized construction systems and
large-volume production, it will be possible to devote im-
measurably more care to detailed design study. It will be
economically feasible to build full-scale models of alternative
solutions and to test them in use. Today it is the exception
when a designer is given enough time or enough money to
allow him to think about such minor but vital details as door
hinges or faucets for longer than the few seconds it takes to
specify them. More important is the time, thought, and test-

ing that can be applied to major details like doors, windows, storage space, and mechanical equipment. When a really large quantity of similar units is produced in a factory, a small fraction of 1 per cent of the cost of each can pay for thorough study of such details. Thus it is fair to expect that the quality and utility of the product of advanced building technology will be far higher than anything we now know.

Variety in Detail

When mass-produced house parts arrive on the scene in full force, appearing again and again in every community, will we have a mechanistic environment as delightful to behold as a case of tin cans? Actually abundant examples of inhuman, mechanistic environment already exist in very many of our handmade, site-built communities. The character of the environment is, after all, determined not so much by the method of fabrication as by the values and intentions of the designer (and usually today this means the builder). As J. M. Richards points out,[6] "the time has come to remind ourselves that machines are tools to be utilized exactly as far and as frequently as it is to our advantage to do so, but no farther." The long-standing precepts of good design—unity, harmony, variety, balance, rhythm—can be realized in industrial building components as well as in forms produced by traditional building methods (see photograph 16).

To gain the broad market needed for commercial success, the basic character of mass-produced house components will probably have to be rather generalized and neutral, with individual preferences, satisfied through a range of surface treatments, colors, textures, and the like. Uniformity in the basic character of components might in fact turn out to be an asset for our communities. It might bring back something of the unity of a common design vocabulary that makes our pre-

[6] J. M. Richards, "The Next Step," *Architectural Review*, vol. 107, no. 639, March, 1950, p. 165.

Industrial Revolution towns or the architecture of old Japan so appealing. Surely the goal of a visually harmonious community can more readily be reached by this approach than by the addition of countless carloads of pseudo-Colonial ornament to our houses.

Calling contemporary architects to account in his article, "The Post-Modern House," Joseph Hudnut, former dean of the Harvard School of Design, comments:

> We have developed in our day a new language of structural form. That language is capable of deep eloquence; and yet we use it only infrequently for the purposes of a language. Just as the [historical] styles of architecture are detached from modern technology and by that detachment lose that vitality and vividness which might come from direct reference to our own times, so our new motifs are detached from the idea to be expressed. They have their origin not in idea but in techniques.[7]

The ideas to be expressed are undoubtedly to be found in the emerging social patterns discussed above; the language with which the ideas are to be expressed is to be found in the new technology.

One of the many factors that greatly influence this new language of form is the need for large dimensional and finish tolerances. It is difficult and costly to eliminate noticeable irregularities in large manufactured parts. A more natural approach would be to emphasize rather than to cover up joints, thereby obtaining new rhythms that actually enhance a design. If irregular surfaces are textured and coated in an imaginative way, the necessary irregularities may not only cease to be regarded as blemishes but actually come to be considered normal parts of the best new designs.

The degree of precision in handicraft building has always been exaggerated. Such precision as has existed is fast disappearing from the contemporary scene (unfortunately it is

---

[7] *Architectural Record,* vol. 97, no. 5, May, 1945, p. 70.

doing so before the disappearance of handicraft methods). Few are happy about the loss; fewer still face the fact that we can accept and even enjoy a new quality of workmanship in factory-finished products. However, we should not make the mistake that some designers have made, i.e., to claim that a precision of finish even greater than possible with handwork would be the hallmark of the industrially produced house. Those who have felt this way took their cue from the mass production of small objects, a notion which has caused some notable failures and probably delayed our progress toward a going components-manufacturing industry. More pertinent are such contemporary illustrations as that of the mass-produced automobile engines, where costs are cut but performance levels maintained through the use of parts roughly produced with large tolerances that are countered through the use of inexpensive gaskets.

In housing, too, we see the development of new gasketing and calking materials (see photograph 8). It may seem at first thought that mere improvements in the way we seal the joints of buildings, however dramatic, would not have an important affect on design. But it was precisely the effort to obtain weather-tight joints that led house designers in the past to develop the characteristic details—such as window frames and sills, door frames, moldings and cornices, overlapping shingles, and clapboards—which give the familiar quality and scale to traditional houses.

Unless designers using the new methods of joining factory-made components can find a way of providing character and a sense of scale, we are very likely to hang on to the old familiar details long after they have become outmoded, inefficient, and downright wasteful. Most people feel that material waste is preferable to ugliness.

So it seems to rest clearly on the designers' shoulders to find new ways of providing for the old human values, variety and richness as well as unity, using to reach this goal the time-honored means of surface finishes, joints, proportions, and rhythms of components, devices for controlling light and air, and color schemes.

Structural Form

Science has given us materials with unheard-of properties and ways have been discovered of shaping them into geometrical forms of enormous strength, rigidity, and economy. A thin shell of structural material can be curved or folded so that the weight of the loads it must carry is brought down to the foundations, thus eliminating the need for heavy beams or girders. At the present time, hand methods are usually required to achieve such results and the cost of labor for "thin-shell construction" very often exceeds the savings in material. But once machines are set to turn out the necessary forming quickly and economically, new possibilities in design will be opened. When this happens we may begin to break away from our well-known house form—the rectangular box capped with pitched roof and its minor variations (see photograph 14).

Economical lightweight structures which can span great distances with ease and which permit free interior planning are becoming more feasible (see photograph 34). Both support and enclosure can be obtained from a single curving shell, and joints can thus be eliminated at the most vulnerable places, i.e., at the connections between floor and wall or roof and wall. An astounding variety of bent, curved, or three-dimensional trussed shapes is now available to the designer (see photographs 17–22). He can, moreover, choose his structural elements at almost any scale that suits him, in units 1 foot across or 100.

Today, designers are exploring three main approaches to structural innovation. First, there is the rectangular panel in two variations, load-bearing and non-load-bearing. Both these variations are in accord with the familiar rectangular-coordinate system followed by virtually all contemporary building practice. Consequently the advantages of interchangeability, simplicity, and ease of manufacture with present equipment are retained. Of the current structural innovations, the rectangular-panel system is the only one that can with relative smoothness make the transition from present-day practice and prejudice.

The Acorn House designed by Carl Koch and Associates (see photograph 15) is an example of a load-bearing system using stressed-skin plywood panels, the structure and enclosure being one and the same. Walter Sanders's own house, built of Unistrut space frames developed at the University of Michigan, illustrates a nonbearing system [8] which incorporates a network of steel struts designed to extract the maximum strength from the steel by using it only in tension or compression, never bent. In a non-load-bearing rectangular system the enclosing walls can be very thin, lightweight, strong insulating panels. The so-called sandwich construction with dense skins and a lightweight insulating core permits free use of a single factory-made component instead of the complex series of layers of material previously required.

The second category of structure which has aroused the interest of designers is what might be called the "umbrella type." When the potential economy of thin-shell or space-frame constructions is realized, it will presumably be possible to roof over great areas at low cost. Underneath a large protective umbrella of structure, plans completely free of the usual space restrictions can be devised. Free and loosely related living areas can be spread out over a large part of the site and the whole site can be actively used day or night, rain or shine.

The thin-shell wood roof Eduardo Catalano designed for his own house (see photograph 21), curved for strength in the shape of a hyperbolic paraboloid, is a notable example of the umbrella idea. The spread-out plan students at M.I.T. devised

---

[8] "Unistrut Used for House Framing: The Sanders House," *Progressive Architecture*, vol. 35, no. 10, October, 1954, p. 106.

for Buckminster Fuller's geodesic-dome enclosure (see photograph 13) gives a hint of the completely new approach to planning it makes possible.

A closed sculptural form, or egglike shell, is the third basic structural type being explored (see photograph 9). Such a structure derives enormous strength—as does an egg—from the constant curvature in all directions and the uninterrupted continuity of the strikingly thin shell. Of all the new structural forms, this is the most difficult to adapt to the demands of house design. The basic egg shape, although the most efficient structurally, tends to become the dominating feature of all the spaces inside the house. It is difficult to avoid a sense of constriction in this kind of enclosure or to make free use of the important outdoor spaces. In addition, perforations impair the strength of the structure so door and window openings of small size and with rounded corners are usually required in order to prevent cracks in the shell. Variations on this theme are the single cell such as Fuller's Dymaxion II or the agglomeration suggested by Wallace Neff for his "Airform" houses.

In the development of our new structures, we are still at too early a stage to predict which design approach or approaches will prove most workable in practice. The chances are very good, however, that we may see a radical change in our man-made landscape and in the traditional symbol for "house" which has endured for two hundred years in our Western culture. The possibility places a great responsibility on the designer, one which will increasingly command his attention.

Climate Control and Mechanical Services

Research concerning the effect of natural environment and climate on human comfort provides another growing influence in housing design. Standards of comfort expand with amazing speed when new devices for comfort control, such as the room air conditioner, hit the market. In this century, we have generally overlooked the fact that proper planning of orientation, plantings, and shading devices for windows and walls can startlingly improve the control of temperature within a house.[9] Assuming that the use of mechanical aids for comfort conditioning will continue to increase, planning for natural aids will take on even greater importance because they can substantially reduce the burden on mechanical equipment, thereby providing greater comfort for less cost.

For centuries people living close to the land have known that a considerable amount of comfort could be built right into the design of a house. This knowledge is largely responsible for the specific character of the many regional folk types of dwelling. Designers must again give more critical attention to the relative costs and benefits of mechanical and natural aids. The builder may well find it a real economy to save the trees on a house site and to plant new ones for the specific purpose of blocking the sun's rays in summer and letting them pass in winter.

The sharply contrasting elements of clear window or solid wall, which are two basic elements of design today, may give way in the future to walls and roofs that can filter light; that can be adjusted to opaque, translucent, or transparent; that can be shifted in panels from place to place, as needed, to control the amount of light and heat entering the house. Climate-control systems, changing with the weather, season, and mood of the occupants may bring a fluid ever-changing appearance to the house. Fixed façade compositions, long the main stock in trade of designers, may give way to dynamic, constantly varying designs which will be just as lively as the people who live inside.

The fantastically complex intertwining of the basic construction of a house with mechanical equipment and its adjunctive piping and wiring is probably the most costly and irrational part of conventional building practice. Perhaps the greatest single benefit to be derived from a shift to factory production

[9] For further documentation of this point see A. and V. Olgyay, *Solar Control and Shading Devices,* Princeton University Press, Princeton, N.J., 1957.

of housing components is the liberation it would bring from the typical "spaghetti" that lies unseen but very much paid for inside the walls and floors of today's house.

The fabric of a house a century ago was essentially the same as it is today, but the cost of its mechanical services has risen from next to nothing to a major element of the total cost. As electric lighting, modern plumbing, central heating, and now air conditioning have become available through the years, builders have learned to work them ingeniously and laboriously into the walls and floors. Mechanical equipment still is being installed as though it were an entirely new and unexpected addition to the basic house structure. Pipes and wires are squeezed into every available opening, holes for them are drilled everywhere and they are painstakingly threaded through the structure at great expense of time and energy. Repairs and replacements are correspondingly difficult and costly.

With increasing industrialization, mechanical equipment will tend to be produced in "packaged," self-contained units (see photograph 3). The manufacturers of such units may well follow the lead of the electronics-equipment industry, which has learned to keep working parts completely free and independent of supporting framework and enclosure, thus permitting easy removal of the equipment itself for maintenance or replacement.

With self-contained mechanical units at his disposal, and thus no longer constricted by need to intertwine services with structure, the designer will be able to concentrate on the space and traffic-flow planning of a house. He will have two clearly defined types of space at his command: an enclosed service core and clear, unobstructed living areas, with the juxtaposition of these two determining the plan. All services may be localized in a single mechanical core, which usually would result in a centrally located core area with all the remaining spaces arranged around it. A more flexible but possibly more expensive arrangement would be to use several interconnected mechanical units, each with some adjoining living space. Most flexible of all would be free space provided with continuous power sources into which mechanical elements could be plugged wherever desired.

As the essential efficiency of producing packaged units brings the cost of mechanical equipment down, more of it will go into the typical house—too much to remain hidden from sight. Some way will have to be found to make equipment packages easy to look at and good company in anyone's living room.

Over-all Value

It is difficult to predict how long it may take for changes in technology and living patterns to be reflected in the design of a house that is truly of our time. Some innovations may be right around the corner, but many will have to wait out a gradual readjustment of the fractionated and traditionally slow-moving housing industry.

With expansion of our technical knowledge and understanding of our own social goals, changes which seem radical today will, one by one, be absorbed into common practice. As this occurs, the industry will benefit, for it will be able to offer the public a product more clearly suited to its needs and more efficiently built, thus providing a greater value in terms of livability for each dollar spent on housing.

Check List of Considerations for the Designer

The following outline is an attempt to summarize some of the social and technological considerations that will affect house designers freed from the traditional impediments of the field:

Housing Design Considerations

1. Land planning
    a. Coordinated planning framework. Housebuilding should be preceded by regional, community, and neighborhood planning, which provides a coordinated framework for siting

houses for optimum location, access, visual and social relationships.

b. Increased density and intensified use of land. Land development and accessibility are not keeping pace with population pressures, hence densities may increase sharply around the old city centers. Site-planning techniques which are known but seldom developed today can be called upon to cope with the increase. Some of these are row housing, courtyard housing, intensive landscaping and screening to maintain and even enhance present levels of privacy and land utilization.

c. Optimum adjustment to natural environment. The location and orientation of the house can be planned to provide the optimum adjustment to local climatic conditions, prevailing winds, outlook, natural lighting, noise, and atmospheric impurities—leaving a minimum amount of supplementary adjustment to be made by mechanical equipment.

d. Respect for natural landscape. Elements of natural beauty in the landscape, such as trees, rocks, rising and falling terrain, bodies of water, ground cover, etc., can be preserved and often used to form a focus or framework for the siting of houses.

e. Opportunities for friendship formation. Placement of houses can strike a balance between provisions for privacy and provisions for the casual meetings with neighbors which lead to friendships. This can be accomplished by the provision of attractive public areas so located as to promote natural use by all.

f. Freedom from public utility connections. More nearly autonomous utility design can free the house from connections with costly and inflexible facilities for sewage disposal, water supply, electricity, telephone. This will allow much greater freedom in location of the house.

g. Simplified foundation systems. Simplified foundation systems can reduce the disturbance of natural conditions and ecology to a minimum during construction. Foundations can be light in weight, economical of material, easily assembled or dismounted and can allow the house to be freely expanded or contracted.

h. Unity and variety of neighborhoods. Siting can be carried out so that neighborhoods have social and visual unity through the use of common elements (e.g., contiguity, height, module), while variety is provided by permitting expression of actual individual differences between families (e.g., size and arrangement of interior spaces, color preferences, lavishness of materials).

2. Structure and equipment

   a. Fewer and larger components. The number of parts of the house assembled on site can be greatly reduced. Parts can be combined into components under carefully controlled, highly automated factory conditions. The maximum size of components, and thus the maximum number of parts which can be successfully combined, will depend mainly on the limitations of the transportation system.

   b. Ease of joining. Dimensional and finish tolerances normal in high-speed manufacturing processes, and the use of relatively unskilled labor in joining components, can be made possible by the development of new plastic and rubber compound gaskets and adhesives.

   c. Integration of functions—wet and dry components. All the functions of the shelter can be gathered together and integrated into two basic types of components, wet and dry. Wet components can integrate into one unit the heating, ventilating, and all sanitary functions. Dry components can integrate into one unit the functions of structural support, protective outside skin, insulation against heat and cold, durable interior finish, radiation of artificial light or transmission of natural light, distribution of heating, cooling, and ventilating media, absorption or reflection of sound, etc.

   d. Flexibility of connection. The dimensions and joining details of components can be so determined as to allow completely free and flexible creation of space. Houses can be expansible in any direction with spaces of any shape and size related in any way—limited only by the dimensional coordination of the components used.

   e. Mechanical aids to assembly. Transportation of components from the factory assembly line to their assigned place in the house can be a coordinated and almost completely mechanized process, with manual handling and sorting of parts minimized.

   f. Structural innovations. The use of the enormous strength properties developed by three-dimensional space frames and by thin skins, when given continuity and compound curvatures can reduce weight and material costs.

    g. New materials. Development of plastics and laminates, new alloys, and lightweight metals permits new methods of fabrication, making integration of functions into building components easier.

    h. Variety through mass production. Although the number of industrial components of a particular design produced in a particular year may be very large, we can expect many different manufacturers to produce them. Each manufacturer will be able to produce a variety of models in a variety of sizes and shapes, each varying in quality and price and range of functions, refinements, features, and "extras."

    i. Demountability. Dry components can be made easily demountable after the house is occupied, to permit changes in accommodation for increasing or decreasing family size, new ideas on living patterns, substitution by improved later models or higher-quality models when they can be afforded.

3. Accommodation for living

    a. Fully mechanized housework. The tendency toward increasing scope and refinement of mechanical household equipment is likely to continue.

    b. Increased space. As the desire for mechanical equipment reaches a plateau, further benefits of rationalization and industrialization of housing production can be realized in the form of increased space in the house. At the same time, population density will be rising. The average house, therefore, may be between 2,500 and 5,000 square feet on a lot as small as ⅛ to ¼ acre, thus approaching a 1:1 proportion between enclosed and open space on the site.

    c. Variety of spaces. Increased space will make it possible to have several kinds of living area in the house, providing for the various moods and rhythms of family life. Part of the living area of the house can be devoted to open, active, and extroverted functions, while another part can be intimate and introverted.

    d. Free circulation patterns. Increased space may mean that the tyranny of the tight circulation pattern will no longer dominate house planning. There can be greater freedom in the arrangement and juxtaposition of functional areas and more freedom of movement through the house.

    e. Real integration of indoor and outdoor living. Partial enclosure with walls and fences, insect screening and trellises, as well as outdoor heaters and coolers, can extend the use of the outdoor space associated with the house to almost the entire year in most climates. The limits of active living area can be at the lot lines of the site rather than at the walls of the house.

f. Acoustic separation. The acoustic problems inherent in the use of lighter materials can finally be solved by the most effective means: spatial separation of conflicting noise sources.

g. Rationalized storage space. As basements become impractical or undesirable, storage space can be provided nearer the living areas which require it. The need for storage space can be more carefully analyzed, and storage space designed to accommodate objects with a minimum waste of cubage.

h. Changeable space relationships. Components that make up interior partitions and parts of exterior walls can be designed for mobility (e.g., tracks), making it possible to vary interior space relationships and the relation of interior to exterior space according to needs or moods.

i. Control of natural and artificial light. Filters, perhaps on the polarized light principle, can control the quantity, quality, and color of natural light entering through wall or roof components. Artificial light can also be controlled in quantity, quality, color, and source.

j. Fewer and better furnishings. The functions of blinds, drapes, carpets, lighting fixtures, and cabinets will be incorporated into the fiber of the house, leaving chairs, tables, and beds as the probable surviving furnishings. Even beds may be ultimate victims, since the entire floor of the sleeping area can be used as sleeping surface if properly treated.

k. Expressive spatial forms. Changes in ceiling height, floor level, and angle between planes should be feasible with a flexible system of joining components, thus making possible an expressive and varied progression of spaces within a house.

Chapter 3
DESIGN AND THE INDUSTRIALIZED HOUSE

> *Here Carl Koch considers the added responsibilities and opportunities given the designer and producer when houses are produced in large numbers by industrial procedures. After stressing the importance to the producer of the designer's comprehensive viewpoint, the chapter deals with the breadth of choice and complexity of aims confronting the designer, the inadequacies of his present training, and the need for designer and producer to draw upon each other's creative abilities.*

Design, always an important element in producing a house, becomes vital when production is in large volume by essentially industrial methods. In most industrialized products, full design advantage is taken of industrial potentials. This is obvious in aircraft and bridges. In automobiles and toasters it is less clear but nevertheless definite. So far as the American automobile is still a good buy, it is because its basic design is still good. The stylist who appears so important today is only diverting attention from the design; hence in increasing numbers we shut our eyes and buy cars because they still work well and because ours will look no worse than our neighbor's!

The industrialized house is a different matter. We are still only trying to produce units which make effective use of our technical potential; their design must not be allowed to deteriorate into mere "styling." What then is the role of a designer in this emerging industry?

Basic Design Objectives

The first responsibility of any house designer is to understand the house as a statement of an ideal. He seeks to appreciate the needs and yearnings of buyers and, even more important today, to translate into buildings their strong—but ill-defined, if defined at all—desires for the satisfaction of primary needs. In a house these requirements are exceedingly complex. Here, in a small over-all space, almost every human function is performed from the womb to the tomb. Besides eating, sleeping, working, and playing, family activities include numberless variations of all these—formal and informal entertaining, family and club groups, meetings and reunions, business and monkey business. To the family, besides all this, the home is an emotional refuge and a traditional symbol. The buyer is very apt to take most of these functional needs for granted, appreciating their importance only when they are not provided for. Many of them are conflicting. For instance, a woman's kitchen must be as easy to work in as possible and as efficient as an operating room, but also as capacious as an attic; as sumptuous as a Roman bath, but also as cozy and snug as a rug for a bug.

A good architect learns to meet these conflicting demands tastefully and effectively. A house must appeal to the age-old urge to find a cave, build a nest, or fortify a castle. This has nothing to do with a slide rule and cannot be short-cut with persuasive advertising, production estimates, or hard-hitting distribution programs. And these human requirements must be met all the more positively in an industrialized house.

The architect's second responsibility is to synthesize the literally thousands of alternative materials and items of equipment, parts, and pieces, which must be fitted together to make a house. The tremendous amount of choice is not appreciated by industrialists, who are used to products infinitely more simplified and standardized. The 10-volume edition of Sweet's catalogue [1] contains 15,868 pages, weighs about 150 pounds, and yet offers only a selected list of the better-known companies' products.[2] The complications of selecting a heating system are described later in this chapter. To them may be added those of selecting plumbing and utility connections; cooking equipment; structure; wall, floor, and roof materials; waterproofing; heat and sound insulation; electrical installations; fixtures and equipment; finishing; and furnishing. No engineer is trained and equipped to make a design synthesis of all these problems, relating each one to human needs, social, psychological, and economic.

The house designer must take a number of other factors into account: zoning and building codes; local customs and prejudices; fire, health, and safety regulations; climatic requirements; and financing facts of life. All these add to the problems which must be solved by design.

Finally, the architect seeks to make a positive, concrete statement of these requirements and to produce more than just a package—a fully integrated house. No wonder that David Slipher, president of Webb & Knapp Communities, Inc., which shows evidence of becoming the country's largest builder of integrated communities, says that good design is the key to marketability.

Designing for Industry

When houses are produced in large numbers, the architect must relate his basic design objectives to the tremendous industrial potential for accomplishing them in a far more effi-

---

[1] *Architectural File,* Sweet's Catalogue Service, F. W. Dodge Corporation, New York.

[2] Although the president of a steel company had spent seven or eight months studying the housebuilding industry, he was genuinely shocked to see just the sample of the house products displayed for a few days at an annual convention of the National Association of Home Builders. After an hour or two, he retired with sore feet, feeling sorry for himself but even sorrier for the designer.

cient way; at the same time, he must learn to deal with a number of economic limitations—budgets, capital funds, markets, and profits. He must understand and appreciate the rules and limitations of big industry. This is not easy; few architects have experience in this field and many are antagonistic to the idea. The job to be done requires the utmost ingenuity of the best architects helped and backed by the best, most flexibly minded, and imaginative industrial executives and engineers.

So far there has been no fully industrialized house. Our houses are full of well-designed modern products but they do not add up. The sum of all the parts does not begin to make a whole. One of the main missing links is an architect-designer who understands and appreciates the industrial potential and who still has a knowledge of the human meaning of shelter-design.

The needed level of design is not provided by the typical architect who must approach the job by treating each family as unique, which to some extent it is. Nor is it provided by the typical builder who more practically has looked for the highest common denominator and has been variously successful at finding it, giving people less and less of what they need and want at the cost of more and more of their living budget. Rather, it comes from a man (or, more likely, a team) who, gaining some of the builder's know-how and pragmatic approach, has equipped himself to design a house which, making full use of our technological, economic, and industrial development, offers such deep and lasting satisfaction that it will exert a pull strong enough to justify the tremendous expense for tooling and merchandising, planning and production.

To illustrate the broader range of this sort of design, consider the factors involved in changing from wood to steel. Every industrialist knows that steel is a better industrial material than wood—high strength-to-weight ratio, predictable and standardized characteristics, subject to precision size and shape limits, high-speed fabrication, and finishing machinery.

Every architect knows that wood is warmer in appearance and feel, has a human, workable, changeable, give-and-take quality which we like next to us in our everyday living. There are good and bad ways to take account of these facts; painting artificial wood graining on steel is generally bad; putting wood handles on steel doors, or wood doors on steel cabinets, or wood table tops on metal legs is, by and large, good.

More basically, in designing steel elements, the designer must recognize that an entirely different over-all process is involved. Wood is suited to craft handwork. It is easily cut and fitted. There is no necessity and little advantage in taking many wood fabrication and finishing operations into a large, mechanized factory. Steel is another matter. It is hard and expensive to modify, cut, and fit, by hand or even with light, portable machinery. Its production expense must be covered by high sales volumes. Any part made of steel should be finished as far as possible in the factory and assembled with the least possible modification in the field. These qualities of steel are both an asset and a liability to the designer. His components, if steel, must be more carefully handled, must fit together with appropriate tolerance for error, and, where possible, should be completely painted before arrival. By way of compensation, steel can be roller-coated with any pattern or combination of colors and with a wide variety of coating materials to provide an infinitely better, longer-wearing, cleanable surface at about one-tenth the price of hand painting on the job. And with many wall surfaces the cost of hand painting is considerably more than the cost of the material itself. So the designer, if he understands the nature of the material, the equipment to fabricate and finish it, and the human requirements to be met, can accomplish a far more satisfactory job at real cost savings (see photograph 39).

His comprehension must go beyond technical understanding of material and equipment, however. What colors and textures must be chosen to provide a reasonable balance between infinite variety and a reasonable stock in hand? What is the best balance between flexibility—fewest parts to accomplish largest number of jobs—and most efficient use of material—just enough in the right place to accomplish each particular job? An attempt to make a single product highly versatile may make it too costly for normal use. On the other hand, limited production runs of large numbers of different parts for highly specialized applications may be prohibitively expensive in tooling, inventorying, repair, and replacement.

The Responsibility of Selection

The modern designer performs one of his most necessary functions merely in selecting the best process and combination of materials from the welter of alternates which face him in this prodigal age. For there are no longer any technical, functional imperatives.

The first Americans, by contrast, had no choice. Trees, rocks, clay were their raw materials, hand tools such as axes and handsaws their only equipment, and imported refinements both expensive and difficult to obtain. Immediate protection from the weather and human enemies was imperative. The solution then was obvious. Log cabins went up as fast as our speediest prefabs do today. This kind of imperative still exists with some products. Most moving vehicles (aircraft, railroads, boats, and even the basic works of the automobile); industrial and farm equipment and machinery; bridges, dams, weapons; and a considerable list of man's real or fancied requirements have sufficient functional imperatives to make their design logically consistent with the means and techniques available to produce them. Not so houses. We all know that we are technically able to produce far better solutions for our requirements than we do. Our solutions are shaped by a series of economic, psychological, and social pressures which, in their reaction on us and our housing product, are tremendously difficult to predict.

Selecting Mechanical Services—the Heating System

Let us take heating equipment as an example. It took several hundreds of cool winters for the evolution from the fireplace and wood and coal stoves to general use of furnaces. Since the 1920s, things have gone a good deal faster. Steam heat was first refined to "vapor" heat—at lower pressure and temperature—and then into forced, warm-water systems. The hot-air heating industry, fearful of being left behind, adopted the same principle and brought out forced warm air. In both cases, to an already elaborate system of furnace, radiators, and ducts or pipes were added motors and blowers and pumps. And the furnaces themselves were particularized in order to make use of fuels like oil and gas as well as coal.

Then along with the one-story slab-on-ground house came so-called radiant heat and a whole new set of mechanisms and requirements. (The technique, as has often been pointed out, was known to the old Romans and Koreans, but they made less fuss about it.) With radiant heating, the warmth of the circulating medium is transferred to a larger surface—floor or ceiling usually—which itself acts as radiator at still lower temperature. The first popular radiant systems used hot water circulating through tubing. The hot-air industry contributed new developments in ductwork and plenums (the Lustron house, referred to later, used a radiant hot-air system in the ceiling). The electrical industry joined the fray (having, after all, made toasters for years).

Once more the result was a tremendous proliferation of alternative systems and equipment: pipes, pumps, wires, fuels, fans, and so on and on. For the designer, further complication of choice and more things dependent on the choice he makes. Shall heat be radiant? What kind? Floor or ceiling? If floor, should ductwork be included in the poured slab, or in a hollow block system, or should the floor itself be raised? What are the relative costs? What kind of floor covering? What effect will the decision have on other elements of construction

—framing, shape of rooms, and the schedule of trades work? At the outset of any new development the architect is often more daring than the engineer. (My office had to design our own first radiant heating system.) As the systems improve and become complex, the architect more and more often must turn to the heating engineer, another professional, and ask, "What do you recommend?"

Here surely are concerns enough. But we have only just begun. The heat pump is already adequate in mild climates, and researchers everywhere continue to seek new basic approaches. Why, for instance, burn fuel to get heat, when the sun sends quantities of it free? Recent developments in storage and recirculation systems have made solar house heating a practical possibility (see photograph 33).

Other basic researchers are investigating the possibilities of true radiant heating (as opposed to heating by transfer or convection, which are the main components of present-day "radiant heat"). Because of heat radiating directly from the sun, a man outdoors on a bright day may stay comfortably warm though the temperature of the surrounding air is low. To radiant may be added "reflective heating," where radiation is enhanced by reflection. Skiers are tanned in subfreezing snow fields. The same principle, moved indoors, could lead to arrangements whereby the walls, floors, and ceilings of rooms are given reflective surfaces, and electric panel heat sources are so oriented as to beam against the occupants both directly and by ricochet. Presumably we would snap on this kind of heat like an electric light on entering a room and turn it off when we left. Undoubtedly such heat would work best in particular shapes of rooms with particular shapes of walls; perhaps there would be no need for solid exterior walls at all but only arrangements of metalized fabric on frames which we could leave open in warm weather and close when it gets cold, to increase the reflective surfaces. Quite likely, also, there will be applications of atomic or solar energy to problems of heating.

Of course, even to talk about heating may seem a little old-fashioned. In some parts of the country, staying cool is of greater concern. And the big thing now is what the admen fondly call "year 'round climate control," which implies yet more cunning methods of humidity control and air cleaning and will keep us as wonderfully separated from nature and as pure as laboratory rats.

Now let us take all these things together. Or, rather affirm that they cannot be taken together. Some systems which now appear likely are not. Some will prove disadvantageous in comparison with others, or will be applicable only in special climates or as partial solutions, or will offer spectacular comforts at certain stages of our technical development and then, like steam heat, slowly fizzle out. But which and when and in what manner? The designer knows only that he is already perplexed in his choice between systems, that it bears more and more heavily on his choice of construction techniques, and that tomorrow—in his conscientious regard for the latest, best, and most economical solutions—his perplexity will be several times worse.

The responsibility of selection alone has, as shown in this review of heating systems, become tremendously complicated. Nevertheless, the designer's problem here has not been as difficult as in other elements of the house. At least the heating system is often provided by one company (which, to be sure, may assemble its components from a number of subcontractors).

Selecting Building Materials—the Sandwich Panel

Selecting the materials for the structure, insulation, vapor barrier, and skin of the dwelling is even more difficult, so much so that the designer is often drawn to the notion of putting all the layers and pieces together in a single industrially produced panel system. The sandwich panel is a very good example of the problems that stand in the way of such an industrial solution to the selection problem.

The sandwich panel, both as complete wall and structure and as curtain wall alone, has been the subject of theorizing and development by designers, inventors, and builders for years. In this country the U.S. Forest Products Laboratory and the J. B. Pierce Foundation were among the first research agencies to concern themselves with this subject. The honeycomb core with plywood or metal faces is largely the result of the former's activities, the Celotex Corporation's Cemesto board (asbestos cement faces bonded to fiberboard cores) the result of the latter's.

To illustrate the potential of this approach: in the original Acorn House my office was able to provide a practical wall, roof, and floor material in a total of 2 inches of thickness, using two layers of ¼-inch plywood resin-bonded to 1½ inches of plastic-impregnated-paper-honeycomb core. This material spanned 6 feet 8 inches easily, had a fairly reasonable K (or heat transfer) coefficient, was light and rigid, had the qualities of any plywood surface, including impermeability and low maintenance, and was conducive to fabrication in large house-wall-sized sheets. We developed our panels on the basis of original research done by the Forest Products Laboratory, and we built the first house in 1947 and 1948. In the 2-inch-thick Acorn sandwich panel, ½ inch of wood, plus the equivalent of ⅟₁₆ inch of wood in the form of paper, creates an effective wall equal to one made up of the conventional ¾ inch of rough boarding, ⅜ inch of shingles, the equivalent of ¾ inch of 2 x 4 studding 16 inches on centers, plus an interior finish which in comparable plywood would add another ¼ inch for a total of 1½ inches to 2 inches of wood.

One of the potential assets of a sandwich panel for building purposes is light weight. The Acorn panel, a relatively heavy and cumbersome example, weighs approximately 3 pounds per square foot; aluminum-faced panels would give the equivalent strength for approximately 1.5 pounds per square foot. The sandwich panel has a high volume relative to its weight, however. Compared with a 6-inch wall, a 2-inch wall is a big saving, but the core material packed in its unexpanded condition, plus the facing material, either flat or corrugated, would occupy a still much smaller space. A development to be looked for is a method of expanding or blowing up the sandwich at or near the building site, which would greatly simplify the packing, storing, and inventorying of this material.

It is noteworthy that although several other studies and developments were going on simultaneously a dozen years ago— one interesting house designed by Dreyfus and Barnes used aluminum faces—relatively little further development occurred until the mid-1950s. More recently, research and development data are beginning to accumulate.

The General Motors Technical Center, one of the early examples of curtain-wall construction, used steel of such a heavy gauge that there was no real reason for the sandwich; several bonding agents and calking compounds failed and had to be replaced before a satisfactory final surface and seal were achieved. Price was no particular object, however, and much valuable information was derived from this building. Since then, extensive developments have been initiated, making use of various combinations of glass, gypsum, plastics, composition boards, aluminum, and different kinds of steel.

For general commercial construction at the present time an inexpensive and satisfactory type of sandwich appears to be one consisting of a very thin facing of roll-formed and continuous-sprayed porcelain-enameled steel bonded to masonite, which is in turn bonded to a plastic-impregnated-paper honeycomb core with a suitable backing material. It should be noted, however, that this sandwich is definitely not a one-operation material. Steel companies make the steel suitable for enameling. Enameling companies make the frit for the enamel; they usually do not apply the enamel. Enameling fabricators prepare the steel and apply the enamel, though there is often a joint ownership of the enamel-fabricating company and the enamel-manufacturing plant. The glue used to cement the porcelain-enameled steel to the masonite may be manufactured by a plastics company, but very often only the ingredients of the glue are manufactured by a plastics company; the glue itself is formulated by a glue company. The next layer, the masonite, is manufactured by still another company making neither bonding agent, nor paper honeycomb, nor any of the other ingredients of this sandwich. The paper honeycomb itself, relatively useless without these faces, is currently made by two or three large-sized producers for whom it is definitely a side line.

Under the circumstances, it is surprising that commercial development has proceeded as far as it has. Furthermore, for housing purposes, the full potentials of a sandwich panel system can be realized only when the design of the entire dwelling and its mechanical services are planned from the start with this industrial principle in mind. Clearly, the development has become so complex that a team of experts is required before real progress can be expected. Such a team does not now exist. Needed is the continuing interest of a single, powerful producer, able to control all the elements of choice.

Selecting the Construction System—
Factory-finished House versus Components

No less important than mechanics and materials is the decision regarding basic construction. Should the house be an entirely factory-finished unit, an assembly of highly standardized components, or something in between? Designer and producer alike seek to learn from existing examples.

One industry, trailer production, has successfully bypassed the barriers to change and improvement which stand in the way of housing generally. This industry has avoided the pitfalls which have kept the house from becoming an industrialized product—primarily by producing a finished unit and not calling it a house. It has been constantly expanding its share of the market and indications are in favor of continued expansion as mobile home designs more closely reflect the use pattern for the product.

Trailers have constantly increased in size, weight, and complexity. As the Acorn house design indicated in the 1940s, materials and techniques are available for constructing dwellings which are truckable over the highways and can be expanded at the site very simply (automatically, at a price) to as much as five times the package size (see photograph 15).

A major reason for the continuing popularity of the trailer is that it provides far more "housing" for the money than any other dwelling type. Divorcing the house from the land makes possible many economies. The illusion of mobility excuses crowding which no fixed-housing planning would tolerate. Equipment is lighter, more compact, less expensive. Few aesthetic, traditional prejudices—which can be expensive—need be taken into account. Most important, the whole trailer can be finished in the plant and is amenable to mass fabrication, purchasing, and distribution techniques (see photograph 35).

A partial development along these lines which has been suggested several times in the past is the mobile mechanical core: a package on wheels including the equipment for kitchen, heating, cooling, plumbing, electrical service. Such a unit could be marketed with a do-it-yourself panel package or alone, to allow local building labor to supply the shell of the house in the traditional way. Certainly this part of the house, plumbing and heating particularly, could provide the most dramatic savings if mass produced and marketed as a complete unit.

The trailer offers the best current example of an entirely factory-produced, complete house. Far less easy to illustrate is the other extreme in the designer's choice of system, the rationalized component product which, together with a number of other separately produced and marketed parts, can be assembled in many different ways to make a complete house. For as yet we have very few standards and therefore very few modern products designed on a reasonably standardized basis.

The Unistrut system may serve as an example, however, because it is an extreme case of multiplicity of application through the use of very few completely standardized parts. The company approach has been to use parts developed for other purposes and already in mass production, so that they have already largely paid their way. The Unistrut space frame, for example, is a three-directional truss system developed from four basic parts—a tension and compression member 4 feet long, a pentagonal or hexagonal heavy-steel pressed cap member which receives up to eight of these truss members, a bolt, and a nut. These four parts make up the whole truss, which can span any width from an uneconomical minimum of 4 feet to a present maximum of about 46 feet in one direction, and any length in the other. An adaptation of the truss is now being used in a school building to span 56 feet. Each part has been very accurately engineered and can be manufactured on a completely automatic basis with the very best and most up-to-date equipment.

The space frame is used both for roofs and for an ingeniously leveled and supported floor system. In addition Unistrut has developed an electrical distribution system utilizing the same members. A complete cathode or fluorescent lighting system may be installed in the trusses, and a modular luminous ceiling panel manufactured which fills the truss spacing below, making a complete ceiling construction with built-in lighting.

Also developed have been a warm-air forced-circulating radiant heating system and an interior partition system utilizing the same elements with the addition of a number of lighter ones, allowing the customer to use his own in-filling materials which, usually made to the same 4-foot module, can be installed with the least possible waste.

A number of interesting points have emerged in the development of this system. In the first place, in order to give satisfactory performance under maximum loading, each member is made heavier than would be required in other applications. The cost of site labor, the difficulties of training crews, and the great advantage of standardized rapid-assembly technique have convinced Unistrut that the waste of steel involved in this way is far more desirable than the provision of a range of variations which save on steel but introduce complications in site assembly, inventorying of parts, development of additional connections, and a whole host of other multiplying factors. Indeed, the designers were able to effect a 60 per cent saving in the cost of assembling the space frame after a careful study which ended with the simple elimination of the washer on the connection bolt.

Unistrut is an outstanding example of the design approach to factory mass production of simple components offering a broad variety of assembly possibilities. The rolling, fabricating, and finishing equipment in the factory, which is a very small plant by present-day mass-production standards, is superior in quality, automation, and installation to that in many far larger plants. This is possible solely because the company has rigorously followed the principle of developing a maximum range of uses for an absolute minimum of parts. It is worth noting that it has taken Unistrut over fifteen years of continuous design study to arrive at this point.

Present Role of the Architect

Let us now look at the present "designer" of our houses—the architect as he exists today. No doubt he is, in varying degrees, influential in housing design. He has generally been responsible for developing, or at least adopting, the prototypes of our variously styled and built present-day houses, be they Georgian, Cape Cod, contemporary, or even ranchburger. Generally he must be content with exerting influence in a distant and relatively unremunerative way on a product for which, as built, he will disclaim any responsibility.

For many years most houses have been developed and built from plans furnished free, or at a very nominal price, by several major sources, among them our so-called shelter magazines. Many of these are republished or edited in quarterly or annual form as books of plans and plan ideas. These designs are furnished free to the editors by known and unknown designers (who are often, but not always, architects) and by the builders of their designs. The designer is usually willing or anxious to receive the publicity which is thus afforded him, as this is a variety of free—and ethical—professional advertising. (The American Institute of Architects does not allow any direct advertising on the part of its members.) He may get some further custom work as a result of the publishing of his design, but, of course, thousands of builders, amateur and professional, may use the plans in whole or in part without applying to him. In fact, most of the magazines offer complete blueprints and specifications for houses for from $1 to $10 with, or without, a small royalty to the designer.

A second source for architects' designs of houses is the materials manufacturers, who employ architects or draftsmen to draw complete plans, which are then furnished free or for a nominal fee as an inducement to purchase the company's materials. Most of the major materials suppliers for the house-building industry have promoted plans or designs for houses, either in trade brochures or other advertising media, or through the agency of trade and consumer magazines as editorial material.

Since the Depression of the 1930s, competitions or contests have proved a prolific source of designs for houses or for rooms in houses—many of which have been quite influential in affecting trends throughout the country. Prizes to the winners—usually students or very young architects—make a large number of free or relatively free designs available directly to the builders of houses.

The builder himself in many cases thinks of himself as a designer and often does actually take over this role. Alfred Levitt, for example, though not trained as an architect, has definitely influenced, if not controlled, the designs first of the famous Levitt houses and most recently of his own apartment houses being built in Long Island (see photograph 27).[3]

---

[3] Levitt was the first to use on any scale a sprayed-on paint which, through actual texture and through a spatter method of coagulating

On a smaller scale, some builders actually develop the design for their own speculative housing, but many more merely use designs provided from one of the other sources—perhaps doctoring them up to suit their own tastes.

Financing and insurance institutions are very influential in the design of houses. Although the Federal Housing Administration does not actually publish designs as recommendations to builders, through its minimum property requirements and various reviews and approvals, it does come very close to specifying the designs of housing. Its "acceptable designs" soon are adopted by the builder who quickly learns that the easiest, surest way to FHA approval is to present something previously accepted for mortgage insurance.

Currently, the architect who really exerts a major influence on specific designs in the housebuilding field is rare. Foremost is the man who has as his clients operative builders. West Coast architects do most of this work, though individual practitioners work on a more or less standard architectural basis with builders in various other parts of the country. These architects are few in number and rather specialized in

---

separate colors, provides both a pleasing surface and real concealment of flaws in the material underneath. A number of other firsts were developed for Levitt houses. One of these is a hot-water oil-burning unit completely contained in a counter-high exposed cabinet which was added to the kitchen, provided with a stainless-steel counter top, and backed up to a fireplace, thus furnishing a unique exposed heating system for panel-slab hot-water heat. Levitt was able to obtain new designs because the size of his project meant a tremendous order for whatever company obtained his business and because he could afford a staff able to suggest not only designs but also reasonable production costs; the companies he contacted were more than willing to engineer and develop an entirely new product under the circumstances. He was also among the first to use split bamboo as closet doors, now common in the operative builder's house throughout the country. He has, working with Johns-Manville or the Celotex Corporation, developed several types of asbestos siding, which have been extensively used first in his project and then in others. He has thus acted as a very influential designer of components for the mass housing market. It is clear that this type of design for a large market is an increasingly important field for design development.

their activity; they consist generally of firms starting as designers of custom houses whose interest or experience has led particularly in the direction of relatively low-cost housing. They have familiarized themselves with the very specialized problems of the operative builder and have learned to understand his language, work within his requirements; conversely, they educate him to the value to be derived from well-designed and carefully thought-out operative houses.

This type of practice appears to be growing with the success of the builders who have employed the services of the few architects well qualified in this demanding field; it requires an active, wide-awake attitude on the part of the architect, an interest in cost, and a knowledge of cost-estimation, of labor factors, of materials prices, and of general building procedure and habit—far more than is necessary for the designer of larger buildings where cost is not as penny-pinching a problem. The basic difference between design for the operative builder and design for the large building is that for the former the operation is always a repetitive one, whereas for the latter an operation is carried out generally throughout one building and then developed and improved, or at least somewhat changed, in the design of the next building, no matter how similar its nature.

In addition, a considerable amount of specialized design work is unique to this kind of practice. One problem at the present time is simultaneously to achieve and to conceal a standardized construction method. Repetition of the same operation throughout a large project of identical houses is one of the principal sources of cost reduction in the building of speculative housing.

An architect working for an operative builder provides service in several ways: one is in creating with each new development a fresh, up-to-date house which catches the public fancy and thereby makes sales for the builder, yet may economically be so sited and varied as to avoid the monotonous project appearance to which most house buyers are relatively allergic. Currently this is generally accomplished by concealing the essentially identical construction, plan, and appearance of a large group of houses with small variations in the way of external accessories, changes in roof pitch, differences in fenestration, and other relatively simple surface treatments within a basically repetitive operation. Increasing attention is being paid to the elements of site planning: placing and setback, landscaping, and use of accessory fences and structures.

In some cases the role of the architect in the building operation extends to the point where it is difficult to separate him from the builder. One such architect has described his job when working for an operative builder as follows. In addition to the preparation of the preliminary sketches, all the variations, the site plan, the working drawings, and the bill of materials, he also carried on all the negotiations with the material and equipment suppliers, passed on the original site on which the builder intended to build, and in some cases, suggested sites for the builder. Further, he conducted all the negotiations with local officials and departments, managed all the operations with the FHA, found and arranged all the details of financing, prepared the permanent mortgages, planned all the landscaping, and handled the furnishing of the model houses. To top it off, he said that he generally acted as a sales agent for the first period after the opening of a model house. Here is one architect who does as much of the building as Alfred Levitt does of the designing.

Many progressive materials suppliers are recognizing the source for ideas and development suggestions in builders', architects', and other design offices. They regularly send men around to the offices to show what they are developing, ask for advice, and use the office personnel as unpaid design critics of their product development ideas. To illustrate this type of approach, a number of companies select a group of designers and architects, invite them either singly or in groups to the plant, and give them food and drink, a visit to their facilities, and an inspection trip on some hush-hush or developmental project, at which time the designers and architects are invited to criticize, make suggestions, and "help" the product-planning department of the large corporation to bring out a product which will meet demanding design requirements. Considerable change, for instance, in the kitchen equipment field has come about in this way.

An Illustration: The Window

The broad field of product-planning design, which is an increasingly important aspect of the design of the parts of a mass-production house, clearly reveals the necessity for a different approach on the part of the architect. We may illustrate this by the window. Though it may become as obsolete as the vermiform appendix, since ventilation and the provision of natural light and view no longer stand in a necessary relationship, the present-day window is a product industrialized enough to illustrate the problems facing the architect for an industrialized house.

Most "designers" have given little thought to the window as a design for mass production. An architect's usual job is simply to make a selection from all the catalogues, picking out the hardware he likes the most and assuring himself that the window is well made and does not leak. He is certainly attentive to price, and he may have his predilections for frame material: steel, aluminum, or wood. Beyond that, his concerns are for the proportions of the window—the relative width to height, thickness of mullion, "shadow line," "reveal," and the like. These concerns are important but have very little to do with production design.

If his window design is going into mass production, the architect must first of all decide—and here his contemporary architectural school training will give him some help—whether the window is to be opened and, if so, how; if one must be able to see out of it or into it; and how it is to be flashed to keep the weather out and heat from going in or out, depending on climate. He knows that he must keep the rays of the sun out in hot weather; he must also know the performance of double-hung versus casement versus in-swing versus awning-type versus sliding versus disappearing versus a few other operating types.

This done, he faces an entirely new and—to 99 out of 100 architects—unknown series of problems. He must study the means of fabricating the chosen material, the number of different uses the window may serve, and a host of other design factors involved in the way it is to be assembled and distributed. If the material chosen is steel, how many designers know the real design elements: the problems in forming (hot and cold rolling, drop forging, welding, bending, or braking), the problems in finishing, the considerations that go into joining, fastening, and assembling? Many designers are aware of the recent and very rapid changes in the glazing field. A few years ago putty or calking compound was the only suitable material for holding glass in frames, but now there are a number of good rubber and plastic materials. Should the window be prefinished, preglazed—what are the problems in doing this, the machinery necessary? What, having settled this, is the best choice in final finishing, in painting, and in masking the glass if painting must be done after glazing?

When he has made all these decisions, the designer has not finished, for he must realize there are still—and for a long time to come will be—architects who insist on using for each large building a window that is just a little different from any other window that has ever been made; and the decision as to the form, the shape, the material used, the method of joining, and everything else about the mass production of the window—if the producer is to be able to quote a low price—must be so fitted to elastic production methods that the producer does not have to throw the job out (with) the window.

What about shipping? The window must be light; it must pack well and economically; it should nest; it must be strong enough to ship. Are there edges that, if damaged, will make it impossible to install? On and on go the problems.

Finally comes the problem of application. At the present time, if it is going to find a large market, a mass-production window should work equally well in a brick wall, a wood wall, a steel wall, an aluminum wall, a stone wall, or any other wall. If it will not fit all these applications and still cost as little as those of the competitors—which may fit just one or two—back to the drawing board goes the designer to start all over again.

Estimating production costs, however, is a problem in itself. Our firm recently undertook to design a versatile steel window and wall panel. But how to get at cost, this vital design factor? The best analogy we could find for a first rough-cost check was an internal steel door frame. We were able to get from a door manufacturer prices for the door frame as separate from the door itself; the indication was that our design might be practical in terms of cost. We then developed a preliminary design, and at M.I.T. got an immediate check on its practicality from a technical production point of view. But since we knew that the crux of the matter was cost, we spent a painfully long and difficult time checking estimated costs with local fabricating firms who would be in a position to produce our panel system.

We got answers that were absurd, in view of our preliminary figures on doors: costs of $50, $60, $70 a panel as compared to $10, $15, or $20 for the similar door panel. The standard present method of checking out design costs got us nowhere. Finally we got in touch with an entrepreneur—a man who has started several companies and is familiar with the problems of capital equipment costs and with the machinery necessary for doing analogous work—and in the end he gave us an analysis coming very close to our first estimate based on the steel door frame.

This example of a mass-produced window panel illustrates a type of approach to design that is essential in working toward industrialized components for housing. To a production man in any field other than housebuilding, it is largely elementary and obvious. To most architects, and to most schools of architecture, it is terra incognita.

The Producer's View of Design

Even more important than the paucity of qualified and interested designers as an obstacle to the emergence of the sound industrialized house, however, is the general failure of the producers to understand the importance of the designer's role. There appears to be a widespread opinion that anybody can design a good housing product and that the only problem is to price and market it. In fact, on at least one occasion I have been amused to discover, after a half hour's conversation with an industrial executive about the creative approach, that each of us assumed that the word "creative" applied only to his own part of the problem. Probably nowhere has good design been more thoroughly divorced from industrialization than in the housing field in this country. Nowhere has the desire for a well-designed product at a reasonable price been so thoroughly unrequited.

Techbuilt, Inc., may serve as an illustration of the existence of this desire and of the difficulties experienced in requiting it. The company was started because my firm, concerned primarily with good housing at an economical price, had over the years come to appreciate the fact that a marriage between design and production was essential. In New England, however, almost no houses with any pretense to good design were being built by operative builders, whereas all those with pretensions to good design were extremely high in cost. Good design was therefore a luxury that almost no one in New England could afford.

We could not interest any operative builder in producing our design; the reason given was that there would be no market for it. (It is very hard to gauge the market for something that has never been offered for sale!) In view of all this, we started on a very small scale to build houses ourselves, skirting precariously around the strictures of the AIA regarding the connection of professionals with a building enterprise.

Our first small efforts were very successful and perhaps, if we had not obtained fortuitously a tremendous amount of favorable national publicity, our business problems might not have multiplied faster than we could handle them. Faced with a mushrooming building enterprise, I began a search for a business-trained management. The problem of finding one with an honest conviction that good design was half the problem (not more, but not less either) was all but insuperable. The first businessman, who managed Techbuilt for a full year, was faced with a product whose design was highly acceptable, but whose production was undertaken over a much wider geographical area than could be justified by the volume of sales and the personnel available to control quality. As a result, many of the completed houses were not built well enough to be completely satisfactory to their owners; for that reason they provided neither a profit to Techbuilt nor a real saving to the purchaser. A year later, however, because of the lack of understanding between the representatives of design and business, not only were many of the good elements of the design scrapped, but good design had been so deemphasized that as much ground had been lost in this area as had been gained in the business end. At this writing Techbuilt has solved the problem but only after a very painful and expensive struggle.

This experience is of interest only as an illustration of the unfortunate and, I fear, generally established chasm between the designer and the business executive as to the function and value of the services each performs.[4]

---

[4] This split has some bearing on the plight of the automobile industry. Foreign automobiles like the Volkswagen are making a remarkable showing for themselves in this country on the basis of really good design integrated with really good management, whereas the most skilled advertising in the world can no longer whet our appetites for chrome-covered juke wagons.

More recently, our firm has worked with a large producer of steel who is interested in examining the potential of the housing market as an outlet for fabricated steel components. One of the main features in this association has been the presence in the company, and in a responsible position, of an executive with an architectural background. Without this liaison, communication between designer and producer would be tremendously difficult. Even so, it has been surprising and sometimes discouraging to realize the amount of time that must be spent to reach understanding on objectives between the two groups. One longs for the combination of American know-how and European understanding of what and why.

Producers seem to believe that any change or improvement in fundamental housing design is questionable, because, if it were any good, it would have been thought of, tried out, and in effect already. Presumably habit makes most producers prefer to steal ideas and products from their competitors and rely on heavier advertising, added gimmicks, and peripheral advantages (like better service, free giveaway, and what not) to capture their share of the market. This approach seems particularly wasteful in the field of housing production. Where technical knowledge is so far ahead of practice, it seems unpardonable to wait for someone else to take the first step. Business judgment in this untapped area might well favor the searching out of products not already produced by energetic competitors.

Broad Scope of Production Design

Two further examples from experience may serve to illustrate the broad scope of design in the industrial production of houses. The Lustron Company in the late 1940s invested in a press to make a steel tub in a single draw, which represented its largest, heaviest, and most expensive piece of manufacturing equipment. This was done because a preliminary cost estimate indicated that at the rate of 40,000 houses per year, including a reasonable amortization rate for the equipment, they could produce their own tubs for $15 each as compared with $45 a tub if purchased from an outside manufacturer. They were preparing to punch out the first tub when they discovered a very serious planning mistake. Their tub was to be 5 feet 1½ inches long, the unusual dimension justified by the high estimates of house production. However, the new press was capable of turning out 120,000 tubs per year. To take care of Lustron's own requirements at their rosiest, the machine would operate at only one-third of its capacity. It immediately became apparent that with all the plumbing industry standardized on a 5-foot tub, they would have little or no market for 80,000 extra tubs a year that were 5 feet and 1½ inches long (and had no unusual selling points or advantages). Needless to say, they retooled their press and redesigned their bathroom to take a 5-foot tub.

Another less unhappy example was that of the electrically operated window. The president of Lustron felt that the market for a proposed new model might well be built around the idea of automatic windows, which at the time were almost unknown for houses though they were already installed in the more expensive automobiles. As architectural consultant on the new model, my firm was rather reluctant to go ahead on as expensive-sounding an idea as automatic windows for a low-cost house. However, a little research into the matter with the Lustron production people soon disclosed the power of mass production. On the basis of the never-achieved figure of 40,000 units per year, the windows could be electrically operated, one window per habitable room of the house, at a total cost of $3.50 per operating window. Compared with the cost of standard hand-operated hardware, this obviously held promise. Design potentials of mass production, in other words, are considerably greater than the architect, as a custom designer, realizes.

In our discussions with the Lustron production people, we found many other illustrations of the importance of having

the designer become thoroughly familiar with the entire production process. This was our answer to their often reiterated
suggestion that the architects should determine the kind of
style that would sell and then let them work out the production details.

Implications for the Future

What are the implications for designers and for industry in
the future production of housing?

The designer must first recognize that the parts used to
make up the house are increasing in size and complexity. This
means that more and more of the house he designs will be
completed in the factory. If he persists, as by and large he
does today, in leaving to others the production design of these
components, he will acquire more and more of the attributes
of the purchasing agent and retain less and less of those of
the creative designer. In the case of panelized components, he
may still retain some of his creative planning function, putting
larger and larger pieces together to solve a modular puzzle
each time he lays out a house. In many instances, this part of
the job may become the mere selection of harmonious group-
ings of factory-completed houses with the creative role of
the architect restricted to choice of colors and juxtaposition
of varying housing types, roof arrangements, accessory buildings, fences, and other embellishments.

If he is willing and able to learn what makes the machinery
turn, to familiarize himself with the requirements of big business, and to acquire the coloring of, or an immunity from,
the organization man, the designer will find that he has a large
contribution to make in the production of better, more efficient, more beautiful and satisfying parts and pieces of the
industrialized house.

If, on the other hand, for good reasons or bad, he decides
to leave this to others, he still has an important and difficult
role to perform as a site, neighborhood, town, city, or regional

planner. Here, too, he will find that he must increasingly deal cooperatively with larger and larger entities. No matter how new the community, he is immediately faced with planning boards, building inspectors, government and private financing agencies, citizens' groups, labor organizations, utility commissions, and the like. He must either act as, or make use of, a market analyst, soil engineer, psychologist, educational and recreational expert, and other assorted trades and professions. He can no longer draw a line at the property boundary—closing his eyes to the adjoining mistakes conveniently beyond his control—and create an oasis of beauty in the city desert or a temple in the unspoiled countryside. Beauty he must create or he is no architect, but he cannot turn his back on surrounding ugliness. For more and more frequently he is being faced with the opportunity and responsibility to do something about the surroundings. The means are being created. Urban renewal is sure to be followed by suburban renewal. Whole new towns are being built. Many of these offer the opportunity to create a satisfactory over-all environment. What he needs for the job are knowledge and persuasiveness.

The designer thus seems to be moving toward a time when he can choose between two vital and exciting roles and a tremendous job to do in either—as a product designer or a city planner—but little will remain of his present-day custom services. To fulfill either role he needs considerably broadened training and experience.

What about the industrialist? To conquer the enticing but elusive housing market, one of his greatest needs is the designer. He needs the designer's idealism, enthusiasm, knowledge, and belief in ends as well as ways and means, for essentially he aims to create a product which does not yet exist, though many of its parts are ready to be put together and its promise has excited many for years. This product must be designed to surmount all the obstacles that have so far blocked its development. It must be designed to take full advantage of mass-production materials and processes. It must be designed to appeal to the emotions, reason, and pocketbook of the home buyer. The designer who is trained in production and the housing market and who has the imagination, enthusiasm, and ability to do all this is a vital party to the emergence of a new industry.

Chapter 4

LAND DEVELOPMENT AND DESIGN

Hideo Sasaki considers the effect on land development of emerging urban relationships. He balances central-area opportunities against the forces spurring outlying development and discusses the prospective character of the new community and of the development organization that would bring it into being.

Growth of the Land Problem

A member of one of the largest and most successful realtor and developer firms in the United States was quoted recently as saying, "...unless ways are found to break the log jam in land acquisition and land development—the biggest problem of most home builders today—we just won't be able to build all the houses we will need. That would hurt a lot of industries besides housing." [1] In nearly every issue, journals on the building industry carry articles on some phase of the land problem.[2] This interest and concern regarding the use of the land is to be expected. Never in the history of the United States has such spectacular growth in the intensity

[1] William Zeckendorf, Jr., of Webb and Knapp, *House & Home*, vol. 12, no. 4, October, 1957, p. 94.

[2] For extensive discussions of land development, see Frank Fogarty's three articles in suburban areas, city core, and retirement or recreation land, *Architectural Forum*, vol. 106, nos. 2–4, February, March, April, 1957; and the series of five articles, "The Exploding Metropolis" by William H. Whyte, Jr., in *Fortune*, vol. 61, nos. 3–6, September–December, 1957; vol. 62, no. 1, January, 1958.

and in the extensiveness of land development taken place within such a short span of time. And probably never have community problems emerged so quickly to confound both citizens and governmental bodies at all levels. The rapid development of residential land, straining the utilities, transportation, and school systems of the community, has replaced all others as the major housing problem.

In the future, sizable increases in population will compound the demand for land, and equally large increases in superhighway mileage and in the numbers of automobiles will spread the problem ever farther over the countryside. From 1946 to 1957 we added more automobiles than people to our stock. Conservative estimates for 1975 predict 50 million new cars and 56 million more people. These figures cannot of themselves show the magnitude of needs that community developers will have to satisfy. Of the 56 million added to the population, it is predicted that 45 million will live in the suburbs, 9 million in the core cities. The pressures of expanding numbers, human and vehicular, will probably push westward that conurbation which has reached out over the 600 miles of Atlantic seaboard from Portland, Maine, to Norfolk, Virginia.

Perhaps as disturbing as the more widely heralded problems of design and use of land is the possible shortage of land itself. As spelled out in a recent magazine editorial:

Right now every human in the U.S. commands an average of 12 acres. Seven raise food for him, leaving an average of five for all other purposes. Optimistically assuming that the same farm acreage supporting 162 million people now will support 218 million in 20 years, the average acreage per person for all other purposes will drop about 20%. And because asphalt will not grow potatoes, the pavement that will be demanded by two cars for every one we have today will have to come out of other-purpose acreage. There's the rub. For the car is not only a monstrous land-eater itself; it abets that other insatiable land-eater—endless, strung-out suburbanization.[3]

[3] *Architectural Forum,* vol. 105, no. 3, September, 1956, p. 103. The editors' calculation is rather optimistic. Land uses are not readily interchanged.

Water is an important aspect of land resources, for a shortage of water could seriously deter the development of new residential communities. In Massachusetts, for example,[4] it is estimated that by the year 2000 more than 830 persons per square mile will be occupying land now serving only 598 persons. Commercial activities and industrial processes require more water. New homes have multiple bathrooms and such water-absorbing appliances as air conditioners, dishwashers, washing machines, and garbage grinders. Suburban developments use large quantities of water for lawns and shrubs. In the next decade water consumption in Massachusetts will double. There is serious questioning of the adequacy of the resources of even a state so rich in water to meet such a demand. Given this situation a description of optimum development, for example, can be but a guess.

If the pattern of the fifties is continued, it is estimated that land will soon be changed into residential and ancillary uses at the rate of a million acres per year. Under such conditions, land accessible within reasonable driving distance to the core city would soon be nonexistent.

Lengthening the journey to work affords no remedy. In many cases this accelerates the process of decentralization. Industry and commerce, moving outward from the core to improve their own accessibility, successfully compete for choice development land. Residential communities must be serviced by shops, churches, and schools which require convenient locations and also compete for the stock of land available for housing.

Land is one of the commodities in our economy whose value may be tremendously increased by altering external

---

Relatively definite natural limits—climate, topography, subsoil conditions—are set on agricultural and residential land. Even more important is the limitation of access. One can usually identify the use of land around the city by the type of road that serves it; if it is a dirt road the land adjacent is agricultural; if concrete and asphalt, then it is residential!

[4] According to a report by Richard L. England of the *Christian Science Monitor*, June 24, 1957.

conditions. Raw land is valuable only to the degree of its productivity for agriculture, forestry, mining, etc.; with change in its relationship to other geographic factors, land may double or triple in value without any alteration in its inherent characteristics.

As late as 1944, an authoritative study of the housing problem stated:

Urban land today is not a scarce commodity. Great quantities are made available, (1) by increased distance from the main centers of commercial and industrial activity within which land may be put to urban use, and (2) by the intensive utilization of land possible within these wide limits. With current rate of population growth, housing is not likely to be hampered for lack of land. Considering the over-all picture, the problem is no longer that of a shortage of urban land forcing values continually upward, but rather that of a surplus tending to limit the rise of values.[5]

In the years since the end of the war, however, a unique combination of factors led to a dramatic rise of land values, especially in areas surrounding the major metropolitan centers. During the decade and a half of the postwar period, more than four-fifths of the increase in the total population of the United States occurred in and around the metropolitan areas. Coupled with the greater buying power, and the increased use of the automobile as the principal means of transportation, the resultant physical expression was suburbia. The growth in the so-called suburban areas was about seven times that in the central city (see photographs 2, 26). Average cost of improved building sites during this period almost doubled. The effect of this rise in land costs is reflected in the sales price of the builders' houses. According to a 1957 survey by the National Association of Home Builders, the average lot cost was 10 per cent of the sales price in 1950, 15 per cent in 1955, and 18.4 per cent in 1956; where land is difficult to develop, the developed lot cost may run as high as 30 per

[5] Miles L. Colean, *American Housing: Problems and Prospects,* The Twentieth Century Fund, Inc., New York, 1944, p. 13.

cent.[6] Thus, the rise is an absolute one and not merely a reflection of the inflationary spiral.

In-town areas have not risen in value at a rate equal to that of suburban areas. According to one writer the situation may be summarized as follows:

Within the old business districts of most cities, land prices show either little change from 1947 or only a slight rise, when measured by the constant dollars of the consumer price index. In some cities there have been absolute declines; in almost all, prices, in constant dollars, are still well below the peaks of the twenties. . . .

Beyond the central zone, land prices show a crisscross of trends; a few sharp rises where there has been an upgrading of use; little or no change where neighborhoods are unaltered, but well-preserved; sizeable declines where deterioration has set in.[7]

A second problem is that of insufficient supply of land classed as suitable and available for housing. This may be a debatable subject from the quantitative point of view; statistically it may be demonstrated that land for housing, whether inlying or at the fringes, is still plentiful.[8] However, much remains to be desired from the qualitative point of view. For residential use, an area should be integrated within itself as well as with the larger community, with adequate and accessible facilities and amenities.

Because circumstances during the immediate postwar period created a seller's market, the second problem did not affect most builders. Any house at any reasonable price could be sold, and land itself, although a problem, was available for the astute and aggressive entrepreneur. Such problems as the available supply of land, land prices, and community and

[6] In some parts of metropolitan Boston, lot costs range as high as $6,000, with the houses themselves priced from $16,000 to $18,000.

[7] Frank Fogarty, "Land II: The Strange Case of the City," *Architectural Forum*, vol. 106, no. 3, March, 1957, p. 134.

[8] See Robinson Newcomb, "Are Urban Land Pressures Easing?" *Urban Land*, vol. 17, no. 5, May, 1958, p. 1; *House & Home*, vol. 13, no. 6, June, 1958, pp. 130ff.

consumer resistance have constantly grown more acute; hence a critical reevaluation of the future is needed.

Problems of Outlying Land. The consequences of community development in outlying areas, which we have been witnessing during recent years and which will accelerate in the future as highway and utility programs are extended, tend to contrast with the classical form of a metropolitan area—the mother city of great concentration at the center and a gradual decrease in intensity and density of land uses away from the center. In its place is seen a more continuous and horizontal spread of industries, commercial areas, and housing, with no dominant or well-defined centers and with areas of greater density generally found closer to access routes.

A recent publication by the J. Walter Thompson Company and the School of Architecture of Yale University calls the emerging pattern "Interurbia," and describes its characteristics as follows: ". . . It contains two or more adjacent metropolitan areas with either two cities of 100,000 or more, or one city of 100,000 and 3 cities of 25,000 or more, plus adjacent counties with less than 25 per cent farm population and more than 100 people per square mile." [9] Other terms commonly used to describe this pattern are "scatteration," "conurbation," and "regional urbanization." Whatever the term used, *suburbia*, as traditionally defined to mean that residential fringe area associated with the central city, no longer is appropriate. Interurbia as defined above contains industrial and commercial establishments as well as residences. Moreover, the residential areas are apt to be related to a range of centers, with industry in one direction, office areas in another, shopping facilities in another, and recreation in still another. Only elementary schools are likely to be reasonably close, for a primary basis for school site selection is still geographic proximity to the pupils.

Few communities were prepared for the speed, scope, and

[9] *The Changing Face of America,* an informal undated publication of J. Walter Thompson Company and Yale University School of Architecture.

vigor of urban development following World War II, but many are now engaged in frontal attacks on these problems with whatever means they have at their disposal. The most common problem of an expanding community, of course, is that of schools. With the influx of new population, usually young families with young children on hand or to come, these communities are faced with the need to expand school facilities and budgets beyond any possible hope for the comfortable balance of yesteryear; hence most communities are anxious to regulate residential development.

Zoning for large lots is among the devices frequently used to reduce the influx of the childbearing population. The requirement of lots of an acre or more has been widely upheld, on the basis of drainage requirements for septic tanks and tile fields, need to avoid sewer and other public installations in areas of unusual difficulty, and the general complexities which high-density development inevitably creates for the municipality.

To discourage speculative profit from badly planned land development, the burden of furnishing community facilities is often imposed upon the builder under subdivision control, and requirements for improvements are increasingly becoming stringent. Already builders are required to put in the paving and other improvements before the city will accept the development or to post bond to the effect that they will do so at a later date. Another device communities are using under subdivision control is to require subdividers either to dedicate land for park and playground areas or to pay fees in lieu of dedication. The area required may range from 5 to 7 per cent of the total area, the fees from $50 each for ¼-acre lots to $150 each for 2-acre lots. Sewer treatment systems are another control point to inhibit development or to gain free community facilities. Thus the builder sometimes becomes the scapegoat of a national problem.

Problems of the Developer. From a public-policy point of view, building as an industry is a source of economic livelihood for too many to permit its neglect and abuse. On the other hand, because the building industry touches upon the dreams, hopes, and investments of all citizens, whether home-owners or renters, and because it determines the fixed pattern of communities and leaves a legacy to the future generations, the builder must face up to his design responsibilities.

Many problems confront the builder. He must first locate land for development. This the average builder accomplishes on a hit-or-miss basis, consulting local realtors, scanning the classified ad section of the daily papers, or driving around the countryside on weekends. The land available for his operation is apt to be a remnant, poorly situated in relation to over-all community structure and not protected against intrusion by incompatible land use. Only the large builders, or those who have combined resources for the purpose, can afford to carry out a long-term program of land acquisition based upon some degree of rational market or community analysis.

After locating a piece of land and arranging financing, the builder must obtain legal assistance to complete the process of transferring the title. Various title complications may make the process of assembling land extremely costly, time-consuming, and on occasion, impossible.

In determining his program for development of the land, the builder must conform to various local regulations and often to those of the Federal Housing Administration,[10] which in many ways are representative of institutional benefits and impediments to rational land design. These and other require-ments virtually dictate how a dwelling unit may be laid out and where it is to be located on the site. Small wonder that so many housing developments result in the same layout and monotony.

[10] A new set of regulations called Minimum Property Standards has been prepared by the FHA. The regulations are based upon performance and not upon specifications for structural considerations. The attitude toward land planning is likewise more flexible. The regional offices are granted the power to judge each design on its own merits.

After plans have been prepared, they must usually be submitted for approval to the local planning board. In theory this is a very desirable procedure, but frequently the planning board members, although conscientious citizens, are not qualified to evaluate design. When the community has a technical staff to advise in the evaluation process, the results are apt to be more satisfying. The FHA technical staff, the Urban Land Institute, and other such organizations have done much to bring about an improvement in this respect. Well-illustrated booklets and handbooks [11] have been made readily available to both the communities and the developers, to the mutual advantage of each. As suggested earlier, however, conservatism is characteristic of institutional approaches, and in the past these groups have not always kept in step with the tremendous pace of changing needs and patterns of U.S. life.

The essential objective of controls is to encourage more efficient land design. If rational methods can demonstrate that both visual and auditory privacy is assured, that light and air will not be obstructed, that ample area for contemplated activities will be provided, and that the over-all design will operate efficiently and safely, then such a design should be permitted. When the housing industry generally insists on standards of performance verifiable by up-to-date testing methods, it will be able to create a production climate in which development designing may be appreciably improved. It is indeed an anomaly that so much of the building industry has cared so little for so long about land design and development, other than to complain about the shortage of good and cheap building land. Good land design and land development need to be recognized as an essential concern of the building industry, as good road design and road building are to the automobile industry.

[11] The National Association of Home Builders, *Home Builders Manual for Land Development*, rev. ed., Washington, D.C., 1950, is an excellent example.

Potentials of Development Design

Increasingly skilled attention is given to land design by the developers, the real estate fraternity, and the professions most concerned—city planners, architects, landscape architects—and a wealth of basic material and practical experience is now available. Here, as in housing design generally, creative individuals and teams long ago worked out design improvements which are only now beginning to be applied in practice. It is not so easy, however, to find a wealthy client who can provide the opportunity for physical expression of a land-design concept in relatively pure form. Most of the ideas, therefore, must still be found in books and magazines and in the underlying analyses contained in planning studies made for individual communities. Only in a few places in the world has an enlightened development group (Welwyn in England, Radburn in New Jersey), a major industry (Ciudad Bolivar in Venezuela, Kitimat in Canada), or a government program (the United States Greenbelt towns, the British New Towns) given us a clear view of the development possibilities of communities as a whole. More recently, growth pressures have led to many other new communities, such as the three Levittowns (see photograph 2) and Park Forest in this country, and the lessons from these are being added to the literature of planning.

On a modest scale, principles of land-planning design have been more widely applied in practice. The handling of automobile circulation and access and of drainage and utilities is now an area of high skill. Many of the functional requirements of industry, commerce, institutional uses, recreational areas, and residential development have been identified and systematized in standards of good practice and in municipal regulations.

Without attempting comprehensive coverage, we may offer a few examples of other design innovations. Since design is a process of problem solution, the particular details of each proposal depend on the individual requirements of each problem.

The "patio house" is an instance of a design innovation which, although developed by designers to meet in-town situations, could as well be used for outlying developments.[12] This is a house featuring an interior courtyard, completely private to each unit, with fenced-in front and backyards and reliance on common or public areas for more extensive recreation. Usually, such houses are one story high. A density of about seven to ten units per gross acre could be obtained through the use of this type of development.

Currently, designers are experimenting with the modification of conventional row houses (see photographs 23, 29, 30, 31, 32). These are frequently referred to as "patio houses," although they actually are row houses with fenced-in rear gardens. Densities as high as thirty families per gross acre may be developed by some of these designs. Direct auto access and off-street parking for each unit, a private plot of ground for outdoor use (somewhat small, but supplemented by a reasonably large "common area"), complete privacy, a safe place for children to play in the "common area," and a pleasant level of natural planting—all these can be provided, despite this high density.

Apparently the requirements of "single family living in the suburbs" could be met with a vastly higher level of economy by improving the design of the structure.[13] Yet there is nothing new about the fact that row houses can be good design. The well-known Baldwin Hills Village in Los Angeles stands high as a tested example of how the full range of amenities may be provided by this method of land development. Chatham Village in Pittsburgh has been a successful venture from its outset over twenty-three years ago.

[12] See *House & Home*, vol. 12, no. 4, October, 1957, pp. 140, 140A.

[13] For an extensive study of row-housing designs, see *Eastwick Row House Study*, The Philadelphia Redevelopment Authority, Philadelphia, 1957.

To achieve ever-greater densities without involving high-rise elevator-serviced units, the so-called "town house" or "maisonette" types have been evolved by designers. These are three-story structures in which the upper two floors are used for one dwelling unit. Three-story economies in construction as well as land use may be obtained by the stacking up of only two dwelling units. A similar idea is that of placing two two-story units one over another to create a four-story structure. Such units have distinct advantages over conventional four-story walk-up apartments where the top floor units are reached only by climbing three full flights of stairs. In certain situations where the topography is auspicious, it is possible to enter such a building at the middle level, thus equalizing the convenience of access to the two units.

To illustrate what contribution a designer may bring to the use of the land, Eichler Homes [14] on the West Coast demonstrate the effectiveness of the very simplest measures. The units in this development are standard single-family detached units located on conventional individual lots, which are rather small. Since the side yards were to be only 6 feet wide on one side, and the rear yards only about 30 feet deep, the designer simply fenced each lot completely with a 6-foot-high fence. Each house was one story high, thus providing complete privacy for units. Large panes of glass and a well-designed floor plan permit free flow of interior spaces to the exterior (see photograph 1) creating an over-all effect of spacious dimensions for a very small house and lot development. The street scene itself is harmonious, with the fences tying the simply designed units together.

In other instances, where the topography is varied, and vegetation more plentiful, a good land planner may, by the alignment of streets, the location of lots, and the skillful placement of houses, lower the builder's cost for cutting and filling and foundation work, avoid the need for special drainage or

[14] Designed by A. Quincy Jones and Frederick E. Emmons, Architects.

sewerage structures, and at the same time preserve many of the natural amenities of the site for the eventual occupant.

By judicious arrangement of roads it is not unusual for the skilled land designer to improve the builder's layout by providing:

> —more lots, frequently larger in average size
> —more area for recreational use
> —more freedom from traffic hazard
> —more visual interest in the spacing and grouping of houses
> —less road area
> —less utility length

The ultimate result frequently is like having one's cake and eating it, too; the trick is in reducing the total requirements for road and utility purposes. If the designer were given the additional freedom of determining what road widths to use in view of the functional use of the roadways, instead of being tied to rigid subdivision regulations, the effectiveness of his design would be increased even more.

Economies may be furthered, also, by planning in the design for the efficient execution of the work in land development. By proper scheduling, by use of proper tools and machinery, the builder may cut the cost per acre of development as compared with current practice. An impressive example of efficient management is given by a builder in Ohio who was able to develop a 15-acre tract of raw land into forty lots with an approximate savings of $1,000 per lot over the normal costs of buying developed lots.[15] When asked where this profit goes, the builder replied, "The economy of every phase of building must go into the total operation. The total operation is building houses for sale. Land development is only a part of it." [16]

Regarding their operations as a total process, some builders

[15] "Land and Lots," *House & Home*, vol. 11, no. 2, February, 1957, p. 154.
[16] *Ibid.*, p. 155.

are able to boast that their profits are made on the land and not on the house, which is given to the consumer at cost. The "product," in its real sense, becomes a complete environment for a family's living needs, and it matters little at what particular stage of the building process the actual profits are made. Indeed, it may be possible to withstand a loss in a particular stage in order to increase the total value to the customer and, therefore, the profit on the entire operation. This same principle applies to the larger relation of the house and site to the community. Frequently, by dedicating sites for schools, parks, or some such equivalent beneficial community purposes, the ultimate value of the total project may be increased appreciably.[17]

Problems of Inlying Land. In the main, problems of residential land use in the inlying areas are related to programs for conservation, rehabilitation, and redevelopment.[18] There are some new developments on vacant land, but these are of more sporadic nature and their consequences are not of the magnitude resulting from suburban growth.

Despite extensive programs of conservation, rehabilitation, and redevelopment, at both public and private levels, the sheer magnitude and complexity of the urban problems lead many professional and lay individuals to believe that only a very slow and evolutionary pattern of change will occur in our existing cities. Some of the impediments to over-all community renewal may be generalized as:

1. Inability to reach rapid decisions when there appears to be a conflict between public and private interests in renewal programs.

2. Lack of design coordination between public and private building programs. On one hand, the emphasis of public

[17] In Levittown, N.J., the developer plans to build schools at the same time as houses and turn them over to the new community, thus solving one of the most troublesome of new community problems.

[18] Of these, only redevelopment involves total clearance of the land within a project area. The cleared land may but does not have to be rebuilt for a use different from its original use.

policy tends to be on using renewal land to house only one income class. On the other, there is little contribution toward over-all redesign on the part of private builders. Buildings are still conceived as existing on single and isolated plots. Few understand or seek the flexibility that would bring a neighboring new building into the over-all design, for example, by sharing common service areas, directing pedestrian movements along other than lines parallel to the streets, or pooling areas in the center of the block for open space.

3. Magnitude of the price for public programs. Urban highways cost between 2 and 17 million dollars per mile. What little park space exists is grabbed as the cheapest sites for public institutions, and later, when growing population makes the need for recreation space critical, the expense of withdrawing built-up land for this purpose becomes prohibitive.

4. Inflated land values. Even with the write-down made possible by the Federal urban-renewal program, there are relatively few areas where private investors can be found to develop more appropriate land uses. Yet even these few could rapidly exhaust Federal funds.

5. Cost of services. The responsibility of the city to provide basic services, in a period when its income is falling and costs are rising, makes city rebuilding difficult.

These reasons suggest that the redesign of the inlying areas of the central city in terms of housing, public facilities, active recreation area, and green space is likely to proceed slowly in the next half-century unless some drastic changes in public temper or policy should take place, despite the clear advantages for many groups in the population of living in such areas.

Central Area Opportunities. In the in-town area, the problem of design is quite different from that of new land development. The individual desires of the prospective occupants play a lesser role than institutionalized notions of what people desire. Methods and conditions of land assembly, financing, ownership, and management are more variable than those of single-family detached development; hence the opportunities for innovations both in the design of the units themselves and in the use of the land are often greater. With the encouragement of an enlightened public policy and the cooperation of an astute developer, the designer may often create an in-town development competitive with suburban residential areas.

Since strong inducements are required to attract private investment, and since in-town projects are usually planned and designed in an integrated manner, concessions regarding design details are frequently made, and it is not unusual to be allowed variations from regulatory provisions of codes and ordinances, such as zoning setbacks and yard regulations, distances from parking areas to units, and roadway design standards. Although these variations are often minor, a small degree of flexibility, plus the specialized ownership and management patterns, allows the designers to produce ingenious innovations of considerable merit.

The difficulties of the problems or the requirements of the program are not the basic impediments to good design, for it is the role of the designer to solve problems. It is when his hands are tied, so to speak, by arbitrary requirements which predetermine the solution that impediments are created. Such requirements prevent the designer from evaluating the many complex factors involved and integrating them in a meaningful whole.

Because the in-town situation is currently so distressing, the climate of public policy is tending to be more tolerant of new ideas of management, financing, and design. Thus with creative leadership, public support, and flexible regulations, in-town areas can be a breeding ground for significant innovations in the use of the land and the design of the housing environment.

Forces Spurring Outlying Land Development. At least three basic forces have been and are spurring the development of land for housing outside the central cities. The first is a system of social values, the demand for a suburban way of life. The purchaser of a subdivision house today believes that he is buying better welfare for his child, i.e., educational and social opportunities and a degree of security from urban menaces. Though this value system may not be shared by all buyers, he typically feels that his deed represents social prestige and economic attainment. Other than in special cases, he knows he has more "elbow" space and experiences less noise, less traffic, and less dirt. This attitude toward the suburban areas is not new to the middle-income class and it is not entirely a postwar phenomenon. In the last half of the nineteenth century there was already a substantial migration to the suburban house, the weekend cottage, the summer estate. Considering the suburb as a value symbol, as a social demand transposed into market demand, there appears no significant alteration in this attitude toward the decentralized, low-density residential area. This continuing desire for a new way of life may engender a new phase of housing production and technology.

The second force which appears to encourage the development of the outlying new residential community is the functional inadequacy of the central city. Some of the aspects of this inadequacy may be generalized as:

1. The city's current inability to provide the broad band of services called for in middle-income housing. Because it lacks the land needed for "on the ground living," it has not sufficiently experimented with new design opportunities and social organizations (e.g., cooperatives), and it provides a low level of such key facilities as schools and recreation areas. Some housing economists believe that investment in rehabilitation of the in-town stock will satisfy the market. However, significant investments have not been made as yet outside of specially subsidized case areas, and in most trial projects the rentals have passed the upper medium-income range.

2. The inefficiency of the mass transportation system and

the failure to integrate it with the automobile. Some of this may be due to a double-standard policy of subsidizing automobile and not mass transport, some to the lack of initiative of mass transportation in competing for the transportation dollar. A large part simply reflects the facts of life in modern urban transportation, where a system scaled to ten rush hours per week must carry charges and expenses with little return throughout most of the remaining service period of more than one hundred hours.

3. The timidity or political necessity of small projects. Urban renewal tends to be considered as a series of small, strategic investments scattered throughout the city. Perhaps the total scheduled investment of any one five-year slum-clearance and housing project should be concentrated in one broad area, to build total effect piece by piece.

4. The increasing strain on municipal budgets of providing and maintaining municipal services. With the dispersal of the tax base to the outlying areas, while problems continue to mount, nearly every city in the United States is hard pressed to continue minimum services, let alone provide capital improvements such as new schools and recreational areas to compete successfully with the suburbs.

5. The intangible of appearance. It is suggested by some that today's tattered and tawdry city form is in itself tension-producing. With the city economically unable to strengthen its perceptual qualities, idealization and idolization go to the suburb by default.

6. Overbalance of low-income groups. The city continues to draw a disproportionate share of the lower-income groups and to hold the highest percentage of the aged. Providing appropriate shelter and services is increasingly draining the cities' dwindling resources.

7. The failure to add to, or maintain, existing green areas. Most planners agree that green areas are essential for the family group, for psychic and visual relief, for play space, and

as a device for reducing congestion. But in-town park development in the last three decades has failed to keep pace with increasing population.

The mere existence of functional inadequacies in the city will not mean the triumph of suburbia. In varying forms and to varying degrees the metropolis has always had these problems. The new element today is the possibility of a seemingly better way of living. Aided by rising income and level of education, those seeing the defects in the existing situation and the potentials of suburbia—as an alternative, not a substitute, for central city living—continue to exert pressure for outlying community development.

The third force which will ever increasingly stimulate the creation of outlying developments is the new leisure and the manner in which it tends to be used. The work week has been shortened—from 60 hours in 1900, to 47 in 1933, to less than 40 in 1957, and there is talk, sometimes serious and sometimes wishful, of a four-day week—and paid vacations are longer and more predictable. Furthermore, a new value is being attached to leisure time, a sort of revolution in attitudes and philosophies as to its use.

> To a lessening degree is a man's job the central focus of his concern. Work no longer appears to him as the only road to virtue and salvation. Outside the job lies the world of family and cultural pursuits. And attainment of satisfaction in such areas seems hardly less significant than advancement along the straight and narrow path of the career.[19]

Community Prospects. What type of community might evolve in the future to meet these requirements better than today's suburbs? It is safe to assume that the majority of the population would consist of families engaged in bearing and raising children. By comparison with counterparts in today's subdivisions or suburbs, however, the families in the residential

[19] Director's Report, *1956 Annual Report,* The Twentieth Century Fund, Inc., New York, p. 9.

community of the future are apt to be more articulate in their housing demands. Mobile, consumption-minded, actively sharing in the new leisure, these families will demand not just shelter, but "living" in their new communities.

The father may be employed in commerce or a service industry. His work area probably would be within reasonable driving distance from his home, but his range of choice in jobs and job locations would be less linked to residential location. He would probably work a shorter week. If not in a service industry, his work may tend to be repetitive and sedentary. Psychologically, this may be compensated for by an active and diverse personal leisure, a significant portion of which may be with the family.

The mother's routine may still be tied to the activities of the children. The amount of time she spends in maintaining the home, however, would be reduced through the use of mechanical devices and dust control. It is more than likely that she would actively engage herself part time outside the home. As the chief family disciplinarian, chauffeur, and secretary, hers would be the responsibility of organizing and planning the family activities. In this child-oriented community, the school could determine the extent to which she participates in community affairs, both social and political.

The number of hours the child is in school may tend to increase, and members of the family may join the child there by participating in extension courses. To balance child-oriented leisure, adult groups may participate in music, drama, and active sport. In design terms, this means that many specialized areas, both indoors and outdoors, must be considered as extensions of present requirements, and we may anticipate that more of the family income would be spent on supporting this type of facility than ever before.

When it comes to family leisure, the automobile could easily bring the group to areas at some distance from the residential community, where the stay may be of three to four days' duration. It is possible that special recreational developments will be built to serve this form of family life, as has been a commonplace outside of Scandinavian cities. We have seen the notion of a "two-house" family emerging.

Today's consumer pattern, in which all the family participates in the selection and purchase of food, clothing, household articles, and entertainment, would continue. Advanced shopping centers already cater to this need by building into a single structure a variety of goods and a fair-like atmosphere, making the weekly shopping trip a family recreational enterprise.

It is unlikely that the subdivisions of today will evolve inevitably into balanced communities. Flaws in the existing procedures for developing residential areas often seem insurmountable. Socially and economically the subdivision tends to be a one–age group, one-class, one-function community. Although this in itself is not a barrier to human development, the lack of facilities to enjoy other than the most limited range of activities tends to divert leisure time to television-gazing and other forms of escape. Help is needed to clear away current restraints.

The implications for the builder, and they are already apparent today, are that the American value system is shifting, and that increasingly he must sell *community* as well as shelter.

Land-development Organizations

As one means of opening the way for land-design innovations, developers have begun to form organizations of considerable size and resources—some integrated units and others on a federated or cooperative basis—to handle the purchase and development of land in significant acreages so that full advantage may be taken of values added by land development and of freedom from localized restrictions. Mass production of housing in the assembly-line sense, which has long intrigued more than a few minds, requires organizations capable of mass production in raw-land development.

Based on the purpose of large-scale community development and servicing, the structure of the raw-land development operation tends to reflect the following activities:

1. Raw-land acquisition—the assembling of land, handling of controls and restrictions, and selling of land development programs.

2. Community development—the planning of communities, arranging for provision of access roads and municipal services, setting standards for housing production, and development of community facilities.

3. Shelter and community production—the actual construction of houses, site improvements, landscaping, paving, and installation of utilities.

4. Community service—maintaining and operating all facilities owned by the development corporation and providing service to the houses.

5. Continuing evaluation and research—product control, interpretation of land-use data, marketing research, experiments in housing and community design, and analysis of consumer motivation.[20]

Operations may have two major phases. First is making and implementing plans for the first stage of the community. This includes the construction of the residential sections (which would offer a wide range of price, type, and prestige choices) and of the first community institutional buildings. During this phase, growth potential may be determined by the research staff on the basis of market attitudes and population projections for the area. In the second phase, the developer gradually sells off his residential holdings but retains control of and operates the service areas, plus the land available for expansion.

[20] Aside from product research, for some interesting and valuable types of investigations of which there are too few in housing, see Leon Festinger, Stanley Schacter, and Kurt Bach, *Social Pressures in Informal Groups: A Study of Human Factors in Housing*, Harper & Brothers, New York, 1950; and Leo Kuper (ed.), *Living in Towns*, The Cresset Press, London, 1953. The latter study was sponsored by the city of Coventry to further a more enlightened view in formulating public policy for housing.

The community is incorporated and the citizens assume responsibility for maintaining the institutional and community facilities. Phase two includes the construction of additional residential sectors and the marketing of sites for custom-built houses, which might or might not be built by the land-development organization.

In order to create a fuller social community, a limited amount of rental housing could be operated, some on a contract basis for the central-city housing authority for low-income groups and the elderly; some to serve the transient market. These units could be spread throughout the community and not isolated and segregated. Under certain circumstances, entire communities could be operated by the organization with the residents paying a single monthly fee for all charges. Prestige projects of this sort could be developed for industrial corporations who would use them as a way of attracting and holding personnel.[21]

Some raw-land development organizations may do no housebuilding,[22] leaving the actual site preparation to subcontractors, both local and national specialists.

The essential role of these organizations is to lead the way out of the morass of current obstacles and restrictions. Once the path is open to innovation, many alternative possibilities could become available. Prospective buyers could choose their

[21] There are many examples of developers who have gained some of the economies of scale, among the most publicized of which is the Levitt organization, which is geared to produce an entire community at a time (see photograph 2). In developing Levittown, Long Island, Levittown, Pennsylvania, and the projected Levittown, New Jersey, the organization not only made its purchases and plans well in advance—incidentally, testing many of the community-design ideas long urged by land planners—but provided a standard of efficiency in the process of land development that served to stimulate the entire industry. In the true sense of the phrase, Levitt mass-produced lots and the making of sales, so that his fabrication methods could also gain the benefits of mass production.

[22] Fritz Burns and Dave Bohannon on the West Coast are examples of land developers who prepare the way for others to do the actual construction work.

homes from catalogues of prefabricated-unit components, select manufactured models of their choice, or hire architects for custom-designed houses. The development organization could order houses in quantity lots from independent fabricators, controlling the design of continuous sectors in the community by limiting the number of models available. Greater choice could be encouraged, and a wider range of model types and prices could afford a greater flexibility in community design of residential sectors. The increase in potential ways of grouping such choices—that is, the broadening of the land designer's palette—would add variety to the community design. Factory production of housing units could come into its own with the complete separation of the building processes from the site.

Land developers already plan to operate the community's service facilities, including the shopping and industrial areas which return the largest and most consistent profit to the developer. Full service and leisure areas increasingly tend to be included at the project's inception. The expected consistency of profitable return tends to attract development capital to the organization, and the very scale of development opens the way to innovations on the part of major producers of materials and equipment. Over the whole range from the individual to the balanced community, a larger share of the economy could be channeled into housing production as a result of operations at large scale.[23]

[23] Although not conforming in detail to our broadly brushed description, the Don Mills Development, Ltd., of Toronto, Canada, serves as a prototype (see photograph 28). The development corporation assembled and purchased the land, planned and developed the entire community, invited as many as seventeen different builders to participate in erecting the units, and retained interest in the shopping center. A mixture of type and price range of housing was provided, including rental units as well as units for sale. Industrial areas, a high school, several elementary schools, large internal park and play areas as well as a greenbelt all around the community, a mile-long recreation lake, a country club, a "sports bowl," and a $1,250,000 sewage-treatment plant were provided for!

In this country Webb and Knapp are proposing similiar developments,

Summary

The first decade of postwar subdivision construction has left a housing residue which is inadequate in quality, often misplaced in relation to strategic metropolitan location, and lacking basic visual, social, and physical amenities. The typical developer's interests in community design have been minimal and short-term because of the critical shelter shortage. Community pressures and various regulatory laws have improved the situation somewhat in the last few years, but builders still have not, for the most part, significantly improved community design. People are leaving not only the central cities but also the earlier subdivisions because of dissatisfaction with the physical and social design of their communities.

The demand for better land-development design has rarely been probed by the housing industry, although there may well be a sizable market for it. Should it come to pass, it could (1) attract a greater part of the personal income into the housing and community-building sectors of the national economy, (2) create a more consistent market for the production of housing units by the rational development of raw land and provide the opportunity for housing production to become industrialized and stabilized to an extent not heretofore possible.

---

and may serve to illustrate the role of the raw-land development corporation. The extent of the land purchases for their operations may be indicated by such illustrations as a 1,100-acre tract in Vancouver, a 5,000-acre purchase between Fort Worth and Dallas, 11,000 acres in Los Angeles, and 32,000 acres in Louisiana between Baton Rouge and New Orleans (*House & Home*, vol. 12, no. 4, October, 1957, p. 84). The firm itself plans to utilize local groups of builders for each project. It is interesting to note that this organization is negotiating with a leading prefabricator, National Homes, to erect some of the units in one of the projects.

Chapter 5

CURRENT PATTERNS
OF FABRICATION

This chapter, primarily the work of Albert G. H. Dietz, describes the different patterns by which houses are currently produced, emphasizing typical operations rather than over-all considerations of organization and scale. Castle N. Day and Burnham Kelly supply additional detail on those producers who most fully understand and benefit from industrial potentials: the large operative builders, the prefabricators, and the manufacturers of mobile homes.

The pattern of fabrication for a house warrants careful study because it has a significant influence on the production volume, on the industrial resources that can be made available, on the detailed and over-all design of the house, and on the general attitude with which it and its producer are viewed by the consumer and his community.

In today's housebuilding industry, we find four principal types of producer. Three of these are familiar: (1) the custom builder who typically erects individual houses to plans and specifications for specific owners; (2) the development, operative, or merchant builder who erects groups of houses for sale on a specific site or sites; and (3) the prefabricator who builds house packages in a shop and sends them out to be erected on sites located anywhere within an economical shipping distance. The fourth type, too often left entirely out of consideration,

137

is the manufacturer of mobile homes. Examining the operation of each of these will help to put the housing industry into focus and to point up impediments, trends, and potentials.

The Custom Builder

Although his relative position in home building is steadily dwindling,[1] the custom builder who deals primarily in individually planned and built houses is still a central figure in the dwelling-house picture, and the industry is largely devoted to meeting his requirements. The character of his operation may be brought out by tracing briefly the steps involved in the construction of a single house for a given owner.

Typically, by the time the custom builder enters the picture, the owner has acquired a lot and has a reasonably definite idea of what he wants in his house. If he has retained an architect, the plans are completed. The builder's first step, then, is to prepare an estimate of cost. This involves making a quantity survey, estimating the labor requirement, obtaining bids from subcontractors, obtaining costs of materials and equipment, putting all these together, adding social security and similar charges, determining what profit he will attempt to make, and submitting this estimate to the owner or to his architect. The cost is often too high, and the builder and the owner proceed to cut. Eventually a compromise is reached; on this basis, a contract, commonly for a lump sum, is signed and a building permit obtained. The owner arranges his bank loan with provision for final mortgage when the house is completed to the satisfaction of the bank and of the Federal Housing Administration, if the latter insures the loan, or of the Veterans Administration, if the owner is a veteran who wants and is entitled to VA help.

The typical builder expects to do some of the work with his own force and to subcontract the balance. Usually he re-

---

[1] Basic statistics on the production of houses by different types of producers are given for the conventional housing industry in Chap. 1. Mobile home statistics appear later in this chapter.

tains carpentry because this trade carries through the entire job and coordinates the others. The work progresses in a number of separate operations. Subcontractor No. 1 enters, after the house is laid out on the lot, and with his bulldozer, power shovel, and other equipment strips the top soil and excavates for the foundation. He also digs any necessary trenches. He is followed by subcontractor No. 2 (masonry), who erects the sectional forms for a poured concrete foundation, for which dealer No. 1 then provides the ready-mixed concrete. The forms may, of course, be custom-built by the contractor, utilizing lumber which will later be reused in the superstructure, and the foundation may be concrete blocks or other masonry supplied by dealer No. 1 and erected by subcontractor No. 2.

The contractor, drawing on his first construction loan from the bank (if he plans to use one), brings in his carpenters and erects the framing for floors, walls, partitions, and roof, with material procured from dealer No. 2. Subcontractor No. 3 (the plumber) begins to install the rough plumbing, including sewer and water connections to the street. Subcontractor No. 2 erects the chimney. While the roofing is being applied by the contractor or by subcontractor No. 4 (the roofer and sheet metal man), subcontractor No. 5 (the electrician) and subcontractor No. 6 (the heating man) install their rough lines and make necessary connections to street utilities. In the meantime windows and exterior doors are being hung. These are obtained from dealer No. 2 (lumber) or from dealer No. 3 (millwork).

By this time the owner has made at least one payment, so the builder is in fairly good financial condition to meet some of his obligations and to proceed with subcontractor No. 7 (the plasterer) after the building inspector, the plumbing inspector, the wiring inspector, and possibly the heating inspector have approved the construction to this point. A FHA or VA inspector may also have to pass on the construction.

With the insulation installed, and lath and plaster applied

and dry (unless dry-wall construction has been employed), millwork and flooring arrive from dealers Nos. 2 and 3 and are erected by the contractor's own crew, or the flooring may be installed by subcontractor No. 8 (the floor layer). Eventually the time comes for subcontractors No. 3 (plumber), No. 5 (electrician), and No. 6 (heating) to install fixtures and appliances either supplied by themselves or purchased by them from dealers Nos. 4, 5, and 6 or supplied by the contractor or, in some instances, by the owner. In the meantime, subcontractor No. 2 (masonry) is finishing the fireplace and subcontractor No. 4 (sheet metal) is installing the hood over the kitchen range.

Subcontractor No. 9 (the painter), who has already applied at least one coat of paint outdoors, arrives and applies paint and whatever other finishes are called for at the same time that he hangs wallpaper purchased from dealer No. 7, from whom he may also purchase his paint if he does not obtain it directly from the paint manufacturer or from a wholesaler.

Finally, the contractor installs the finish hardware purchased from dealer No. 8. He also grades the yard and he may plant it with grass seed purchased from the hardware man or from dealer No. 9 (the nurseryman); on the other hand, the owner may elect to save a little money and undertake to do the final grading and seeding himself.

After the last bit of haggling over changes and extras has been completed, the contractor has furnished proof that all bills have been paid, and the inspectors have made their last inspections, the owner makes the final payment which the contractor hopes will provide a profit after he pays off his last bank loan.

Although this story is typical, it is by no means invariable. Any combination of dealers, subcontractors, and financial arrangement is possible. There may be more or fewer dealers and subcontractors depending on how much the contractor decides to do himself and the kinds of specialized subcontractors and specialty dealers available in any particular locality.

This approach to house construction is as loosely knit as it can be and still be workable. It is ideally suited to handling highly localized and unpredictable orders and at the same time makes possible the maximum degree of individuality in any given house. Whatever the owner or the architect calls for can be produced; the necessary combination of skills and supplies can be had. No other housebuilding operation has this extreme flexibility.

Typical Pattern. The custom builder of single dwellings is in many ways the archetype of the small businessman. His volume of business is not large, and it may fluctuate widely from year to year; his organization and overhead are minimal, and he is in turn dependent on many other businesses both large and small over which he has little or no control. Still, taken collectively, he represents an extremely large segment of the economy, and his fortunes have a strong bearing on national and local well-being and policy.

Typically, the small builder erects between five and twenty houses per year. These may all be custom-built, some may be custom-built and some built for sale, or occasionally all may be built for sale; the proportions probably vary from year to year. For each house there may be what amounts to a new team; hence one of the custom builder's major skills is that of command. Each house is designed to meet the requirements of a different owner on a different site, and different subcontractors, dealers, and financial and legal organizations may be involved. This calls for maximum flexibility, but it also tends to lead to low efficiency because there is little opportunity to achieve the smooth coordination which comes from long association. However, when a builder has been in business for a period of time, he frequently finds a combination of dealers and subcontractors with whom he works well, and he is likely to use this combination for every house if he possibly can.

Obviously, a complicating factor is the typical owner for

whom this house is a once-in-a-lifetime project, larger than anything else he will ever undertake. He is ignorant of building, unable to visualize his house from plans and specifications, subject to changes of heart as the building takes shape, and always on hand with comments and suggestions. Maximum individuality is achieved in the custom-built house, but at high unit cost and little assurance of complete satisfaction all around.

The builder's office organization requires a minimum of paid office help. Frequently his wife, daughter, or sister keeps his books and looks after his accounts; the statements from his bank help him to keep his finances in order. With the growing complexity of government regulations on taxes, social security, workmen's compensation, liability insurance, and mortgage insurance, he finds it increasingly necessary to have legal and accounting help, and his overhead is therefore increasing. His office organization is still minimal compared to that of other builders and to many other small businessmen, but it is no longer quite true that this builder can keep his office in his hat.

Generally, the custom builder receives a series of partial payments made as various phases of construction are completed. The usual method is to have the owner deposit sufficient funds to cover the entire contract with an escrow agent before work starts. If a loan is involved, the bank usually performs this function and holds the owner's equity and his note to cover his loan. The contract between the owner and builder specifies when payments shall be made; they may be based on the monthly percentage of completion achieved, the amount of bills paid by the builder, or some particular portion of construction when it is finished. The contractor usually must furnish proof that all bills have been paid before the final payment is made; otherwise his creditors might apply mechanics' liens against the house.

The system of partial payments means that a contractor's personal investment in construction is at any time considerably less than the full value of the contract. However, he must have sufficient working capital to bridge the gap between successive payments. Otherwise his investment in work in progress will exceed his available capital. Typically, he supplies most of his own working capital through personal investment. If he needs additional funds, he borrows from a bank, using personal notes for security. Most small firms are proprietorships, and consequently personal property serves as additional security against which working capital can be borrowed.

In contrast with the large-scale operative builder, land is often not a major problem for the builder of single dwellings. If the house is custom-built, the land has already been acquired by the owner; if not, a few lots can usually be obtained by a local builder. Seldom is the site far from his familiar territory. Frequently it is one of the many individual lots remaining open in developed communities.

Although architectural design trends undoubtedly have a strong, if delayed, influence on house design, the services of an architect are infrequently employed on custom houses. The typical builder considers the architect an expensive luxury and a downright nuisance. His attitude is likely to influence the owner who in turn looks on the architect's fee as an expense that can be saved, forgetting that the experienced architect, if given the opportunity, can more than earn his fee by providing a better house and one more suited to the owner's needs than will result from the owner's fumbling one-time attempts to meet his own requirements. The builder generally draws up the final minimal plans and skeleton specifications. There is no architectural supervision or advice during building. Orientation is set by lot lines. Color, interior decoration, and landscaping are up to the owner.

If architectural services in this field are minimal, other professional services, such as engineering, are vanishingly small. Except for an occasional surveying check of doubtful lot lines, engineering services are not needed if the house is built according to tradition and rule of thumb as exemplified by the local code, and such services are usually too expensive in any case for the individual house or the small group of houses.

The subcontractor is an essential and vital part of the custom-building process. Very few builders of single houses attempt to do the entire job themselves. Conversely, few go so far as to subcontract everything, in contrast to the practice in large-scale building where the prime contractor may be a coordinating broker who does no actual construction. The carpentry is undertaken by most housebuilders, a large proportion of whom began as carpenters. Other trades that may be retained are the mason's and in some instances all the structural and finishing trades, but the so-called mechanical trades —plumbing, heating, electrical—are almost invariably subcontracted because they call for specialized skills and tend to be regulated by separate codes.

The subcontractor usually supplies both labor and material. Like the contractor, he operates under a lump-sum subcontract which covers all costs. He is distinctly an entrepreneur and purchases primarily from his own local dealers or, when it is possible, from a manufacturer or wholesaler.

In the operations of the custom builders, especially when they are in outlying and smaller communities, labor is likely to be nonunion, following the traditional crafts, but with considerably more freedom in crossing craft boundaries. The crafts tradition works well enough for the custom-built or speculative house built in the traditional manner; however the nonunion builder often operates an essentially family organization, with a nucleus of brothers, in-laws, uncles, and sons, and the rest of the force made up of transients picked up from job to job, some of these in turn sometimes becoming more or less permanent parts of the team.

Materials and equipment are customarily bought from local dealers, who carry the accounts on credit against monthly or periodic billings and often are the principal source of new ideas. Few builders can or do make the effort to go after new things not locally or conveniently available and backed by a knowledgeable local dealer. As for millwork, the trend is toward buying completely assembled, often prefinished, units. This is particularly true if the units are made of metal or if they incorporate materials like plastics.

Local codes and regulations tend to reflect local practice and tradition. Since most small housebuilders simply conform there is little conflict. By the same token there is little incentive to try new ideas and methods, and the result is to freeze existing practice.

The typical builder belongs to a local organization such as a master builders' association whose principal functions, other than social, are to establish local policy, especially in dealing with local unions, fixing wage rates, considering local laws, and dealing with building inspectors. National and state-wide associations also represent the builder, though few small builders are members. The rapid growth and great size of the National Association of Home Builders attest the growing consciousness of builders that their problems are not only local but national in scope. Such state-wide and national associations act as sources of information about changes in technology and materials; they provide opportunities for contact with other segments of the industry and make possible organized efforts for changes in national and state-wide regulations, policies, and legislation.

Custom builders' selling effort is usually confined to making the name of the firm well known locally. They advertise on highway billboards and signs posted in front of current work, but most of their market contacts come through their acquaintances among real estate dealers and through previous customers. Market analysis and construction research are practically nonexistent on the part of the custom builder.

The Operative Builder

From the occasional and often suspiciously regarded "spec" builder of thirty and more years ago has emerged the present-day operative or development builder (or merchant builder, as he prefers to be called). Building groups of houses at a single time with common and similar plans, he has become the largest supplier of single dwellings today, particularly in populous urban and surrounding suburban areas. Many reasons can be found for his rise to his present position. Among them are three major factors:

1. *Land.* Operating on a large scale, he acquires raw land, develops it himself, builds, and sells the completed houses on their developed lots. Therefore, he can control the development pattern to suit the houses to be built; he is in a better position to cope with the web of controls and regulations, and he can afford to buy and develop the large outlying land-holdings that offer the best source of building lots in a growing land shortage. More important—most important in many instances—he is able to realize a profit on the land as well as on the house, particularly if he can hold part of it for commercial or industrial development. Land is, therefore, a powerful factor in the emergence of the development builder.

2. *Construction.* When enough similar houses are built at one time on contiguous lots, the economies of mass construction become possible. These consist chiefly in mass purchases at reduced prices, subdivision of labor into work teams performing the same job on each house, effective supervision of construction, organized delivery of materials and equipment, reduction in waste of materials by careful planning and cutting schedules, and increased use of power equipment. The size of the operation permits the use of large earth-moving equipment; the engineering and site assembly of panels, trusses, and mechanical assemblies; and the effective use of mass advertising and sales techniques.

3. *Public preference.* Not the least of the reasons for the emergence of the merchant builder is the consumer's growing inclination to buy a completed house. People cannot afford the cost, time, and headaches of buying land, planning a house, and building. Custom building involves too many irritating legal and financial details; and only a minute fraction of

owners has any notion of how to get the most from the services of architect (if one is employed) or builder. Consequently, the owner takes the safe path of buying something he can actually see, even if it is quite short of his desires.

The distinguishing feature between operative and custom builders is not necessarily size, but rather the attempt to build with common elements and to make broad production savings instead of tailoring individual jobs. All operative builders have some features in common; in other respects they differ by degrees depending upon the scale of operation.

When the builder of single houses turns to building groups of houses for sale, certain of his problems, particularly that of coping with the owner from the outset, are reduced or eliminated. Typically, he builds several houses at once, on contiguous lots, and he achieves something approaching a smoothly running operation. Very frequently he works at least part time as carpenter or foreman on his own operations, like the custom builder, and his organization is likely to be an unincorporated proprietorship or a partnership. He can build on relatively small parcels of land; and such parcels are easier to find, and closer to the built-up urban and suburban areas, than the extensive tracts required by the large-scale operative builder. The small builder is seldom concerned with putting in streets and utilities; conversely, he pays developed-land prices and does not have the opportunity for profit on the land. Although he does not obtain significant quantity discounts or make extensive use of power tools, he does use powered hand tools, such as circular saws, and he usually sets up a small bench with power tools. So long as he remains small, he has small overhead and high flexibility. He can, and frequently does, make rather significant changes in the house after it has been started if he finds a buyer before completion.

As the operative builder grows in size, he is as likely to build on speculation on tracts developed by others as to develop land himself, but his purchases of lots are likely to be of sufficient magnitude to influence the site planning of the land, particularly if he appears on the scene while land is still in the raw state. He can a.id usually does obtain some work-crew specialization. On the other hand, he is likely to be too large to operate on a nonunion basis, but not large enough to undertake the highly specialized piecework subcontract structure accessible to the large-scale builder. He tends to be in a fairly strong bargaining position relative to subcontractors, but they are likely to be real subcontractors who supply both material and labor, rather than merely suppliers of labor for the mechanical and other specialized trades, as is often the case for the large builder. He buys materials and equipment on a scale large enough to warrant significant price reductions but not to set up a subsidiary for purchasing at wholesale and obtaining specialized designs and individual runs of material directly from the manufacturer. In sum, he uses as many operating efficiencies as he can. At the same time he need not, as distinguished from the large operative builder, confine himself to the major population centers in order to assure a demand at the scale of his production.

Pattern of Large-scale Operative Builder. When he becomes very large, the operative builder takes on some of the characteristics of a true industrialist. He therefore deserves careful study by all those interested in the housing industry.

1. *Volume.* Although the number of large operative builders is relatively small, the group accounts for a large share of total housing production (in 1954, 1 per cent of the builders erected about a third of the new homes).[2] Generally builders are considered large if they fabricate as many as 250 houses a year. However, a few giants in the industry produce ten times this volume. During 1953 the fourteen biggest operators accounted for nearly 5 per cent of all new homes.[3] Largest was Levitt and Sons, who started 7,000 homes in Levittown, Pennsylvania; other giant firms produced as many as 5,000 houses,

2 "Housing Takes to Detroit Ways," *Business Week,* April 30, 1955, p. 63.
3 "Biggest Homebuilders of 1953," *House & Home,* vol. 5, no. 1, January, 1954, p. 40.

most of them by spreading their activity over many projects. In 1957, the largest builder was Centex Construction Company, operating in Arkansas, Hawaii, Illinois, Indiana, and Texas. Between 1950 and 1957, Centex built 17,500 units, valued at $240 million.[4]

Such builders usually build on large tracts (250 to 400 units at least) and develop fairly complete communities. They must pave roads, build sewage treatment facilities, and run in electric lines and water mains. Many build apartment houses and shopping centers and provide for industrial development on their tracts as well as single-family houses. Levitt is able to build schools and community buildings in addition. It has been estimated that as much as half the man-hours spent on Levittown, Pennsylvania, went into the provision of facilities other than houses.

Even operating over a wide area, companies can realize several of the organizational and functional benefits which accrue to the large firm. However, labor cannot be specialized to the extent that is possible when all production is on a single, gigantic project. Frequently the companies that operate at several sites subcontract all building operations, acting as building brokers similar to those commonly found in the construction of large buildings. Ability to assemble organizations in a hurry is a prime characteristic of such builders.

2. *Management.* Most large firms are principally owned by a few men who serve as the top-executive group. These men usually have responsibility for specific areas of operation such as design, construction, land development, financing, government relations, purchasing, and sales. One problem of the large operative builder is the lack of good intermediate personnel between the labor force and the top-management group. Because the firms are tightly owned there is usually no path to promotion for bright young men in staff or line positions. Consequently these firms have few capable junior execu-

---

[4] *House & Home*, vol. 13, no. 3, March, 1958, p. 45. Ten builders in 1957 produced 1,000 or more houses.

tives, and top management must usually handle all negotiations with outside agencies and make most of the routine day-to-day decisions.

Because of the regulations of national, state, and local tax systems and the need to fit into the materials-distribution channels of the building industry, the large-scale operative builder frequently finds it desirable to organize separate corporations for land purchase and development, construction, and the purchase of materials and equipment. The builder is also better able to protect his equity if he spreads the risk over several corporate entities. Although these are separate corporations, they are closely associated in carrying out the entire operation and all are controlled by the central management group.

Most large firms in the industry also attempt to set up some more or less formal system of scheduling controls and reporting. Unlike smaller organizations, management is usually so far removed from the construction process that regular methods for transmitting production information are required.

3. *Finance.* The operative builder usually acquires his equity capital through personal investment; even the industry giants rarely have public financing. This investment is seldom sufficient to finance even a moderate-sized project, and the builder typically relies on borrowed funds for working capital. If the firm is reasonably sound, it can borrow on notes against its general assets. Funds acquired in this manner are usually used for land development and similar operations. Money for actual construction is usually under the FHA commitment and construction advances program. Under this program, the builder borrows from financial institutions using mortgages against the houses in process as security. The FHA insures the loans and thereby guarantees the lender against loss as long as the borrower completes the project. In order to get this insurance the plans and designs must be approved by the FHA in advance.

The operative builder must also arrange for permanent

financing (i.e., the mortgage for the eventual purchaser), and in most cases, he is required to have a firm commitment on permanent financing before he will be lent the construction money, so that funds will not be tied up in completed houses while prospective purchasers search for adequate financing. As he is customarily dealing with a large volume and a middle-class market, most of the final financing also comes under FHA or VA guarantee. The VA will not guarantee a loan if the selling price exceeds its estimate of current market value; the FHA sets a maximum loan on a house according to its appraisal of long-term economic value. Consequently it is to the builder's advantage to secure the highest possible appraisals from these agencies. Often the builder must spend a great deal of time negotiating over the appraised value of the design before he can obtain permanent financing.

4. *Purchasing.* The field of purchasing is one in which the large builder is able to achieve considerable savings over his smaller counterpart. Many of the largest builders buy directly from the mill or basic producer. In so doing, the firm bypasses the retailer and often the wholesaler; thus avoiding the mark-ups that occur at these points in the chain of distribution. However, this often requires special organizational arrangements, for many materials producers sell only to recognized distributors. In order to comply with such a policy, the builder establishes his own building supply subsidiary which buys from the manufacturer and resells (usually exclusively) to his construction organization.[5] Whether the builder buys directly or through a wholly owned subsidiary, the result is the same: the profits and many of the costs of the middleman are avoided. Even if he cannot bypass the middleman, the operative builder can often realize significant savings by buying in volume and receiving shipments direct from the producer. Such a program requires that the builder have some place to store or warehouse large quantities of materials. However the

[5] North Shore Supply has long served this function for Levitt.

cost involved in storage is usually much less than the savings accrued through buying in quantity. Much of the material can be stored at the site at little or no extra cost. Sherman Maisel in his study of contractors in the San Francisco Bay area has estimated that "compared with the small builder the average large builder saves $410 on materials purchased for a typical house, and the largest builder may save an additional $130, or a total of almost a quarter of the small builder's materials cost." [6]

5. *Research.* The large operative builder is in a much better position to engage in applied research than the small firm. His greater financial resources make him more able to afford it and his volume of business is large enough so that there is the possibility of realizing high profits through innovation. However, with the exception of one or two progressive merchant builders, the group as a whole has done little exploration. Large builders do some testing of materials and have worked with suppliers to bring out innovations resulting from their practical experience in the field. But they have rarely attempted intensive pressure on suppliers to develop new materials, nor do they engage in large-scale research activities of their own.

6. *Production.* A high degree of labor specialization is one of the outstanding features of large-scale operative house construction. Here the team rather than the individual craftsman is the basic unit. Crews are organized and given carefully worked-out tasks to perform. Some of the largest firms even specialize work within the crew, giving each man a single job which he performs repetitively as the crew works its way through the project. For example, one firm has broken down sheathing a roof into a three-operation job. One man takes lumber from a stack and leans it against the building; a second man working on the roof draws the lumber up and cuts it to size; a third man does the nailing. Such specialization enables workers to become expert at small tasks, and thereby increases

[6] Sherman J. Maisel, *Housebuilding in Transition,* University of California Press, Berkeley, Calif., 1953, p. 121.

efficiency. Maisel has estimated that large firms save about 26 per cent of the small companies' labor costs through specialization.[7] A few large firms subcontract certain jobs to the working crews on a lump-sum basis. A price is set for a given job and the return to the individual crew depends upon how quickly it performs that job.[8]

Large firms customarily mechanize more jobs and use more power equipment in building than smaller concerns. However, even the largest firms in the home-building field have limited opportunities for mechanization. In a system primarily based on wood technology, the human hand with simple tools is more or less unbeatable even on the largest tracts. Site mechanization usually involves using power equipment to aid the worker rather than to replace him. For example, power saws and drills are often used for finish carpentry, pneumatic hammers for nailing the subflooring, and motorized trowels for finishing the flatwork. One of the few operations which can be almost completely mechanized is that of digging the trenches for the foundation wall and the utilities. In large tracts where the volume of work is sufficient to offset the cost of transporting the equipment, this job is usually done by a rotary trencher.

A certain amount of prefabrication often is carried on at shops located on the site or a short distance from it. Framing lumber may be precut and delivered in bundles, with those pieces which will be used first on top. Dormer roofs, window assemblies, bathroom walls, and stair-well assemblies may all be prefabricated on jigs. Ceiling joists and rafters may be precision cut and delivered on trailers. The advantage of such procedures is that members may be made for several houses at once under ideal conditions with power equipment. Thus

[7] *Ibid.*, p. 114.

[8] These organizational innovations are inherently in conflict with the operational assumptions underlying the structure of the craft unions. Obviously, adaptions are required as the volume of industry production by such organizations increases.

pieces are turned out at a much faster pace than is possible with standard methods of carpentry. In most cases this time reduction much more than offsets the costs resulting from the relatively small increases in materials handling.

Where the volume of work is large, subcontractors also can specialize their labor and do some prefabricating. This is particularly true of plumbing, where the advantages of prefabrication are very apparent. Project plumbers often precut piping into standard lengths and build many of the standard subassemblies in the shop. A few prefabricate the entire "tree" or prefabricate and handle in bundles the coils used for radiant heating. As much as 80 per cent of the work is assembly work that can be done in the shop, and the remaining installation can be broken down into a production-line operation, with each journeyman going from house to house to perform a particular job. Some subcontractors specialize in project work and have made it a point to develop cost-cutting methods; a few work almost exclusively for one large builder. As more units are produced, overhead and profit may be spread thinner, giving a lower unit cost; the large and steady volume of business is attractive enough to the subcontractor to persuade him to pass on these savings to the builder. In such an organizational structure, subcontracting in the independent-craft sense understood in custom building hardly exists.

7. *Marketing.* The operative builder usually has a definite marketing program. He is producing houses for sale and therefore must make some effort to discover what the market wants and to promote his products. Recently an increasing attention to these problems has been forced on him by the fact that most people no longer must buy a new home. This market of "already-owners" is considerably tougher to sell than a market in desperate need of shelter. Before current owners will buy a new house they must become dissatisfied with their present dwelling.

Most firms in other large industries spend a great deal of time attempting to study the characteristics of their actual and potential markets. Through such study they hope to be able to adapt their product precisely to the desires of the consumer, thereby achieving higher sale and possibly also lower costs. Most large operative builders undertake some form of market study, usually not nearly so extensive or so formal as in other industries, but some continue to substitute assumptions based on personal experience gained in earlier (and often smaller) operations.

Such progress as has been made in housing market analysis has been largely the work of government agencies. The Division of Housing Research of the Housing and Home Finance Agency has been particularly active in this area and has sponsored research aimed at developing usable theories and low-cost techniques which may be adopted for local housing market analysis.[9] A difficulty arises from the general inadequacy of local data. The HHFA and the Bureau of the Census occasionally make local surveys of population and housing characteristics; city and county records will often yield information concerning the population (number of registered voters, vital statistics) and construction activity. Sometimes local VA, FHA, and lending institutions will supply useful data on the characteristics of current purchasers (but most of the information in the records of these agencies is confidential). However, except in large metropolitan areas, basic records are apt to be incomplete and unorganized; they are also apt to be in a form not readily adaptable to the housing industry.

Among the largest builders a few maintain their own market research staff but most obtain informal market research infor-

---

[9] Three publications that have resulted from this research are Chester Rapkin, Louis Winnick, and David M. Blank, *Housing Market Analysis*, HHFA, Division of Housing Research, 1953; Maurice R. Brewster, William A. Flinn, and Ernest H. Jurkat, *How to Make and Interpret Locational Studies of the Housing Market*, prepared by HHFA, published by U.S. Department of Commerce, no. PB111653, 1955; Reinhold P. Wolff, *A Short-term Forecast of the Housing Market, Jacksonville, Florida*, HHFA, Division of Housing Research, 1953.

mation through consultation with real estate brokers, or consultants hired on a fee basis.[10]

When market research has told the builder where the market is and what the buyer wants, selling activities take over in an effort to create the market and shape the attitudes of potential customers. The present-day operative builder usually centers his sales campaign around a model house. This prototype is constructed at the start of the development and serves as the showroom for the product. Many builders find it desirable to construct several different models, each representing a dwelling that will appear on the tract (see photograph 5). This trend reflects increasing discrimination on the part of buyers and the need to provide a range of choices.

Most builders have a sales office in or near the model. When a customer shows genuine interest, he is taken there to discuss financial details and to check his qualifications for buying. To attain large-volume production it is necessary to generate large-volume sales; operative builders like William Levitt have therefore developed the making, processing, and closing of a sale into a highly organized, mass-production process.

To make their houses more attractive and salable, builders furnish their models carefully. Landscaping the site helps to create the "curb appeal" which draws crowds into the development. Frequently the model is equipped with signs highlighting the sales features and X-ray sections exposing the framing, insulation, and sheathing. Some builders use tape-recordings to explain new or uncommon aspects of the houses. Manufacturers' point-of-sales advertisements are occasionally displayed for the prestige and confidence that may be obtained by identifying the houses with the brand names of nationally advertised components. All these methods are designed to sell the house once the customer has come to see it. Advertising and publicity stunts are used to draw the crowds

10 Robert B. Filley, "Let a Market Analyst Look before You Leap," *House & Home*, vol. 9, no. 2, February, 1956, p. 134.

—gala openings with guest celebrities, pretty girls, raffles, and giveaway prizes.

Operative builders spend relatively little on advertising, nevertheless. The classified sections of newspapers are the favorite advertising medium, and other outlays go mainly for newspaper display space, usually on whatever day the local papers feature "real estate" sections. A few builders back up these main efforts with radio and television spots or outdoor advertising. Very few builders employ advertising agencies. A recent NAHB convention recommended that large builders spend between $1\frac{1}{4}$ and $1\frac{1}{2}$ per cent of their volume on advertising.[11] This is considerably less than common in other major industries. For example, General Foods spends about 8 per cent of anticipated sales on advertising, and the appropriation at du Pont runs about 5 per cent of consumer sales.[12] But food and chemical sales occur at a much higher frequency, and nobody has really determined the appropriate size of the advertising budget for a house. In the absence of major firms with the resources to invest in general advertising and to wait for it to pay off, much of the responsibility for promotion will have to be shouldered by trade organizations, magazines, and other interested groups.[13]

Many large builders give warranties which guarantee the material and workmanship of the house for a full year. This is a promotional device which costs little and dramatizes well. In general the builder will not be picayune about sticking to the exact wording of the guarantee, feeling that loss in good will is more expensive than the cost of a minor repair.

The package mortgage is a relatively new sales tool for builders of all types; it permits appliances to be sold along

[11] "Are Your Merchandising Methods Up to Date?" *House & Home*, vol. 9, no. 4, April, 1956, p. 169.

[12] Daniel Seligman, "How Much for Advertising," *Fortune*, vol. 54, no. 6, December, 1956, p. 123.

[13] *House & Home* and the NAHB *Journal of Homebuilding* carry frequent articles on merchandising techniques.

with the house and financed as part of the home loan. The chief advantage to the buyer is the fact that the appliances are financed on a long-term loan; even though the total interest paid will be greater than under standard installment plans, the monthly payment is much less. Installation costs are also less when the equipment is put in during construction of a house. Moreover builders pass along part of their discounts on large appliance purchases.

In 1957, appliance dealers sought to secure legislation which would remove from all FHA financing "items which are not an integral part of real estate." [14] The campaign was unsuccessful, but it indicates that the housing industry has been making effective use of one of its more successful selling tools—one that will become more and more useful as builders continue their concentration on the "already-owner" market.

Another recent marketing development for builders of all types is trade-in selling, which occurs whenever the builder helps the buyer dispose of his old house. There are three general types of trade-in operations. One is the straight trade-in, where the builder accepts the old house at something less than market price and sells it; in such a case, the builder often repairs or modernizes the house although this is no longer an FHA requirement. More popular is the trade-in guarantee, where the builder guarantees the buyer a certain price for his old house if it has not been sold before the new house is completed. Sometimes the builder assists the buyer in selling his old house, but the buyer determines the asking price and assumes prime responsibility; if the house is sold before the deadline, the builder is washed out of the deal. The guaranteed price offered by the builder is usually 80 to 85 per cent of the fair market value and in about 10 per cent of the cases he must take title to the house. The third type of deal is the time-limit trade. The buyer signs a contract for the new

---

[14] Joseph B. McGrath, "Home Buyers and Builders Facing a New Threat," *NAHB Correlator: Journal of Homebuilding*, vol. 11, no. 2, February, 1957, p. 3.

house and then the builder or a realtor helps him sell his old house; if the house is not sold within a specified period of time, the original contract is void.

To date trade-ins have not reached the point where they account for a substantial portion of housing sales volume. However, a recent NAHB survey showed that one-third of the builders covered now handle them.[15] The 1954 Housing Act allowed the FHA to liberalize its policies and requirements concerning trade-in properties. It was hoped that the new program would provide builders and realtors with the necessary interim financing for an inventory of such houses. However, there is some question as to whether this is working as effectively as it might,[16] and the industry is plugging for freer trade-in financing under FHA, so that an effective secondhand market may serve to stimulate over-all sales.[17]

8. *Community problems.* In many ways, land is the chief problem facing the operative builder, as was pointed out in the previous chapter, and it becomes more acute the larger the development. At the same time, it is a major opportunity and justifies unusual efforts to provide access and utilities or to solve problems through the use of earth-moving equipment— efforts the builder can afford if the project is large. The large operative builder is much more likely to be in difficulties with typical codes than is the medium or small one, however, because his mass-production methods are more likely to be specially engineered and, therefore, to conflict with the local codes. The small- and medium-scale builders are likely to stay in code areas and go along with the codes, but the large operative builder tends to avoid the issue by moving into outlying areas where the controls are weak or nonexistent.

Because of this, project builders must usually give con-

---

[15] John Dickerman, "Trade-in Houses Open a New Market for You," *American Builder*, vol. 78, no. 12, December, 1956, p. 25.

[16] "Three New Plans to Make Trade-in Finance Easy," *House & Home*, vol. 11, no. 5, May, 1957, p. 150.

[17] *House & Home*, vol. 13, no. 6, June, 1958, p. 132.

siderable thought and time to planning the layout of new projects, in some cases setting high standards for effective community design in suburban areas. They offer one of the bright hopes for substantial design progress in the industry.

The Prefabricator [18]

The prefabrication industry has a long history,[19] but only in the last two decades has it been given general attention as a force for the eventual industrialization of housing. In the period just before World War II, less than 1 per cent of single-family dwellings was prefabricated, and only one-eighth of the crash program of emergency war housing was prefabricated. Following the war, however, the housing shortage stimulated a large number of new companies to enter the field, and by the late 1940s production had reached 3,500 units per year or between 3 and 4 per cent of the total. In the last decade, production has mounted until in 1956 nearly 95,000 units were produced, or about 10 per cent of all single-family dwellings. During this decade, also, the number of companies in the industry has leveled off at about one hundred, and most of those whose attention was limited to a specialized house design, or a super-efficient production system, to the exclusion of sound over-all management, had disappeared from the scene.[20]

The variety of construction approaches to prefabrication may best be illustrated by several examples:

1. One of the oldest prefabricators in continuous production fabricates a set of wood panels with interior and

[18] As of 1958, the industry has decided that prefabricators should be called "home manufacturers." The trade association is now known as the Home Manufacturers Association.

[19] For a history and a detailed analysis of the industry, see Burnham Kelly, *The Prefabrication of Houses*, Technology Press and John Wiley & Sons, Inc., New York, 1951; and Albert Farwell Bemis, *The Evolving House*, vol. III, *Rational Design*, Technology Press, M.I.T., Cambridge, Mass., 1936.

[20] For good discussion of recent trends in prefabrication, see *House & Home*, which annually has given its December issues almost entirely to the subject.

exterior covering glued to ribs (studs, joists, and rafters) smaller and more closely spaced than conventional members. All wall and partition panels are standardized, height and pitch of roofs are also standardized. The basic dimension is 6 feet. Although the company provides a number of standard floor plans, it also builds to the individual owner's plans, which are adapted to the fabricator's standard dimensions. A series of simple connections is employed. Electrical wiring is incorporated into the panels or run in surface conduit. Plumbing and heating are to some degree standardized. Doors and windows are incorporated into the panels and finish floor is shop-applied. Continuous trim, like baseboards, is field-applied, and special floor closure strips are employed. Final coats of paint are field-applied. Although not extreme in construction or appearance, the house frequently encounters building code difficulties because of its unconventional framing.[21]

2. The construction used by many small prefabricators seeks to avoid building-code difficulties by adapting conventional platform and balloon framing to a system of wall, partition, floor, and roof panels. Of all the approaches considered here, this one differs least from conventional framing, but even it has run into code difficulties in regions where essential features of the platform and balloon frames are not permitted. Sheathing, subfloors, and roof boarding are shop-applied, but most finish is field-applied although precut as much as possible. Some preassembly of electrical, heating, and plumbing packages is possible with the standardized plans, but it is not carried to the point of incurring serious difficulties with local codes and inspectors.

3. Stressed-skin panels[22] are a feature of many a larger producer. Typically, the manufacturer of such a system has a series of standard plans in which his standard panels are interchangeable, but no attempt is made to accommodate the sys-

---

[21] A detailed report on nearly every significant prefabrication system has appeared at one time or another in the FHA *Technical Bulletin.*

[22] Construction described in Chap. 6.

tem to an individual owner's plan. Trussed or semitrussed rafters are commonly employed and ceiling panels are suspended from this roof structure. As much preassembly as possible of heating, plumbing, and electrical components is practiced. Field finishing is minimized, but a considerable amount of field installation of trim is necessary. Slab floor construction combined with one-story plan eliminates floor panels.

4. Unlike the other approaches here described, Techbuilt [23] sells a house essentially two stories in height, with the lower floor a concrete slab on ground, partly below grade, and the entrance at mid-height between floors. It uses both stressed-skin and semistressed-skin construction, in that the roof panels have plywood glued top and bottom for complete stressed skin, floor panels have complete ceilings of plywood glued to the underside, part of the floor plywood is shop-glued but part field-nailed to allow access, and walls have full-sized studs with only the exterior sheathing plywood shop-glued. Large glass areas and an open plan demand careful engineering of all panels and their connections in order to support and distribute loads in such a way as to take full advantage of the strong stiff stressed-skin construction. Equipment, including the heating, plumbing, and wiring, is planned for maximum concentration within a central core and as much preassembly as possible. As might be expected, this house has had its share of difficulties with local code authorities, especially because of the stressed-skin principle and the method of panel assembly.

5. All the houses described above employ more or less familiar housebuilding materials and rely primarily on wood, especially in the frames. Attempts to utilize other materials have not been outstandingly successful, although this picture is changing. The largest-scale attempt to utilize metal, and in many ways the most ambitious prefabrication scheme so far set up—that of the late Lustron Corporation—involved porcelain-enameled steel as the basic material for structure and

23 See also Chap. 3.

finish combined. Other materials, of course, were also employed, but the house was essentially a steel house.

Lustron took over a wartime factory and installed large-scale metal-forming and enameling equipment to carry out all the fabricating processes from raw sheet to finished units. This included the manufacture of plumbing fixtures.[24] As nearly complete as possible factory assembly of units such as bathrooms, kitchens, and heating equipment was carried out.

Among the many reasons advanced for the failure of this ambitious attempt are resistance by local officials to a house built of unfamiliar materials; too great emphasis on factory fabrication, with too little attention paid to the distribution, marketing, and erection problems; delays in getting started; and rising costs, so that the prices which had to be charged were substantially above those first advertised. The prices were not significantly lower than those of competing conventionally built houses—indeed the broad acceptability that would be required with huge volume led to raising standards until the houses were larger and better finished (and more costly) than most of the competition at a time when much emphasis was turning to "economy models." The volume of production and distribution did not mount rapidly as had been hoped, and before it ever really got under way, the company was in financial difficulties which brought about its demise.

Objectives. Despite the variety of approaches, the more or less obvious objective of all foregoing examples of prefabrication is to reduce cost or to increase value by these measures, among others:

1.   Transfer of labor from the site to the shop where more efficient working conditions prevail; lower labor rates may be paid; optimum use may be made of power equipment, jigs and fixtures, conveyors, and other materials-handling equipment; and production is not hampered by weather.

2.   Mass purchases of materials and equipment at prices

---

[24] See also Chap. 3.

lower than those available to the builder of single dwellings and better inspection and control of purchases.

3. Better engineering both of the house and of the production process. Components can be designed to utilize the materials to more nearly their fullest capacity, quality control is much improved, and the cost of engineering talent is spread over a large number of units.

4. Over-all management efficiency, since the successful prefabricator is highly conscious of the process and problems of developing land, clearing community controls, making sales, scheduling erection, arranging financing, and turning over capital. For the most part it is not in the product but in the over-all production process and in managerial skill that the prefabricator may be distinguished from the conventional builder, and in many of these respects he is not distinguishable from the large operative builder.

Typical Pattern. The completely prefabricated house, which needs merely to be delivered to the site and installed without site labor beyond that required to move the house from the truck and to make a few field connections, is not yet a commercial reality. Most prefabricated house packages represent only about one-third of the cost of the final house.[25]

1. *Construction.* In structure, prefabricated houses today utilize panelized construction for walls, floors, roofs, and partitions in varying degree, from simple framing adapted from standard construction through stressed skin to a limited use of sandwich construction. Other structural parts include trussed rafters, beams, and special girders in addition to packaged precut lumber for field assembly.

The central heating plant is generally preassembled with the necessary controls and stubs of ducts or piping to be connected to the heating lines in the field. Most designs call for

---

[25] *PF, The Magazine of Prefabrication*, vol. 6, no. 4, April, 1958, p. 20, gives the cost breakdown for a $10,000 prefabricated house in detail. Of a total construction cost of $6,700, the factory package plus transportation was about $2,750. The land cost was $1,500, and profit was $1,000.

1. New building technology enriches the living quality of the home. Steel structure opens up living areas in the Eichler X-100 house.

2. Air view of Levittown, Pennsylvania, shows land planning as the major factor in large-scale home-building operations.

3. Appliances like the G.E. Kitchen Center, which combines seven major household operations in one compact unit, encourage new plan relationships. Kitchen and living area merge.

4. The production line does many jobs faster and better. Aluminum wall panels receive oven-baked finish at National Homes.

5. Mass production requires mass sales. Builder John Long of Phoenix displays merchandising techniques.

6. Skilled designers have long studied the potentialities of the production line. General Panel Corporation in the 1940's developed a three-dimensional load-bearing panel system.

7. Eichler X-100 house uses plywood curtain panels in a steel frame.

8. Panel construction is simplified by replacement of conventional sealants with new materials.

9. Architect Frederick J. Kiesler's work shown on this page explores the aesthetic potentialities of new materials. The egglike "Endless House" of 1950 was a daring demonstration of shaping interior space.

10. *below* 11. *right* Sketch and full-scale mock-up of the "Space House" of 1934, an earlier study of domestic space.

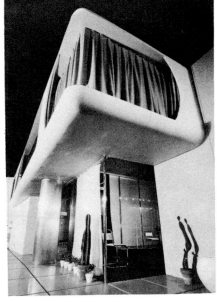

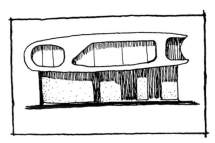

12. R. Buckminster Fuller makes full use of engineering potentials to enclose space. The original Dymaxion house, 1927, suspends lightweight metal skins with cables.

13. Fuller's later Geodesic dome with plastic skin, by enclosing entire site, allows free dispersal of living areas.

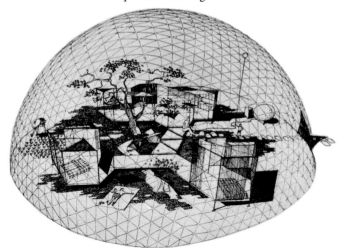

14. Frank Lloyd Wright uses modern machinery to shape a house of earth.

15. To meet the needs of modern production and transportation, Carl Koch designed a house package that unfolds at the site.

16. Standardized industrial parts are skillfully assembled by artist Charles Eames to make a highly personal house.

17. Wallace Neff's idea of spraying concrete on an inflated balloon form is used by Eliot Noyes for a Florida house.

18. Eliot Noyes' projection of the house of 1964 is enclosed by large reinforced plastic shells.

19. John Johansen explores the freedom of form available with concrete shells formed on wire mesh.

20. A full-scale demonstration of plastics as the basic structure of a house. Monsanto House of the Future by Hamilton and Goody.

21. Eduardo Catalano designs a thin wood roof in the form of a hyperbolic paraboloid to shelter his house.

22. Standardized industrial components produce small space units which are assembled to form a wide variety of house plans in this proposal by George Nelson and Gordon Chadwick.

23. Economy in materials and land are combined with individual courtyards in row-housing scheme by Danish architect Aarne Jacobsen.

24. Wall panels for Air Force housing are built at Acorn Houses, Inc. Such large projects encourage use of new, more efficient techniques.

25. Simplicity of the General Panel Corporation component system carries production-line efficiency into field assembly.

26. Piecemeal conversion of farm land into Suburbia is wasteful of land resources.

27. William Levitt brings many suburban amenities to his housing group at Whitestone, New York.

28. Careful advance planning preserves trees, groups housing into attractive spaces at Don Mills, a new town in Ontario, Canada.

29. Carl Koch's proposal for Cincinnati redevelopment mixes row housing with high apartment blocks for visual and social balance.

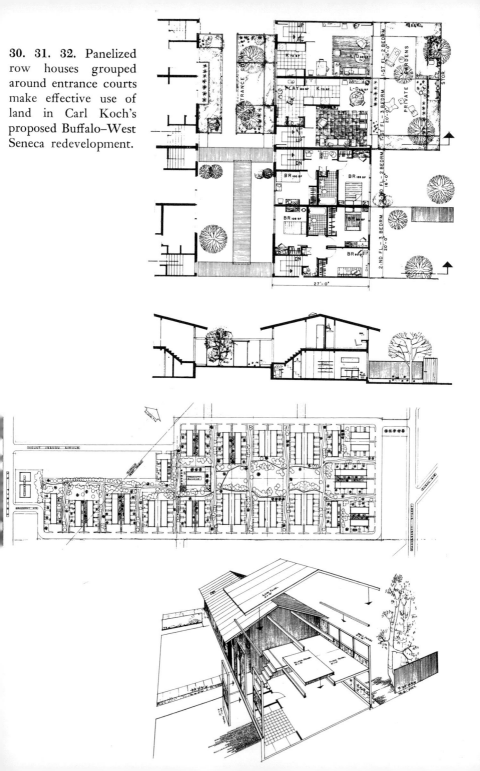

30. 31. 32. Panelized row houses grouped around entrance courts make effective use of land in Carl Koch's proposed Buffalo–West Seneca redevelopment.

33. In order to get 80 per cent of its heating requirements from the sun in the New England climate, M.I.T.s Solar House IV uses new house shape.

34. Laminated wood columns and dihedral beams create attractive exposed structure in Rilco Research House by John Lindsay.

35. Mobile home manufacturers such as Spartan readily adopt industrial materials and techniques.

36. Largest trailers offer comfortable minimum-involvement housing.

37. Lean-to porches, terraces, and gardens tie mobile homes to site.

38. Lighting, heating, and air conditioning are integrated in plastic structural units of Monsanto House of the Future. Family room interior.

39. Interlocking of interior and exterior spaces made possible by use of long span steel structure in Carl Koch's proposal for National Steel Corp.

short ducts or for short piping systems, so that the amount of field labor can be minimized. The ducts and piping systems are preassembled into units that can conveniently be shipped, or are at least precut to size. Various ingenious methods of incorporating ducts or piping into the panels or of circumventing the panels are employed. A major problem in any prefabrication system is that of incorporating plumbing, ducting, piping, and wiring into a system of shop-fabricated structural units.

Like the heating system, a limited amount of prefabrication is employed with plumbing. Although many completely prefabricated bathrooms and kitchens have been designed, little use is made of such units because of the variety and rigidity of local codes and the strength of traditional plumbing distribution channels and trades. In the last few years there has been a significant increase in the number of plumbing packages sold with the house, and when it can be locally approved, a prefabricated stack or "tree," to which the fixtures can be attached in the field, is frequently employed.

Wiring and electrical fixtures raise problems similar to those of plumbing and heating. However, wiring can be and typically is run in surface conduits or in a continuous outlet applied in the field. Where local detailed inspection is not required, conduit and other means of wiring can be built directly into the panels at the factory.

Numerous attempts have been made to design and build complete mechanical cores, including heating, plumbing, and major electrical equipment in a single unit to be installed and connected in the field to the necessary utilities, and to heating, plumbing, and electrical lines feeding the rest of the house. Such cores have had limited success except as they have been built by prefabricators for specific installation in specific plans and in areas free of restrictive code and labor regulations. Somewhat simpler versions, containing kitchen elements in convenient form, have had some success in other applications —notably for the remodeling or conversion of apartment units. This is one of the areas in which significant developments may be expected, in particular because of the interest of large appliance and equipment producers.

2. *Site problems.* Some measure of site preparation is inevitable even with prefabricated housing. It is at least necessary to install streets, walks, and utilities such as water, gas, and electrical lines, and some grading is necessary. Utility connections to the individual sites are installed in much the same manner as for operative-builder construction; for prefabrication, more accurate placement may be required to make sure that the field-installed connections and those incorporated into the prefabricated house will match.

Foundations employed for prefabricated housing are generally similar to those used for site-built housing. These include full foundation, pier and grade beam, and slab-on-ground, of which the last is the most common. In some instances piers alone are employed and the structure is erected on them. Little attempt has been made to develop a special system of prefabricated units which can be utilized for foundations of houses.

Because of the importance to the prefabricator of being able to sell over a large area, variation in local building codes is likely to be a greater problem for him than for the small builder or for the development builder who operates in a single locality. To the prefabricator, the fairness of each individual community regulation is less important than the establishment of a uniform level and maximum requirements over a broad market area. Many of the advantages of prefabrication are lost if a welter of special designs interrupts production schedules and complicates distribution. Heating, plumbing, and electrical wiring have not been extensively prefabricated because many local inspectors have insisted on being able to examine all phases of each mechanical installation to make sure that it conforms to local requirements. Since it is manifestly impossible to take the inspector to the fabricator's shop every time a house is built, it is necessary to design the mechanical equipment in such a way that the local inspector can make his inspection on the site.

3. *Labor and management.* As is true for housing generally, it is estimated that only about half the prefabricating shops are unionized. Where unions exist they may be either craft or industrial organizations. Furthermore, if the shop is unionized, the field force may not be or vice versa. If both are unionized, they usually belong to the same organization; if the field force is unionized, it is almost sure to be a craft union.

Wage rates favor field labor over shop, since shop employment is considerably steadier and has better working conditions than field employment. Clashes between shop and field, even when one is unionized and the other is not, have not been widespread and have not so far constituted a serious hazard. Jurisdictional disputes among various crafts are usually avoided by arranging the plans and work in such a way as to employ a minimum number of craft unions. Labor generally is not a major problem to prefabricators, who can adjust to its requirements more easily than to those of the codes. Furthermore, with the situation so evenly balanced between union and nonunion, the industry as a whole is glad to avoid having to take any stand. In the long run, however, as the bulk of housing is produced by larger organizations, a trend toward unionization seems highly predictable.

Unlike the custom builder or the development builder, the prefabricator has essentially two distinct organizations: (1) the shop and (2) sales and house erection in the field. Generally speaking, the prefabricator's central organization must be larger and more elaborate than the site builder's. Besides supervising the shop, it must handle planning, purchasing, marketing, financing, distribution, and relationships with the field offices and community officials in general. There is more fixed plant, and overhead is therefore generally greater than for the site builder. In compensation, the organization offers regulatory and financial support, operating stability, quality control, and the benefits of brand-name merchandising.

Field organization varies from prefabricator to prefabricator and, for a given prefabricator, may vary from locality to locality. Typically dealer-erectors take care of the distribution, erection, and selling within a given territory. Dealers are recruited from materials dealers, local builders, or from outside the traditional building field. The prefabricator may sell a substantial number of houses to large-scale developers, so that prefabricator and operative builder become collaborators rather than competitors in a given market, gaining the benefit of economies in both production and site development.

Unlike the site builder, especially the large-scale operative builder, the prefabricator has a large potential market in outlying rural areas. Once the house is loaded on the truck or other means of transportation, it makes relatively little difference whether it is delivered to an urban or to an outlying site. The local office can take care of a considerable territory and is in an excellent position to handle sales of this type; the reduced site labor is a big advantage; and there are fewer local restrictions in rural than in urban areas.

For a product as expensive as a house, financing is of primary concern. There are three principal aspects of the problem for the prefabricator: the financing of the central organization, of the dealer organization, and of the purchaser.

Financing the central organization is similar to financing any business operation.[26] Equity capital can be provided by the sale of securities such as common stocks, if other means of raising equity capital are not available. Production is financed partly by sales and partly by back loans as is customary for industrial production. Acceptance corporations, growing in importance, help to provide fluidity.

Dealer financing may be undertaken by the central organization, or dealers may provide their own financing. The picture here is not as clear-cut as it is in the automobile industry

[26] To a high degree, financing depends entirely on advance commitments on mortgages for individual sales. The rates and regulations of VA, FHA, and FNMA are critically important to prefabricators.

where manufacturer-dealer relationships have settled down to a reasonably definite pattern. Dealers in prefabricated housing may operate on a commission, percentage, or other basis, depending on the individual circumstances.

It is in the financing of the purchaser that heaviest reliance is placed on government aid. Prefabricated housing, like operative-builder housing, is largely purchased by families who require VA aid or FHA insurance. Mortgages guaranteed or insured by these agencies carry upper limits on interest rates, and political pressures keep these rates low. In times of stringent credit, the available money tends to seek other markets where the return is more attractive, and FHA and VA mortgages are purchased only at a discount. This, in turn, reduces the borrowing capacity of families dependent upon such government support. Strong pressure, consequently, is brought to bear to relax the restrictions on interest and discounts in order to stimulate the flow of money into the market for prefabricated and other large-scale housing. When it is hard to arrange, the financing of any type of housing can easily far overshadow all other management problems.

Transportation is a major item in prefabrication operations. No matter how carefully planned and engineered, the floor, wall, partition, and roof panels are bulky and occupy considerably greater space than the same materials would occupy if stacked together before assembly. In addition, materials are generally shipped twice: once from the manufacturer of the raw material to the shop of the prefabricator and again from the prefabricator to the finished site. Furthermore, prefabricated units are at least partly finished and so must be packed and handled with greater care than raw materials; hence shipping rates are higher. For long distances (over 1,000 miles), some use is made of rail, but eventually the units must be packed on a truck to be taken to the site. The general practice, therefore, is to use truck transportation directly from the shop of the prefabricator to the final site.

Some manufacturers operate their own trucks; others rely

on contract carriers. It takes from one to three trucks to ship an entire house package, depending on the size and weight involved. The cost of transportation largely determines the area within which the manufacturer can operate. Beyond certain distances, transportation costs are so great that the prefabricator cannot compete with the conventional builder.

Prefabricators are following closely the development of "piggyback" transportation of trucks or truck trailers on railroad cars. Some are convinced that when the rates and procedures for this method of transportation are worked out, houses can be shipped economically over much greater distances than is now possible.

4. *Marketing.* There are three basic types of prefabricated-house dealers: the dealer–contractor-builder who sells to the consumer, primarily on a contract basis, and then erects; the dealer–operative builder who builds mainly on a speculative basis; and the dealer-nonbuilder who sells to the consumer but does not engage in the building operation.[27] This last group is by far the smallest of the three. There are now over 7,000 dealers in the United States; *House & Home* reports that six manufacturers have over three hundred dealers apiece.[28] There are dealers of all sizes, but the biggest share of prefab production goes to the big dealer-erectors. A *House & Home* survey of fourteen manufacturers showed that during 1956 thirty-seven per cent of the total sales were made to big dealers erecting more than one hundred prefabricated houses a year.[29]

In general, the dealer in prefabricated homes faces the same marketing problems as the operative builder, described earlier, and relies on the same sales techniques, although most dealers get some sales aid from their manufacturers. For the manufacturers, there are new marketing requirements in the form

---

[27] On this subject, see Glenn H. Beyer and Theodore R. Yantis, *Practices and Precepts of Marketing Prefabricated Houses,* Division of Housing Research, 1952.

[28] "Annual Report on Prefabrication," *House & Home,* vol. 10, no. 5, December, 1956, p. 130.

[29] *Ibid.,* p. 133.

of programs of improving dealer relations and sales promotion campaigns.

The inherent advantage of prefabrication is that large cost economies may be achieved through mass-production techniques. Such methods necessarily imply a fairly constant level of output over an extended period of time. Unless the manufacturer secures an even flow of orders into the shop he must either accumulate large inventories (i.e., tie up considerable cash in finished stock) or suffer the dis-economies of sporadic production (labor turnover, etc.). The efficiency of the plant operation is therefore largely determined by the ability of the dealer organization to provide a steady volume of orders.[30] In the past, however, many prefabricators have ignored marketing activities and most of the company failures during the 1946–1948 period can be traced to this fact. Today the surviving firms are vitally aware of the importance of their marketing functions; few, however, have formed strong dealer organizations which operate at maximum efficiency.

Manufacturer-dealer agreements are very varied and most of them tend to be rather informal. Few manufacturers grant exclusive franchises, but most of them give assurance that a second dealership will not be established in a particular area as long as the original dealer's operation is satisfactory. In general, manufacturers have little control over dealers; dealers may shop around among manufacturers, purchase demonstration models from several companies, and even erect conventional housing. A few manufacturers have established a firm price schedule but most have no control over the final sales price. Sales quotas are seldom used; manufacturers rarely attempt to control dealer advertising or to require the maintenance of model homes.

Most manufacturers give their dealers sales assistance. Many provide point-of-sale advertising kits and contribute funds in

[30] See "700 Sales in 4 Weeks," a description of a project by prefabricator Hamilton Crawford, *Architectural Forum*, vol. 95, no. 3, September, 1951, p. 206.

the form of prepared copy and allowances for local newspaper and radio advertising, so long as the manufacturer's name is mentioned along with the dealer's. One, American Houses, distributes specially designed model kits with which prospective purchasers may arrange standardized components and determine their own favorite plan. Some manufacturers hire professional decorators to help their dealers furnish the models; some provide aid and guidance in connection with site planning. Several of the largest perform an important service to the entire industry as well as to their dealers by clearing away problems of local codes and regulations—going to court if necessary to dispose of the most obsolete and arbitrary.

Dealers also get aid on financing from manufacturers, many of whom have created acceptance corporations to cope with the problems of consumer financing and to help the dealer finance his own purchases of packages. A few of the largest companies supply funds for everything from site preparation to permanent mortgage, and many firms offer 90- to 120-day financing to help their dealers build demonstration houses. A survey of 110 firms showed that 75 per cent offered financial aid.[31]

The manufacturers generally do little direct advertising, although a few advertise extensively in national media. Most use mainly trade journals and seek to acquire dealers. The sales organizations vary widely among different firms. Some of the larger firms have factory representatives who serve as liaison between the dealer and the plant. These men act as technical advisers on erection, inspect the finished product, locate new dealers and sources of mortgage money, and advise on sales promotions. In smaller firms, most such functions are carried on by top management.

Despite recent gains, several basic weaknesses in the form and methods of marketing organizations still exist among the prefabricators. They have too little control over dealers, espe-

[31] "Annual Report on Prefabrication," *House & Home*, vol. 10, no. 5, December, 1956, p. 135.

cially in regard to price policy. In the future more firms are likely to offer their dealers more advertising, merchandising, planning, and financial aid, and this will probably be accompanied by closer manufacturer-dealer ties. The manufacturers' own sales organizations will probably be expanded and become more highly trained. These trends are currently evident and should eventually result in more efficient sales programs.

5. *Research and development.* Since the prefabricator generally operates on a large scale, he finds it to his advantage to undertake some engineering and research. The amount varies from firm to firm and depends to a considerable degree on the size of the company's operations. Basic research is left to the materials and equipment manufacturers; the prefabricator's research concentrates on the development of cheaper and more efficient details in the structural systems, mechanical equipment, and shop and erection procedures. Some engineering time must also be devoted to convincing local building officials that the system is sound and safe.

Many of the larger companies work closely with suppliers in developing better products or assembly processes, and a good deal of attention is paid to the development of prefabricated commercial structures, schools, and churches. Recently a number of prefabricators have begun the independent distribution of panels and other components, for purchase and use in any structure or design that the buyer wishes.

Illustration: National Homes.[32] Currently, the largest prefabricator is National Homes, and the key to its long record of profitable operation is an order of management priorities which put marketing first, then distribution, and then—only in third place—construction (see photograph 4). Started in 1940 with $12,000, the company climbed in worth to about $20 million in the late 1950s, when it had sold about a quarter million houses. Its production has been steady (best month, August, is only 25 per cent above the January–March valley).

[32] Information from a talk by James Price at M.I.T., June, 1958.

Though the labor rate has doubled since the initial 50 cents per hour, plant labor cost per unit has dropped slightly from the original $175.

The largest single buyer of products like wood, masonite, and gypsum, National keeps no finished inventory at any time, never produces to stock. Distribution is by trailers, owned by the company in order to control schedules, and these travel as much as 30,000 miles per night. When railroad techniques and rates are improved, it is expected that 90 per cent of the units may be distributed by rail. At the site, 400 to 600 hours of labor are required to complete the house, at a cost of as little as $450. Help is given the dealer on planning, building, and selling (there is an extensive program of national advertising), and loans are made at the rate of $90 million per year. Dealers build largely the low-price units, almost entirely in large developments. The company cannot insist on exclusive dealerships, and it gives no exclusive sales areas. The plant is entirely organized by the carpenters' union, which cooperates fully. As many as 40 per cent of dealers never have labor troubles. Local codes and controls are no problem, since the house is designed to comply with major national codes, and the company has not hesitated to take legal action against arbitrary local rulings. In design, management's aim has been standardization and simplification, hoping to sell 80 per cent of the units without change. The only real future scarcity seems to be land, which rose from $500 per lot in 1940 to $2,000 per lot in 1958.

The Mobile-home Manufacturer

One of the most significant developments in the production of housing often is entirely overlooked—the growth of the mobile-home industry, known in the past as the trailer industry. There has long been a tendency to regard the trailer as a special-purpose vehicle having little bearing on the supply of permanent housing. Nothing could be further from the truth.

TABLE 9. Sales of Manufactured and Mobile Homes Compared

		Trailer sales			
Sales in year, millions of dollars	Percentage change in dollar volume from previous year	Sales in number of units	Percentage change in unit sales from previous year	Unit sales as a percentage of unit sales plus permanent nonfarm dwelling units started	Prefabricated house sales
1951 248.3	+15	67,335		5.8	50,000
1952 319.9	+29	83,054	+23	6.9	60,000
1954 324.0		76,899		5.9	76,000
1955 435.0	+34	101,000	+31	7.1	93,000
1956 501.0	+15	121,000	+20	9.8	94,791
1957 579.0	+16	140,000	+16	11.9 [a]	90,000 [a]

[a] Estimate.

Source: Figures for trailer sales for 1951–1952 are from Andrew W. Shearer, "Trailer Coach Industry Becomes Big Business," *Automotive Industries*, vol. 109, no. 3, August 1, 1953, pp. 52–59; for 1954, Norris Willatt, "Trailer Parks: They Mushroom into a Thriving Business Across the Nation," *Barron's*, vol. 35, no. 39, September 26, 1955, pp. 15–16; for 1955–1956, Jerry Zakosky, "Mobile Homes Get Roomier, Less Mobile, but Gain Sales Mileage," *Wall Street Journal*, March 8, 1957, p. 1; for 1957 *House & Home*, vol. 13, no. 3, March, 1958, p. 45.

Figures for prefabricated house sales for 1951–1952 from Burnham Kelly and Phyllis M. Kelly, "The Housing Industry in the United States," in *Prefabrication*, vol. 1, no. 1, November, 1953, p. 17; for 1954, *House & Home*, vol. 8, no. 6, December, 1955, p. 102; for 1955–56, from survey by the prefabricated Home Manufacturers Association.

Production statistics for mobile homes are not currently reported on any regular basis. The Senate Committee on Banking and Currency has expressed the hope that the Bureau of Labor Statistics will include mobile home production figures in its home-construction reports. See U.S. Senate Committee on Banking and Currency, 85th Cong., 2d Sess., Report no. 368, Calendar no. 374, May 20, 1957, pp. 9–10.

The trailer-coach industry was born during the 1930s. At the start, a high percentage of purchasers were vacationists, but with the advent of World War II people began using trailers as year-round dwellings, and clusters of trailer camps sprang up around military installations, construction jobs, and defense plants. Many trailers were purchased by the government to serve as emergency housing in newly industrialized areas. The critical housing shortage following World War II gave the industry tremendous impetus; since then sales have continued to increase, until in 1957, 140,000 mobile homes were sold, or well over 10 per cent of all new dwelling units. Trailer sales compared to prefabrication house sales in the 1951–1957 period are shown in Table 9.

Since the post-1950 growth occurred when the housing situation was easing, it cannot be attributed to a market demand for temporary housing. Nor is it explained by an increased use of trailers for recreational purposes. The growth in the industry has been caused by the fact that an increasing number of people prefer to live more or less permanently in trailers. The stock of trailers in use was well over the million mark by 1957.

The Buyer. Mobile home owners today tend to be construction workers and others whose occupations require relatively frequent change of dwelling place (see Table 10), and who are therefore apt to adopt trailer living as a permanent way of life. Mobility of the trailers is not essential, for the owners frequently leave them behind when they move; in the new location they find another "mobile" home. A significant number of retired people and others buy mobile homes, and in general buyers consider that they get good value for their money.

The average mobile-home family has an income slightly more than $1,000 above the national average,[33] but average family size is only 2.9 persons compared to a nationwide average household size of 3.4 people, and a high proportion of

[33] "The Changing Function of Trailer Parks," *Planning Advisory Service,* American Society of Planning Officials, Information Report no. 84, Chicago, March, 1956, p. 6.

the smaller number of children is in the preschool, kinder-garten, and primary-school age groups.[34] Apparently although a trailer may be a practical home for older people or young couples, it is less satisfactory for adolescent children or for large families.

TABLE 10. Occupations of Mobile-home Owners in Per Cent for Three Selected Years

	1937	1950	1955
Total number of trailer dwellers	. . .	1,500,000	2,000,000
Mobile or semimobile occupation (in per cent)	15	35	63
Retired	35	15	10
Vacationers	50	1	4
Military			20
Other		49	3

Source: 1937 and 1950 percentages from "Trailer Coach Industry Survey for the Year 1950," HHFA, *Housing Research*, Spring, 1952; 1955 percentages, estimates of the Mobile Homes Manufacturers Association, Chicago, February, 1956. The figure for the number of inhabitants in 1950 is from "Notes on the Trailer Industry," *Fortune*, vol. 44, no. 6, December, 1951, p. 163. The number of inhabitants in 1955 is estimated in "The Changing Function of Trailer Parks," *Planning Advisory Service*, American Society of Planning Officials, Information Report no. 84, Chicago, March, 1956, p. 1.

The unit, to serve better its housing role, has become both large and heavy (see photograph 36). Easy mobility is no longer a major consideration; once bought, the trailer is fixed in one place for an increasingly long period of time.[35] The

[34] *Ibid.*, p. 10.

[35] The Mobile Homes Manufacturers Association's figures show that the average mobile home is moved only once every twenty months, despite the special character of the unit and of most of those who own it. This figure includes long-term occupancies and vacation travelers so that the median could differ as a rough indicator. By comparison, the average United States family moves once every sixty months; the twenty-year-olds, once every thirty months.

mobile home is considered a full-fledged, fixed home in 85 per cent of the cases.

Some take up trailer living primarily because it is cheap, but in many cases convenience seems the primary motive. An industry publication reports:

In a continuing market survey of mobile-home buyers, 19 out of every 20 purchasers queried said they would not leave their mobile homes even if offered a house or apartment at what they consider a reasonable price. Sixty per cent of these purchasers had lived in mobile homes before, and their new purchase indicates a preference based on first-hand experience.... Even though the mobile-home owner may never move his apartment on wheels ... the advantage of being able to do so if necessary or desirable is an important factor in the popularity of mobile homes.[36]

TABLE 11. Increasing Size of Trailers

Year	Percentage of manufactured trailers over 35 feet long
1952	47
1953	51
1954	61
1955	76

Source: "The Changing Function of Trailer Parks," *Planning Advisory Service*, American Society of Planning Officials, Information Report no. 84, Chicago, March, 1956, p. 5.

Current Characteristics. In order to adjust to the changing market, manufacturers have turned their attention to developing models more suitable as homes. One survey covering about 25 per cent of the 1954 output showed that 75 per cent of those units were designed to meet the call for small compact homes.[37] To provide more of the functions of a permanent home, trailers have become longer and to a certain extent wider.

[36] *Homes for the Mobile Population*, Mobile Homes Manufacturers Association, 20 North Wacker Drive, Chicago 6, Illinois, 1955.

[37] R. R. Kay, "Trailer Boom Adds to Steel Demand," *Iron Age*, vol. 175, no. 4, January 27, 1955, p. 57.

In 1956, 61 per cent of all the trailers built were at least 40 feet long,[38] and 25 per cent of the production was the relatively new 10-foot-wide model. This trend toward longer and wider units has considerably reduced the mobility of the trailer. A truck or heavy car is required to move the bigger models and many owners rely on professional towing firms to perform this function.[39]

Trailers are usually well made, of light metal construction, and show the built-in ingenuity and efficiency of an ocean-going cruiser or a Pullman car. Short on room and individuality, they are long on the efficient use of space, operating simplicity, ease of housekeeping, and durability with minimum maintenance.

The basic design is fairly well standardized and includes a living room, kitchenette, bedroom, and bath. Two-bedroom trailers are not uncommon, and some two-story, three-bedroom models are being sold. Trailers are sold furnished and include a stove, refrigerator, and space heater. Extras include television, garbage grinders, washers, washer-dryers, air conditioning, and fireplaces. Sold f.o.b. factory, the average trailer, 27 to 35 feet long, retails at from $2,800 to $5,000. The standard range for the two-bedroom, 40- to 45-foot models is between $4,500 and $7,500. Prices can go to $12,000 and sizes to 10 by 51 feet. The average trailer loses about 10 per cent of its value in the first month. After that, depreciation is rather small if the unit is well maintained.

An important aspect of the industry, and one underlining the only nominal mobility of most trailers, is the large volume of business in awning structures to improve the insulation of the roof and add sitting-out areas, finished room units designed to be added to trailers, and special trailers themselves. Given space and money, an elaborate home can be assembled from

---

[38] Zakosky, *op. cit.*, p. 1.

[39] Most states require permits before the 10-foot-wide models can be taken on the highway, and some ban them altogether. Most states also regulate the length of trailers allowed on highways, these restrictions vary from 35 to 45 feet. "The Changing Function of Trailer Parks," *op. cit.*, p. 5.

trailers and accessories, and the volume of this accessory business is increasing (see photograph 37).

The trailer industry is not large by comparison with other United States industry; in 1955, 81 industrial firms reported higher sales than the entire trailer industry. The 1954 Census of Manufactures reported 275 establishments, "primarily engaged in the manufacture of trailers for attachment to passenger cars." [40] One hundred and twenty-five of these firms had 20 or more employees each. The industry had a total of 11,131 employees; 9,491 of these were production workers. No one firm produces more than 10 per cent of the total trailer output. The larger firms may turn out as many as 100 trailers per week whereas the smaller ones produce only 2 or 3 units a week. Most of the manufacturers are in the Middle West or in California, chiefly around Los Angeles. In the future many of the smaller firms will probably be eliminated from the field because of the marginal nature of their operation.[41]

Trailer manufacturers are primarily assemblers. Many of the component suppliers are concentrated in the automotive industry and to some of them the trailer field represents a sizable source of income. Suppliers of building materials and home furnishings also find substantial markets in the trailer industry. The major portion of the dollar volume of supplies to the industry is accounted for by household equipment.[42] Mass pro-

[40] U.S. Bureau of the Census, *1954 Census of Manufactures: Motor Vehicles and Equipment*, Advance Report, ser. MC-37-1, December, 1956, p. 1.

Of these 275 firms, perhaps 75 to 100 are primarily engaged in manufacturing trailers for the transportation of boats, furniture, etc. Therefore the figures for manufacturers of house trailers would be somewhat less than those quoted above.

[41] One authority noted: "Of the nearly 200 firms making house trailers, nearly half of them are on a marginal basis. Many of the latter are not expected to survive the transition in mobile homes. As more people regard trailers as their only and permanent residence, the accent falls heavily on better engineering and design of the coaches." "Spotting Trends in Trailer Facts," *Steel*, vol. 132, no. 18, May 4, 1953, p. 58.

[42] *Ibid.*

duction techniques are employed wherever possible, but the nature of trailer production and the volume of most of the producers do not particularly suit mass methods. As production becomes concentrated in fewer, bigger firms, more of the total output will probably be produced by industrial methods.[43]

Most trailer purchases, like automobiles, are financed on an installment basis. Normally the down payment is about one-quarter to one-third of the price (including trade-in); the remainder is paid off in three to five years, or occasionally seven years. About 60 per cent of all sales involve trade-ins. Local banks or finance companies generally handle the financing, and the dealers are usually cosigners with the original purchaser. The financier often requires that the dealer agree to haul back at his expense any trailers that must be repossessed.[44] In 1954, $400 million worth of mobile-home paper was outstanding and banks seemed to consider it a satisfactory investment. Sixty-four per cent of the banks queried in a recent survey (see Table 12) stated that mobile-home paper was as good as automobile paper. The problems that would arise with the advent of a depression are no greater than in any industry based on installment buying.

Trailers are mainly sold through local dealers. In 1951, less than 1 per cent of the trailers sold were bought directly from the manufacturer. There are about 3,000 dealers in the United States, concentrated, like the manufacturers, in the Middle West and California. Most dealers have a trailer sales lot with

[43] "At Spartan, we use over two and one-half million dollars worth of tooling, machinery, and equipment, plus two million dollars worth of buildings and other facilities for a single purpose—building an average of 20 homes per day by production-line methods," W. H. Shelton, "Spartan Makes Trailers on a Production Line," *American Machinist*, vol. 100, no. 27, December 17, 1956, pp. 110–113 (see photograph 35).

[44] Financing could be something of a headache because of the ease with which an unpaid-for trailer may be moved across state lines. To date this has not been a serious problem, however, and industry figures put the loss rate at less than 0.16 per cent. "House on Wheels: They're Tricky Things to Sell," *Business Week*, no. 1210, September 6, 1952, p. 94.

twelve or more trailers lined up for inspection; often the dealer lives in one of these. Most of the mobile-home advertising is still done in the classified sections of newspapers, but a dozen or so newspapers now feature a yearly mobile-homes section, and two papers have reported they run regular weekly features on trailers.[45]

TABLE 12. Trailer Repossessions

Number of banks replying				267
Number reporting no delinquencies greater than 60 days				190
Number reporting less than 15 per cent delinquencies greater than 60 days				25

	New trailers	Used trailers	New trailers	Used trailers
Reporting:	280	308	283	281
Repossessions:				
None	76%	75 %	83%	82%
Less than 0.5%	13%	11.5%	12%	12%
Less than 1%	4%	3 %	2%	2%
Less than 2%	2%	2 %	1%	1%
More than 2%	5%	8.5%	2%	3%

Source: Kay Marten, "They Called It Gypsy Paper," *Bankers Monthly*, vol. 71, no. 2, February, 1954, pp. 36–40.

Almost all "trailerites" live in trailer parks where they rent space from the proprietor. In 1946 there were 3,000 parks, most of them able to accommodate only 30 to 40 vehicles each. Today there are over 11,000 parks, a large percentage of which can hold over 300 trailers,[46] and they are increasing at the rate of 1,000 per year.[47]

In the past, many of the parks were shoddy and regarded as slum areas. The general level has been rising, however, and

[45] "Mobile Home Dealers Source for 'Pay Dirt,'" *Editor and Publisher*, vol. 89, no. 34, August 18, 1956, p. 20.

[46] Norris Willatt, *op. cit.*

[47] Reported by Mobile Homes Manufacturers Association.

will probably continue to do so. This has been at least partially due to the efforts of the Mobile Home Manufacturers Association. This organization prepares model mobile-home–park regulations that are winning increasing acceptance for enforcement by communities. The organization will provide free architectural service for a person who wants to start a trailer park; it has prepared numerous pamphlets to help the trailer-park operator with construction and sanitation problems. In addition, the MHMA publishes an "Official Mobile Homes Park Guide." A park must meet the standards recommended by the MHMA before it will be listed in this book, the 1957–1958 edition of which includes some 6,100 inspected and approved parks.

In 1955 Congress authorized the FHA to insure loans to finance trailer-park construction. A proposed park must meet certain specifications concerning utility services and minimum space per trailer before the owner can qualify for such a loan. This is expected to improve parks as well as to discourage the establishment of economically unsound enterprises.

In the past, zoning ordinances have generally restricted trailer courts to nonresidential areas and some have even excluded them from corporate boundaries. The industry organizations argue that "if trailer-courts are forced into fringe areas where land is cheap . . . profiteering trailer-park operators may go a long way towards creating overcrowded, unsanitary trailer slums." [48] However, restrictive municipal ordinances are sure to be a major problem for the industry for quite some time.

California has the largest number of trailer parks, with Florida second and Arizona third. Groups of trailer courts are found around most large industrial cities. The MHMA estimates that the cost of constructing a park is about $1,000 per mobile-home lot and that a park must accommodate fifty trailers in order to be a profitable business venture. One writer

[48] "The Changing Function of Trailer Parks," *op. cit.*, p. 22.

estimates that the before-tax return on investment runs from 12 to 15 per cent.[49] Rents usually range from $20 to $25 per month, but in at least one luxury park, where facilities include a swimming pool, television, and a complete shopping center, the rent is $100 a month.

The future should bring an increasing use of the trailer as semipermanent housing. In the next twenty years the number of young families and retired couples will grow faster than the population as a whole. Retirement age may be lowered, and increasing numbers of young men will marry while they are still in school, in the service, or in the early years of work when shifts from city to city are frequent. The trailer offers these groups a highly efficient and relatively low-cost form of housing that can, if necessary, be transported when the owner has to move. The future will see a continuation of the effort to make the trailer more homelike, while retaining the important qualities of high efficiency and minimum care and maintenance. This, coupled with the improvement of trailer parks and a greater public acceptance of the trailer as a respectable home, should enable the mobile-home manufacturer to capture a greater share of his growing potential market.

However, the potential market for the trailer will be limited by the very qualities of minimum involvement and high efficiency that recommend it to its present customers, unless housing production generally turns in the direction of completely finished units and our average families learn to assemble the houses they want from a selection of such units. Too large a segment of the population is represented by the family of father, mother, and several growing children, all of whom like to putter around the house and garden, and to take a keen interest in the affairs of their community.

The market for vacation trailers may grow as real income rises and people have more time and money to spend on vaca-

---

49 Norris Willatt, *op. cit.*

tions. But a trailer will always be a relatively large outlay for purely recreational purposes and must compete with a wide variety of alternatives for the family's recreation dollar. Vacation trailers will probably continue to be a shrinking percentage of the total demand.

Although trailers will probably become somewhat bigger, increase in size is not likely to be as great as in the past decade because of state road regulations and the difficulties of transportation. We may expect a continued development of units that have reasonably small dimensions when on the road and can be expanded or unfolded at the site. Future advances will probably be in the form of more efficient utilization of space and an improved level of equipment and services.

Conclusion

In spite of the deep desire of many, probably most, potential owners to have homes designed to their own special tastes, custom building has lost much of the market which at one time belonged to it exclusively. Only a few attempts have been made to secure through organizations of small builders the convenience and efficiency of operative building. One such is the close working relationship sometimes established between custom builders and aggressive materials dealers as a means of providing the owner all the services he needs. A broad operational analysis of the production of houses might well suggest potential efficiencies in retaining numerous and flexible small-builder organizations for which such complex problems as procurement, finance, and land development would be handled by specially designed intermediate organizations. For a lively builder with fresh ideas and an ability to move fast, small size offers many possible advantages. Bigness as such is not necessarily a virtue; it may lead only to conformity and monotony. Under current circumstances, however, the trend appears to be accelerating away from the traditional custom operation from which other elements of the industry have derived and adapted their basic form. Like the custom tailor, the custom builder tends to be more and more occupied with remodeling and repairs.

As for the operative builder, his has been primarily a triumph of good organization and management; for the most part, he is only now beginning—within rather narrow limits—to explore the design and production potentials of industry. Unless he has become large, he has been much limited by all the localized inheritances that have come to him from the days of custom building; even when he is large and able to move out beyond community restrictions, he is limited by the traditional conservatism of the financial sources upon which he must rely and by his need to show a profit at every step. Under the circumstances, the most successful operative builders have tended to be those who wasted little time on potentials and devoted their very considerable business abilities to the task at hand. On the whole, operative builders have done well, and they will continue to do so in the future.

The prefabricator has many of the same strengths and weaknesses as the operative builder. Typically he sells procurement simplification, quality control, and assistance in speeding up local operations; one of his big advantages is the low wages he can pay at the plant. If there existed a well-considered system for the production, distribution, and assembly of standardized components, many of the advantages of current prefabrication would disappear. Some of the larger prefabricators are now approaching the scale and strength at which they may make significant innovations, but they, like the operative builders, are restrained from taking any bold steps by the localism and traditionalism of the market, the conservatism of those who arrange financing, and the ever-pressing need to keep in the black. It is a commentary on the stage of industrial development of these firms that even the largest regards it as a business essential never to produce to stock.

The mobile-home manufacturer comes nearest to taking

real advantage of industrial potentials, with the courage to face concomitant changes in pattern and appearance. Among his obviously important assets is the fact that his product is not enmeshed in the complications of real estate; hence he is freed from the traditional impediments besetting the more conventional producers. Because the mobile house is regarded simply as an industrial product, it has been better able to gain industrial advantages.

Trailer manufacturers have been more aggressive than most home fabricators in introducing new methods of construction and design. With more and more people considering trailers as semipermanent dwellings, sales are directly tied to the livability of the structure. Thus it is to the manufacturer's advantage to continue a policy of research and innovation; and as his scale of operation grows, he is notably less subject to impediments to the process of innovation than most producers of housing. We may expect continued innovation in the trailer field, probably the production of more elaborate and somewhat more expensive units, and perhaps a greater invasion of the conventional market than now seems possible.

It should be added, however, that nothing prevents other sectors of the housing industry from competing for the mobile-home market. Since true mobility is of secondary importance and increasingly difficult to achieve by the standard trailer approach, attention can be turned to other methods of obtaining the convenience, efficiency, and high degree of mechanical performance desired by this market. These could as well be supplied by specialized unit or component designs for houses or even for apartments. Such ideas have long been familiar in design proposals. It may be hoped that the time has come for a full and fair test in the market, free of artificial impediments.

Chapter 6

CONSTRUCTION ADVANCES

This chapter, primarily the work of Albert G. H. Dietz and James A. Murray, reviews advances in materials and methods already in use in the housing industry and explores some significant trends for the future. Burnham Kelly and Carl Koch supply additional material on some basic considerations involved in housing production. Koch concludes the chapter with a fanciful projection of the operation of a possible component distribution system.

Conventional Construction

Most builders are quick to adapt themselves to local public opinion and to the controls that reflect it. Few try to gain acceptance for new methods, however great their theoretical advantage. Few have the resources needed to see such an attempt through in the face of entrenched tradition.

Nevertheless, change does occur. The house built today is significantly different from that built fifty or even twenty-five years ago; the house built ten to twenty-five years hence will be even more different from that built today. The housing market is so large and attractive and the competition for a share of it is so keen that experimentation and innovation in design, construction techniques, materials, and equipment are constantly under way, despite the traditional conservatism of the field. Some of these innovations inevitably prove superior to the conventional; they find public acceptance and, therefore, become a part of the technology of house production.

Designers are interested in speeding the evolution of architectural forms. Often they are discontented with traditional materials, whose limitations are known, whereas those of the new materials may still have to be found. Opposing these influences for change are the tendency of buyers and builders to cling to tradition at the same time that they are attracted to the new; the doubts regarding performance of new systems in actual use; the problems associated with getting new materials into the hands of builders; and the delays in obtaining acceptance of new materials by regulatory agencies. On the whole, however, results have been positive, and even the producer of typical small houses has made considerable advances in materials and methods in the last ten or twenty years.

Sheet Materials. Sheet materials including plywood, plasterboard, exploded wood fiber, hardboard, cement-asbestos board, the recently developed wood chipboards, and the many varieties of vegetable fiberboards are used in much greater quantities and for a greater variety of purposes today than formerly. These sheets promote speed of erection, reduce site labor, can greatly increase the strength and rigidity of the structure, and provide increased weathertightness.

Plywood itself has had many improvements. Among the most significant of these has been the introduction of completely waterproof plywood, bonded with synthetic resin adhesives, which is usable for the exterior skin of a house as well as in protected areas (see photograph 7). Major development activity now centers in the surface treatments of plywood. The appearance can be altered not only by the selection of face veneers for interior decorative plywood but by surface treatments, such as striation and grooving. Resin-impregnated paper overlays for plywood improve the surface appearance and provide a superior base for finish coatings. Prefinished plywood for interior applications has become common and greatly reduces the field finishing operations required. Decorative, high-pressure, plastics-based laminates bonded to the surface of plywood provide widely used counter stock for kitchen counters and built-in units of all kinds.

Other wallboards are similarly being improved by admixtures, for durability upon outdoor exposure, resistance to insect attack and decay, and strength and resistance to impact. Many varieties of shop-applied coatings are being developed for these materials; they include durable finishes and tough plastic film and sheet to increase resistance to wear and to provide decorative finishes. In some instances, ceramic, plastic, or metal tile is preapplied in the shop to reduce field-installation time.

Because wallboards are already well established in the building trades, the introduction of new varieties generally encounters no fundamental problems. Cost is the major factor. New building boards must demonstrate ability to compete with traditional construction methods on an installed-cost basis. If used outdoors, they must demonstrate their ability to withstand aging and weathering. They do not usually present a code problem unless they prove to be unusually flammable or if the products of combustion include toxic gases. Distribution is generally available through normal channels.

Glass is a traditional sheet material finding greatly increased uses in new ways. It is emphasized in the trend toward openness in dwelling design. Regular glass, both plain and plate, meets most housing requirements, but where areas are large, factory-sealed double glass units have helped to lessen heat loss and to increase comfort by reducing the chilling effect of cold inner surfaces. Heat-absorbing glass can screen out much of the infrared radiation from the sun without greatly affecting the transmission of visible radiation beyond imparting a slight bluish cast. Susceptibility to breakage is greatly reduced, with increased clarity—and cost—by heat treatment to provide a compressed surface on the glass.

Crystalline glass is one of the newest developments, so far largely unexplored in its implications for building. Whereas other glass is amorphous, this glass because of its crystalline nature is high in tensile strength and hence more resistant to breakage while it has other attributes of glass including hardness.

Electrically conductive surfaces can be deposited on glass without appreciably altering its clarity. Electrical current passing through such a surface generates heat and makes possible warmed window areas that act as radiant-heat sources instead of being major sources of chilling discomfort. Other coatings and interior layers may be used to increase strength or to provide a vast range of decorative and light-modulation possibilities.

The major uses of glass appear to be secure and growing. Transparent plastics are challenging it in certain uses, particularly in skylights where the efficient bubble shape is hard to duplicate in glass, and where breakage hazards are great, but such severe breakage hazards are seldom found in the dwelling house. Here glass performs a service hard to duplicate by other materials, and there are few deterrents to its widespread use.

Finishing and Prefinishing. One of the most time-consuming and costly aspects of traditional construction is finishing. Putting in foundations and erecting the framework of a house go forward rapidly. Finishing—especially fitting and hanging doors and windows, installing trim, laying floors, putting in cabinetwork, sanding and cleaning, and finally doing the painting, paperhanging, and other decorating operations—takes the most time, particularly since it frequently conflicts with such operations as installing plumbing and heating fixtures, doing the electrical work, building finished fireplaces, and setting floor and wall tile.

Prefinished units reduce the amount of finishing required in the field; hence the trend in this direction may be expected to accelerate. Also apparent is a steady trend toward diminishing the number of pieces of millwork at the site. This takes the form of assembling door, window, and cabinet units in the shop and reducing and simplifying the amount of linear trim, such as baseboards and dadoes.

It is customary to preassemble and prefinish cabinetwork, which is delivered and installed as units. Indeed, for such items as metal storage cabinets, factory finishing is virtually mandatory. Wallboards for interiors are increasingly being factory-finished; even sheet materials to be used as exterior wall covering are commonly delivered with factory-applied prime and sealing coats. Prefinished wood flooring is becoming increasingly popular. Structural and nonstructural panels are easily given at least a first coat of paint in the shop.

Because of the skill and care required to apply traditional finishes, and because of the labor and time involved in applying successive coats, intensive research is under way to find easily applied finishes that have superior covering and hiding power with increased durability. In short, one of the most fruitful fields for cutting costs and increasing efficiency is in the reduction of the finishing operations in the house. This is also one of the strong reasons for shifting operations from the field to the shop.

Since a wider variety of insulating materials and a better knowledge of the insulation problem are available today than a decade or two ago, the modern home makes much greater use of insulation and associated vapor seals than was formerly the case. Special combinations of materials, preassembled and designed for rapid installation, are common.

The range of selection available to the homeowner and the builder has been increased by the addition of the new group of plastics-based sheets and tiles to the traditional wood, linoleum, and asphalt flooring. Colors, patterns, resistance to wear, and reduced maintenance are values added to the house. Similarly, the traditional materials such as wood are available prefinished both to reduce installation time and to increase the life of the finish.

Site Techniques. Power is increasingly being used at the

site, as well as in the shop, to increase the productivity of labor. The motor-driven circular handsaw has become standard equipment at the site, and builders customarily set up small benches to make use of small planers, jointers, and saws. The spray-gun for painting is commonplace. The horsedrawn plow and scraper have long since disappeared, and the tractor, truck, and bulldozer have taken their place. Power excavation is the normal procedure.

Hoisting and setting parts of houses by power has been avoided in the past on the ground that the rental of a crane or hoist plus operator is far too expensive. The tendency has been so to design the house that any part can be handled by a small crew of men utilizing at most a gin pole and winch. As hoisting equipment becomes more versatile, mobile, and generally available, however, this concept is beginning to change. Increased use of hoisting equipment, incorporated, for example, into the truck that delivers the components of the house, may be expected, and with it a change in the sizes of the components of the house.[1]

An extreme example of the use of heavy power equipment for the mass production of housing at the site is the IBEC system, designed to produce large numbers of essentially identical concrete houses in one place, and used extensively in Caribbean areas. The concrete for walls and partitions is cast in one continuous operation in a completely assembled form, which is then lifted as a unit and placed upon the floor slab, after which a precast roof slab is lifted into place. Although this use of heavy lifting equipment has certain limitations for general application, it does illustrate what techniques are possible.

Customary operations such as screwing, sawing, and hammering are already performed with electrical and air tools. The only thing holding back this development is the dependence

---

[1] See *House & Home*, vol. 9, no. 2, February, 1956, p. 126, on reasons for delays in mechanizing materials handling; *House & Home*, vol. 9, no. 6, June, 1956, p. 154, on steps that can be taken to improve materials handling.

of such tools on a fixed source of power. Should it ever become practical for such a purpose to transmit electric energy over even a small distance without the use of wires, important hand tools of the building trades would be mechanized without exception. Electricity already offers a simple, clean, and quiet means of powering such equipment, and air tools should not be neglected. Homely facts influence the choice. The compressors for air tools generally must be serviced by a member of the engineers' union at rates which tend to make such a power source expensive. On the other hand, the use of air tools protects the contractor from the pilferage often associated with the use of standard electrical tools on the job.

Recent innovations that have proved useful in the field of hand tools include automatic nailers, universal drills, explosive-cartridge fastening tools, and glue and adhesive applicators. An excellent example is the hand or mechanically operated floor layer which nails finish flooring firmly to subflooring without any damage to the face grain of the wood, as so often occurs in the hand application of flooring.

The industry producing power equipment is large, diverse, and inventive, and it is tied neither to housing nor to construction in general. It may be expected to explore new areas of operation promptly and effectively, as it already has in the booming do-it-yourself market.

Many advances seek to bring back into general use conventional construction systems that had been declining in favor. For example, in recent years, the use of load-bearing walls made of masonry units has fallen off. In many cases brickwork is now limited to a surface veneer, with the result that the actual production per day of a bricklayer has been greatly reduced. Since masonry costs have long been high, brick manufacturers realize that improved masonry construction methods must be made available. Recent developments include a packaged unit consisting of about sixty bricks, strapped together at the brick manufacturing plant and delivered as a unit to the mason on his working platform. This method cuts down the cost of getting brick from the factory to the mason in high-volume projects.

Recognizing that a major item in the cost of masonry is the frequent necessity to cut brick to conform to dimensions, the brick industry has developed brick which can be laid to the uniform 4-inch module widely proposed as a basic unit of measure in the building industry. Since the manufacturers of steel windows, block, and facing tile have brought out products conforming to the same basic measure, it is possible to design buildings in which brick walls can be used with a minimum of cutting and fitting.

A careful study of bricklaying procedures has led to the development of techniques involving the use of continually adjustable scaffolding, the proper delivery of packaged brick and other materials to the bricklayer, the use of nylon lines stretched taut between corner posts marked to guide course levels, and other devices which have resulted in increases of at least 50 per cent in output with no increased fatigue for bricklayers. Also developed have been a 6-inch-wide brick which makes it possible to build a wall or partition one brick thick instead of the usual two bricks, and a panel consisting of thin facings of brick backed by a layer of lightweight reinforced concrete, both of which fit into the trend toward combining rapid erection with the advantages of durability inherent in burnt clay.

Not only must labor be introduced to such new materials and methods, but obviously builders also must become familiar with them and, just as important, be convinced of their value, particularly if, as is the case, many of them require the introduction of new materials-handling equipment and methods. Evidently a major educational task is involved.

Plaster is another old-established material with some excellent characteristics and some drawbacks. It produces a smooth finish, has good fire-resistant properties, and is applicable to any size or shape of surface. Its durability is attested by many ancient examples, and it is amenable to a variety of decorative treatments. It is also a considerable block to fast construction because of the curing time involved; it introduces large quantities of water which not only must be removed but which may have adverse effects on other parts of the structure; and it has become more costly than some, but not all, types of more rapidly applied dry-wall construction. Further, its application requires considerable skill.

It is now common to spray plaster on a surface with the so-called plaster gun, instead of troweling it on laboriously by hand. This permits a small crew to apply as much plaster as a crew twice the size using hand methods. If plaster were the universally employed wall-finishing material that it once was, labor might oppose the plaster gun, but with plaster fighting an often losing battle against the encroachments of other techniques and materials, no strong labor opposition has appeared. Since this new device tends to retain instead of supplanting an old material, labor sees the new development as an ally rather than as a threat or a problem in labor jurisdiction.

Research Houses of the National Association of Home Builders. These houses are designed to demonstrate innovations in details that may soon be in use. The 1957 house includes

1. Wall panels of hardboard and stud framing, shop-made according to basic modules and assembled by carpenters on the site

2. Window panels and unit aluminum windows made to slip easily into the framed openings

3. Shop-built trussed rafters

4. Plumbing lines designed to be assembled and installed in one trip to the site

5. Tough plastic-film-covered interior finishes

6. Special ventilated gable panels and eaves soffits

7. A new design for heating and air-conditioning units and distribution systems

8. New cemented-down wood finish for floors

9. Kitchen appliances, cabinets, and equipment dimensionally coordinated, shop-built, and installed in units

10. Rubber-based roofing, shop-applied to large plywood roof boards, requiring only sealing of the joints and a final application of finish in the field

Other examples illustrate experimentation in prefinishing. The roof is made of plywood sheets given a first coat of neoprene rubber sprinkled with neoprene granules, then covered with a second wash coat of gray neoprene. These panels were cured in an oven. They were then nailed to the trussed rafters, the edges were calked, and the entire roof was given a final coat of a paint with a synthetic rubber base. The obvious intent here is to reduce field labor and field construction time, mechanize the procedure as much as possible in the shop, and prefinish a roof of superior quality.

Two experimental wall coverings are used in the same research house: (1) lignocellulose hardboard faced in the factory with a tough transparent plastic film resistant to scuffing and stains. When the sheets are clipped to wall and partition framing, the wall surface is finished. (2) Porcelain-enamel steel sheets backed with a sprayed-on undercoating to act as sound deadener, thereby helping to overcome part of the acoustical problems found in hous. of lightweight rigid construction. When the sheets are clipped to framing and the edges sealed, especially in baths and kitchens, the wall is finished.

The outstanding feature of this house is its use of units or components. Walls and partitions are composed of panels which can be assembled in a variety of ways. The roof is built of unit trussed rafters, spaced so as to accept roof panel units. Kitchen units can be arranged as desired. Mechanical equipment is assembled in units as far as is currently practicable. All these units can be used to build houses quite different in plan. The use of such units or components points up a strong trend in house construction.

This and subsequent research houses illustrate the extent to which innovations may be made within conventional lines, for although they have many experimental features, they are deliberately designed to deviate as little as possible from typical provisions of building codes and to incorporate features which are now or can readily be made available. Their objective is to demonstrate what may be generally acceptable construction features within a few years at the most. Visually, and in over-all design, the houses do not differ from a large number of today's houses.

Trend to Preassembled Units

The general trend in housing is toward an increasing use of industrial methods and materials. Rather than attempt an analysis in terms of price, monopoly or oligopoly status, manu-facturing, distribution, competition, or interdependence, this section seeks to illustrate the trend with selected examples of design and method of construction.

More and more housing products are manufactured units or components composed of parts assembled in a shop instead of in the field and installed in the field by means of relatively simple connections requiring a minimum of site labor.[2] The illustrations given here may be grouped in four categories.

Panels. Much of the structural activity has centered in the development of a wide variety of structural panels. Of these, panels involving the stressed-skin principle have made the greatest progress and this principle is today in fairly common use, notably among the prefabricators. In the stressed-skin principle, the surface material of the panel is firmly bonded to the ribs so that, following the lead of the aircraft manufac-turers, the skin is made to carry a substantial part of the load and the over-all efficiency of materials use is high. This is in distinct contrast to ordinary stud construction in which the outside sheathing and finish and the inside lath and plaster are

[2] Articles on the growing use of components in design appear in *House & Home*, vol. 11, no. 6, June, 1957, p. 130; and vol. 10, no. 5, December, 1956, p. 160. The lead article in the *Wall Street Journal*, September 10, 1957, points up the growing tendency of builders to use prefabricated panels and components. The increasing number of prefabricators selling components independently is noted in *House & Home*, vol. 12, no. 3, September, 1957, p. 63.

merely dead loads added to the other loads which the studs are required to carry. In the typical housing application, a hard, rigid, strong·material, such as plywood, is bonded to relatively thin ribs, and the over-all unit then is relied upon to carry all loads, including vertical loads from roof to floor above and horizontal loads such as winds. The stiffness of the panels is also relied upon to resist wracking of the entire structure by horizontal loads (see photograph 24). The space between the skins is generally filled with an insulating material, and the entire unit is factory-assembled. These panels are usually made small enough so that two, or at the most four, men can handle them. Stressed-skin panels have also been made of lignocellulose hardboard glued to ribs of various types, and metal facings such as aluminum and porcelain-enameled steel have been used to a limited extent. The metals have been used far more extensively in larger structures than in single houses. One of the oldest successful combinations, strictly speaking a sandwich [3] rather than a stressed-skin construction, is cement-asbestos board facings on insulating fiberboard cores.

Stressed-skin panels are commonly used for walls, but they also have found rather widespread application for roof construction, especially if the lower surface of the panel is at the same time the ceiling of the room below. The same materials are employed as are employed for wall panels, but the panels must be heavier to withstand heavier loads.

For roof structures, trussed rafters, nailed, glued, or fastened with the various types of timber connectors, have become common in prefabricated and development housing, but so far have found relatively little use in custom-built housing. The obvious advantages are that trussed rafters can be quickly assembled in jigs either in the factory or at the site and rapidly hoisted into place, in contrast with the relatively cumbersome method of putting up ceiling joists and erecting individual rafters against a ridge board. Trusses allow early closing-in of the house and, in addition, complete freedom from bearing

[3] The ribs replaced by a continuous lightweight core.

partitions in interior design and construction. There is a continuing search for an efficient prefabricated roof; among the systems tried have been sprayed plastic, snapped-on metal skins, plastic skins using air pressure for support, and plastic on fibrous glass.

Because many houses today are built with cast concrete slabs on ground, the development of floor panels has been slower than of those for walls and roofs. In addition, the heavier loading on floors has to some degree militated against the development of panelized floor construction. However, the stressed-skin and sandwich principles are as applicable to floors as they are to walls and roofs, though panels must be heavier and thicker to withstand the increased loads, and stressed-skin floor panels are employed to some extent. Prestressed concrete slabs have also been employed, and metal and concrete joists are finding increasing use as supports for various types of slabs.

In any panel construction, a major design problem is the complications at the site associated with the installation of heating, plumbing, and wiring. These may largely be avoided by developing for these services special units and assemblies which separate them entirely from the structure. Growing competition for all of these structural panels is being felt from post-and-beam construction combined with curtain walls, the only functions of which are to protect against weather. Rapid developments along these lines in the commercial field [4] may be expected to be carried over to housing, even to the individual small house.

Nonstructural panels are being employed in increasing quantities by all classes of builders, including prefabricators, development builders, and custom builders. Wall panels may be generally lighter because they have no structural role, particularly if they are partitions and not exposed outdoors. Both the stressed-skin and the sandwich types are useful. Under the

[4] See *Architectural Forum*, vol. 92, no. 3, March, 1950, p. 81; vol. 106, no. 6, June, 1957, p. 161.

codes, the sandwich can find more ready acceptance for non-bearing partitions because it is only a space divider.

Special Assemblies. It is becoming increasingly customary for doors to be prefitted and prehung to the door frames and the trim also prefitted so that the assembly need only be installed at the site. The same holds true of windows and their trim; they are also being increasingly factory-glazed, fitted, and hung. The obvious additional step, taken as a matter of course by the prefabricator, is to incorporate these assemblies into wall and partition panels.

Increasing use is made of flexible doors which can be folded into a small space, or doors that can be slid entirely aside. These are particularly useful where there is no space for the swing of customary doors. Prefinished stairways are also available, including the folding type which can be raised out of the way when not in use.

There is a growing acceptance of the view that divisions between rooms should serve a double function by acting as storage walls rather than merely as partitions. Storage walls can be prebuilt as assemblies which need only be moved into position and fitted into the space available. In addition, a wide variety of prefinished cabinets is available for storing cooking equipment, clothing, and miscellaneous items. In competition for this market are wood, metals, and plastics, the last fabricated into such items as completely molded drawers which may be fitted into a wooden or metal frame. Lignocellulose hardboard is also a strong contender for this market. The trend is decidedly toward the use of such preassembled storage units.

Mechanical equipment and appliances show many of the most radical developments of assemblies. As the total cost of such equipment and services in the builder house comes to equal and pass that of structure and finish, the giant [5] corpora-

---

[5] All units are not made by giant corporations, of course. Many, furnaces for example, come from small specialty industries and some, for example, fireplaces, from local shops. As was noted above, an increasing number of prefabricators sell assemblies independently of their standard house packages.

tions concerned with them become more inescapably a part of the housing industry. This is illustrated by the growth of design departments in companies like General Electric and General Motors to deal with the future of housing in the broadest sense.

Design developments stress combined functions and simplified installation. The unit sink-dishwasher and the garbage disposal unit, for example, have been combined into a package to which it is necessary only to make relatively simple plumbing and electrical connections. Unit laundry equipment with its built-in cycles of washing and drying requires only an electrical outlet, connections to the hot and cold water supply lines, and a drain. Today's refrigerator requires only an electrical outlet and the same holds true of the electric stove, although this generally calls for a special heavy-duty circuit. The gas stove requires a gas connection and vent. Increasingly these units are being simplified to be built into the structure of the house rather than being designed and sold as separate pieces of furniture. Conversely, many cooking functions are separately supplied by small independent elements that can be plugged in anywhere. Special free-standing kitchens are also available (see photograph 3), primarily of the efficiency type for use in apartments; these provide sink, stove, refrigerator, and some storage and counter space, and they are easily connected to plumbing and wiring.

Central heating has long been customary, but heating units are more and more completely finished, with all controls factory-installed so that field work required is little more than the connection to fuel supply and to an electrical outlet. As is the case with many such assemblies, the possibility is offered for great elasticity in shipping and construction scheduling, since the standardized assembly unit can be installed at almost any time through an opening of standardized dimensions and without bothering or being bothered by other labor and materials schedules. Further savings are realized by multiplying functions to save floor area, as by designing the house heater to fit in the kitchen counter line-up, and thus to add useful counter-top area. Central air conditioning fits into the same type of preassembled unit. Room air conditioners generally require only installation in windows with the necessary electrical connections.

The unit bathroom has frequently been projected; a number of prototypes have been built, but none is generally available on the market. By and large plumbing fixtures are still separately assembled to the plumbing stack which also is generally assembled in the field, although when codes permit, prefabricators and development builders are using preassembled plumbing stacks or "trees" to which the fixtures are attached in the field. There is no inherent reason why the bathroom cannot be constructed like the kitchen, of units permitting wide variation in room arrangement through the placement and handling of only a few assembly elements.

Accessories, such as knocked-down furniture, storage units, and even outbuildings and garages, are increasingly available and can be put together by the do-it-yourself mechanic or by regular building labor. Similarly, stoops and porches or components thereof can be bought as units and attached to the house.

Because conventional fireplaces and chimneys built at the site by the mason are expensive in materials and labor, a decided shift toward prefabricated units is taking place. This is particularly true of the chimney, which is available, for example, in circular units which may readily be set up one on top of another and the joints between them sealed by a cement, usually combined with a surrounding metal strap. To a lesser degree, prefabricated fireplaces are being employed; here a simple wallhung unit, which needs only to be connected to the flue and so saves expensive interior work, is growing in popularity.

Advances for the Future

Advances such as those described above are proceeding at an accelerating pace. Other advances are still in the laboratory or are emerging from the laboratory into development for the housing industry. A few of the most significant of these will be examined, their present status indicated, and the forces tending to speed or to retard their adoption discussed.

Sandwiches. A first level of problems is encountered when one seeks to develop new ways of applying the traditional production systems of the housing industry. A good illustration is the structural sandwich; this involves the advanced concept that well-known materials may be combined and pre-finished in the shop to provide a new composite material possessing properties and advantages not obtainable with the separate materials.

The intent is to combine in a single slab skins capable of withstanding the weathering, aging, and general wear to which the building surfaces are exposed, and a core that provides thermal insulation and, hopefully, an acoustical barrier. The combination of facings firmly bonded to a core may provide maximum strength and stiffness with minimum weight.

The possible combinations are numerous. Here perhaps more than in any other field of development can be found all new materials in combination, all old materials in combination, or combinations of old and new. Evidently the adhesive that bonds the faces and cores is of crucial importance. These versatile combinations can be employed for a wide variety of applications in housing. They are capable of providing the entire structure of the house, combining the strength to carry the loads at the same time that they provide the enclosing envelope, walls, floors, and roof. Depending on whether transparent, translucent, or opaque facings are employed, the panels can transmit light or be completely opaque. Because a structural sandwich of this type is an integral unit, it can be thinner than the customary stud wall and still provide greater strength and rigidity than usual construction. The saving in space can be valuable, particularly in such items as storage spaces. Despite these and other potential advantages, the total quantity of sandwiches found in the structural parts of houses is small. The reasons are diverse and complex. The major ones may be grouped under three headings.

1. *Large-volume production.* To reduce costs to a competitive level, production must be in large volume. As matters stand, many of the organizations actively engaged in sandwich development are small. The larger materials manufacturers prefer to sell to fabricators (although this position is beginning to change and some of them are considering undertaking production and distribution, even though this may involve competition with existing sandwich fabricators), extending them strong assistance in lowering costs and enlarging markets, or absorbing them.

2. *New design approach.* Sandwich construction calls for new design approaches if its full potentialities are to be realized. These composites cannot economically be incorporated into traditional construction. For example, it is easy to conceal piping, conduits, wires, ducts, and other utility lines within the conventional structure, but this is difficult when the individual panels are completely finished and their interiors are inaccessible. The combined attentions of the designer, the builder, and the manufacturer of mechanical equipment are required to overcome such a problem (see photograph 38). Furthermore, designers must be ingenious enough to provide an attractive joint which becomes a part of the decorative scheme. With the newer types of sealants available, making a joint weatherproof is not difficult; the problem is to make it acceptable to the ultimate user.

3. *New basis of analysis.* With sandwich construction, new approaches are needed with respect to tests, standards, codes, and means of securing acceptability.

For any new material, certain questions respecting durability immediately arise. How long will it last? Will it age well? Will it discolor? Will it lose its structural qualities? Will it have to be renewed? In short, can it be depended upon? Unless the material has had a long history of exposure to the expected conditions, some question always remains as to its ability to endure for the periods of time involved in housing. This poses a major research problem (developed in Chapter 7) and also challenges designers to use these new composites in such a way as to make their renewal or replacement, if necessary, as simple and inexpensive as possible.

Because many of the sandwiches are so new, standards of sizes, shapes, and materials specifications have not yet been developed. It is particularly important that standards and specifications be set up not by individual manufacturers but by such generally recognized authorities as the American Society for Testing Materials, the American Standards Association, and the Department of Commerce. Until this is done, architects, engineers, and builders are reluctant to adopt the new materials.

Building codes are frequently a major stumbling block. Most codes, as they relate to house construction, are based on traditional methods employing separate framing members with field-applied facings. The typical sandwich has no separate framing members, but has instead a continuous core to which the facings are bonded, and its fire resistance often is not equal to that of standard plaster or plasterboard on wood studs. Even though most codes do not demand any great degree of fire resistance in dwelling-house construction, code officials are properly reluctant to approve construction which appears to them to increase the fire hazard. Furthermore, few of them are familiar with the structural principles involved in a sandwich and many fail to see how the apparently lightweight construction can possibly be as strong as or stronger and sturdier than the traditional methods of framing.

Like building-code officials, builders, architects, and engineers are also in varying degree unfamiliar with sandwich construction and, consequently, must be educated in its use.

This calls for intensive and patient effort by the proponents of the new systems. At present there is no quick and easy way to bring a new material or a new system of construction to the attention of the entire housebuilding industry, nor are market analyses readily available to give the developer of a new idea detailed and accurate statistics respecting the actual or potential use of materials such as sandwiches in house construction.

Plastics. Plastics illustrate the advanced problems encountered when one introduces entirely new materials and production processes into the housing picture. Even though they are in many ways basically different from traditional materials, plastic products sometimes fit into traditional systems of construction and can be distributed through traditional channels. In other instances they are so widely different that new concepts of their use are required and major obstacles must be overcome before their application can become widespread. The variety of insights they offer into the process of design in the housing industry justifies extensive discussion here.

Plastics manufacturers see the building industry as a large potential market, and the building industry sees in plastics possible answers to some of its problems in the uses of materials. Today on a tonnage basis the total annual output of plastics equals the production of aluminum or of copper; on a bulk basis, because of their low unit weight, the total volume of plastics produced exceeds the volume of all nonferrous metals combined. Production is increasing rapidly; in the period from 1941 to 1957, the growth was well over 1,000 per cent.

Much confusion arises from the tendency to lump all plastics together. Actually plastics embrace some fifteen to twenty basic materials which are as dissimilar as the various metals. Some are soft and flexible; others are hard and rigid; some are weak; others are strong; and all degrees of strength, hardness, and flexibility between the extremes are possible. They may be transparent, opaque, or colored in all the shades of the rainbow. The principal feature they have in common is that they are all moldable, i.e., plastic, at some stage in their history and can be given an infinite variety of shapes and forms.

In some categories of building applications, primarily non-functional and finish applications, plastics are already entrenched; in others, they are just beginning to emerge. Synthetic resins or plastics used as adhesives and coatings are well established, and these uses are rapidly expanding. Similarly, plastics are widely used in floors and, in the form of decorative high-pressure laminates, in counter-tops. Flexible sheet and film are well on their way for wall covering and as vapor seals under slab-on-ground construction. Hardware manufacturers are using plastic parts, particularly molded nylon, as components for hardware items and, in some instances, as the entire item.

In most of the foregoing applications, there are no significant impediments to the adoption of plastics. If they can demonstrate superiority in cost, wearing quality, durability, appearance, and reduced maintenance, or can show any other clear-cut feature of superiority, they are readily adopted by the building industry and usually can be distributed through established channels. No great legal difficulties stand in the way, and most plastics require no strenuous propaganda campaign to win public acceptance.

Of particular interest are plastic coatings, both protective and decorative; their rapid evolution has resulted in greatly broadened properties as well as a blurring of the traditional distinctions between paints, varnishes, lacquers, and enamels. Durability, hardness, toughness have all been enhanced and the ability to withstand high temperatures greatly increased. Progress has been particularly notable in the coatings requiring moderate baking such as is easily attained in the shop. Here the fast-drying coatings and particularly those capable of covering in one coat are important and can be handled by modern techniques of spraying, electrostatic deposition, and baking by infrared lamps.

A revolution is occurring in the coatings based on latex emulsions of rubber or of resins. Rapidly applied roller-coating paints fall in this class and have already strongly influenced interior painting. Much experimentation and testing is under way to determine which of these or which new formulations are especially applicable for outdoor use. Here rapidly applied one-coat, or at most two-coat, paints are particularly needed and can go far toward reducing a costly item in housing.

As is true of all new materials, a major problem with coatings is the determination of their durability, their aging and weathering characteristics over long periods of time; this is of crucial importance in the case of coatings. Ability to bond tenaciously to a surface and the resistance to chalking, peeling, cracking, alligatoring, and all of the other influences causing breakdown in a paint film must be evaluated. So far the only sure method of determining these factors is exposure to the weather. Completely accurate and reliable accelerated laboratory tests to predict the long-time aging and weathering characteristics are still to be found. This lack of reliable, accurate, rapid tests constitutes a strong impediment to the quick adoption of new and promising coatings.

Once a reliable coating has been developed, its introduction into the trade necessitates a massive educational program, not only to call it to the attention of the paint users and specifiers, but to convince them that the new material is reliable. Painters are suspicious of new materials because of previous unfortunate experiences with coatings promoted in glowing terms which in use have failed to come up to expectations. Perhaps in no other field is proper application technique of as great importance as it is in the application of protective and decorative coatings.

In the aforementioned applications, plastics and other synthetics have not found significant obstacles to their adoption. In other applications, particularly as functional building elements, they are apt to meet more formidable deterrents, particularly when the public safety is involved. Plastic piping for sanitary systems, for example, must prove its suitability and demonstrate that it does not constitute a health hazard. Reinforced plastics must similarly demonstrate their structural safety, lack of fire hazard, and ability to endure for considerable periods of time. Plastic foams, when used as perimeter insulation with slab-on-ground construction, find little opposition as far as codes are concerned, but when they are used as the cores of structural sandwiches, their fire rating becomes important.

It is as light-transmitting materials that plastics have had the greatest use and so have begun to appear most widely in building-code provisions. Most of these provisions are applicable to commercial or industrial buildings primarily and only secondarily to dwelling construction. Combined efforts of the industry and code officials have resulted in a series of recommendations respecting allowable areas in skylights, ceilings, walls, and partitions that may be covered by the various classes of transparent and translucent plastics materials.

The degree to which major design changes may be involved in the use of new materials may be illustrated by the consideration of four functional applications of plastics in the housing industry:

1. *Plastic piping.* Plastics as replacements for metal in piping offer many attractive possibilities. The piping may be flexible (polyethylene), rigid (polyvinyl chloride and copolymers), or high strength (reinforced polyester or epoxy piping). The plastics commonly employed for water piping are nontoxic and highly corrosion-resistant, as is attested by their widespread use in the chemical process industries. Since the flexible varieties of piping are easily snaked around, they require a minimum of fittings; when needed, fittings can readily be made by welding, by cementing, or by using molded threaded plastic couplings. In cost, many plastics pipes fall between inexpensive but readily corroded steel and the highly corrosion-resistant metals such as copper.

Flexible plastic pipe is already widely used on farms and in such applications as sprinkling systems to distribute cold water on golf courses. Such pipe is already quite standard for water connections from water mains to the house. The rigid varieties are more commonly employed in industrial plants, such as in the chemical industries, and are beginning to find employment in other industrial and commercial applications. Some varieties of pipe are widely used for irrigation; others are used to handle corrosive crude oil. Installations have been made utilizing plastics pipe for gas lines and this use appears to be growing. In spite of these demonstrated useful applications, relatively little plastic is used for piping in houses. Both technical and nontechnical impediments stand in the way of rapid adoption.

A major technical problem is the fact that, whereas many plastics pipes are quite satisfactory at ordinary temperatures, they soften at elevated temperatures and, consequently, for a given thickness of wall cannot withstand as high pressures at elevated temperatures as they can when handling water at room temperatures. The softer, more flexible varieties may soften so much at the temperatures found in hot water lines that their use for such lines is inadvisable. The temperature tolerances are gradually being increased as better formulations of plastics materials are being found, but there is at present insufficient knowledge of the long-time behavior of these materials to predict what wall thicknesses are required to prevent bulging and possible failure in hot water lines over a long period of time. Consequently, conservative practice is to employ overthick pipe walls, at higher cost.

Several alternatives are possible. First, it may be decided to restrict the plastics to cold water lines only and specify metal piping for hot water. This obviously raises the question of supervision to make sure that the plastic is not inadvertently used in the hot water line, and it also brings about awkward questions of two sets of fittings and two techniques involved in the installation of the same system. For the custom-built house, such complication hardly appears to be feasible. The development builder, installing a great many identical units, might more easily make the necessary differentiation. Second, if all lines are to be made of plastics, then either the hot water lines must be heavier-walled than the cold water lines or the thicker pipe must be utilized throughout the system. If two thicknesses are involved, a difficult supervision problem again arises. If thick-walled pipe is used throughout, it may well cost more than all-metal pipe.

Even if the foregoing technical difficulties are overcome, other impediments still stand in the way of the widespread use of plastics piping. As is true of all building materials, generally accepted standards and specifications must be set up for plastics pipe. Because in many instances metal and plastics pipe will be used in the same system, a problem arises in specifying pipe sizes and fittings that provide for interchangeability of the two types of materials. Standards must not only be established but enforced. This involves policing the industry, a difficult problem, because it is relatively easy for an unscrupulous operator to produce inferior material which to casual visual observation is identical with a top-quality product. This problem, of course, is not peculiar to plastics; it is found in other materials-supply industries as well.

Distribution and retail outlets comprise major concerns for producers of plastics pipes. Indeed, the ease and simplicity with which extruders can be set up have led some producers to think that, instead of producing pipe at central locations and shipping the material long distances, it is simpler to set up many extruders, probably in the shops of the local distributors, and produce the pipe to order. Raw materials can be shipped in bulk more economically than coils or lengths of the finished pipe. This evidently raises some formidable questions of quality control and enforcement of conformance to standards and specifications.

Finally, there is the same problem of general education that exists with all new materials. Architects, engineers, builders, plumbing subcontractors, labor, the eventual owners, and all other users of the material must be made aware of its qualities and limitations. Applications in housing are most likely to occur where the cost of careful design and development can be spread over a large number of units, as in large-scale building, or in components and units produced in large quantities. To the extent that plastics find their way into fixtures, plastics pipes and fittings become natural features of the total installation instead of substitutes.

2. *Reinforced plastics.* Of all the many plastics materials available and under development today, among the most intriguing from the house-construction standpoint are the reinforced plastics in which high-strength fibers, almost always glass but with increasing amounts of other synthetics as well as natural fibers, are combined with liquid resins and formed into the desired shape; after the resin hardens, a light, strong, tough, reinforced plastics part emerges. For their weight, these materials are among the strongest materials known, yet they can be given a high degree of light transmission or can be made opaque. Various colors can be imparted. Their toughness and resistance to breakage is considerably greater than that of other translucent materials. In many respects they seem well suited for use as components of houses.

The principal uses in house construction so far have been as exterior shelter panels, awnings, space dividers, and the like. Corrugated panels are extensively employed as skylights and side lights in industrial buildings. Flat sheets have also found extensive use as glazing, particularly where the breakage hazard with glass is high. They are finding growing acceptance as facings on translucent structural sandwiches for light-transmitting side walls and roofs in buildings.[6]

Molded, reinforced plastics have found extensive use in aircraft applications and in the fabrication of boat hulls. In house construction, the one major demonstration is in the Monsanto "House of the Future" (see photographs 20, 38). Architectural

[6] The first large-scale use of this type appeared in the roof of the United States Pavilion at the World's Fair in Brussels in 1958.

and engineering design of this house were inseparably linked because the fundamental thesis was to use plastics as plastics and not as substitutes for other materials. Consequently, in the design of this house, inherently efficient, strong and stiff sandwiches and curved structural shells are employed to perform the combined functions of structural support and enclosure with a minimum of material. The usual multiplicity of framing members and sheet materials is eliminated. A relatively few large shop-molded shells, limited in size only by shipping restrictions, are assembled on the site. Adhesives, sealants, and gaskets are employed to bond the parts together into a continuous structure and to provide weathertightness. The result is an advanced concept that conforms to no building code and is divorced from the house-construction industry as it stands today.

General use of such structures in the industry is not close at hand. The reasons are various. As compared with wood, concrete, and steel, the per-pound cost of reinforced plastics is high; consequently, they cannot compete successfully on a straightforward replacement basis but must combine structure, enclosure, and in some instances, light transmission in efficient shapes making each pound work to its utmost. The cost of molds must be spread over a large number of parts. Color and texture are both problem and challenge. Further challenges are posed by the details involved in combining reinforced plastics with other materials to make the most efficient use of the properties of all. Finally, imaginative design demands that the homeowner accept structural forms foreign to his background of experience. With imaginative and acceptable design, reinforced plastics may overcome the cost obstacle otherwise facing them.

As is true of all relatively new materials, questions immediately arise with respect to the weathering and aging characteristics of reinforced plastics. Their history is not yet broad nor long enough to answer these questions completely. Some of the early use of inferior resins led to inferior products, especially when combined with the inefficient early production methods. With improved resins and improved fabrication procedures, the quality of the material has been improved, but twenty-year histories of weather exposure are still unavailable. Consequently, uncertainty still exists respecting long-time durability.

Code problems are also involved. Because the materials either burn or can be destroyed by fire, the building-code official must determine in what category he will place these new materials, and they do not conform exactly to any of the existing categories. Code provisions are gradually being developed but widespread adoption by municipalities still remains to be achieved, and until such adoption is general, the large-scale utilization of these materials will be retarded.

Distribution depends upon the end use. For example, flat and corrugated sheets may find their way through regular dealer outlets into the hands of individual builders; they may go directly to prefabricators for incorporation into house components; or they may go to other fabricators for further processing into finished units such as sandwich panels. For entirely new and structural uses, such as are illustrated in the Monsanto "House of the Future," distribution would be as major components of an entire structure, with general channels of distribution created as the new system proves itself in use.

3. *Adhesives.* The introduction of plastics has brought about a revolution in the ancient art of gluing. To a considerable degree, waterproof adhesives have been responsible for the extensive use of plywood. Laminated wood, built up of thin and relatively short boards bonded together, has become important because large pieces and curved shapes can be made that otherwise would be impractical. Modern adhesives have made most of this possible, although casein adhesives that were known to the ancient Egyptians play a prominent part in the fabrication of laminated wood.

Some of the most spectacular developments in adhesives are in the bonding of metals, glass, hard plastics, ceramics such as tile, and similar impervious materials. The strong synthetic resins, combined with rubbery materials to give them the necessary flexibility, can provide for differential shrinkage and expansion among the parts bonded together and have led to the use of construction systems based on the high-strength engineering adhesives. For housing purposes, much interest centers on the possibility of bonding by means of spots or narrow lines of adhesives as, for example, to replace nails or screws in connecting boards to studs, joists, rafters, ribs, or other structural parts. A dream of many builders is a pressure-sensitive adhesive, making it necessary to use only a hammer-tap to bond a building board rigidly to a stud without nails. This remains only a dream, although a high-frequency electronic unit for spot bonding has been developed.

Several technical problems of a fundamental nature face the adhesives field. The major one is that of being certain, without pulling the pieces apart, that a satisfactory bond has been achieved in fact. Another is the nature of the bond itself; the reasons why materials bond to each other are still imperfectly understood. Until these basic matters are thoroughly explored, the development of adhesives will continue to be largely a trial-and-error process.

Except for these technical problems, no formidable deterrents appear to stand in the way of more widespread use of adhesives, at least in otherwise traditional structural systems. Since systems of construction made possible by high-strength engineering adhesives are usually not provided for in the codes, they must be argued with individual code officials. Many of the adhesives require heat and pressure to develop a superior bond; to the extent that fabricating shops must install the necessary equipment, this constitutes a deterrent to their more widespread use. Notwithstanding these and other problems, adhesives may be expected to play increasingly important roles in building.

In the long run, benefit from the new adhesives may best be derived from new forms incorporating more advanced structural concepts than are traditionally employed in housing. Just as sandwiches and shells offer the most promise in the use of composites and materials like reinforced plastics, so these same concepts in many ways make best use of adhesives. Quantity production and distribution are implied, as are components and units made in the shop under the conditions most conducive to efficiency and reliability in the use of adhesives.

4. *Sealants and gaskets.* Because of the trend toward large glass areas and the use of panels and component construction, means of sealing the joints among these various units have become of great importance. Consequently, putties and calking compounds have graduated from relatively minor roles into constituents of major importance in building. The prime requirement of such sealants is that they be able to accommodate changes in dimension occurring in different materials with changes in temperature or moisture content.

Among the newest materials changing the character of sealants are the polysulphides and the synthetic rubbers. Mixed and flowed into place as thick pastes, these convert to rubbery tough materials capable of remaining flexible at high and low temperatures and of bonding firmly to a wide variety of surfaces like glass, metal, wood, and masonry. Although these are relatively new as building sealants, their long history of outdoor exposure in other applications indicates good durability. Older-style glazing and calking compounds are also undergoing considerable improvement in consistency, flexibility, retention of properties, and aging characteristics.

Gaskets can be made of molded synthetic rubber and flexible plastics in a wide variety of shapes and sizes. Not only can they make large glass areas weathertight, but joints between large building panels can similarly be handled (see photograph 8). One type of window now available has an inflatable gasket which tightly seals the window when inflated, but when deflated allows the window to pivot for easy cleaning.

A major problem in increased use of the superior sealants is cost. Compared to older-style putties and calking compounds, they are expensive. Because first cost is often of overriding importance, all too frequently the tendency is to utilize less expensive materials and get by for the time being even though maintenance costs are greatly increased in the future. A second deterrent to greater use of these materials is technical. Many of the best modern sealants are two-ingredient materials which must be used immediately after mixing because once the constituents are combined, they gradually stiffen into their final rubbery form and cannot again be softened. This introduces problems of application, particularly in calking guns.

There appear to be no other major deterrents to the increased use of improved sealants. It can be expected that they will play an increasingly important role in building and that greater reliance will be placed upon them as they demonstrate their ability to seal and to accommodate movement in building components. For the new systems embodying sandwiches and shells the existence of reliable sealants is crucial.

Metals. Metals are ancient materials familiar in building, but the industrial methods commonly associated with them are rarely applied to domestic structures. Although there have been frequent proposals for a house primarily built of metal, such proposals have not heretofore met with much success. Nevertheless, there seems little doubt that metal will be used increasingly in housing in the future. In part, this will stem from the growing need for structural materials as the total demand for housing increases and the lumber supply has to be supplemented.

Steel and aluminum appear destined to move strongly into the housing field, with steel meeting most of the structural needs and both metals competing for the nonstructural applications. Copper, lead, and zinc will continue to fulfill their present specialty uses, with mounting competition from plastics. Magnesium is a question mark and must prove its superiority over aluminum, for instance, if it is to find much use in building where weight-saving is not of overriding importance. In the extremely unlikely event that the cost of titanium is brought down sharply in the foreseeable future, its strength, corrosion-resistance, and lightness will be of interest in building.

Plain carbon steels or low-alloy steels can be expected to meet most of the requirements for steel in housing, particularly structural and semistructural. Stainless steel will be used mainly in trim and in cabinets, washing equipment, and similar applications where appearance and corrosion-resistance are important.

The lightness and corrosion-resistance of aluminum have already brought into widespread use for windows, roofing, siding, flashing, and trim, and its surface reflectivity has given it a big market in reflective insulation. Color and durability can be added to aluminum by anodizing to extend its range of possible applications where decorative value is important.

A number of protective and decorative coatings are now available, such as porcelain enamel, synthetics, and various plastics. These have greatly extended the usefulness of both steel and aluminum. This is particularly true of steel, where corrosion is otherwise a severe handicap, and for both metals the decorative value has been greatly increased. The porcelain-enameled steel houses that have been erected have given a good account of themselves. Many other structures in which porcelain enamel has been properly applied have shown themselves resistant to corrosion. A limitation is the brittleness of the enamel which can be cracked by impact and is difficult to repair satisfactorily. Durable baked-on synthetic coatings are softer and easier to scratch than porcelain enamel but more resistant to impact.

Most of the functions which the metals can fulfill can also be fulfilled by other materials; in fact, in many instances the metals are the newcomers attempting to supplant the established materials. They must therefore overcome the traditions established not only in the building industry itself but in the public mind. A general, vague, ill-defined opposition to the all-metal house appears to exist although metal components, particularly windows and combination doors, have found widespread acceptance. Coldness to the touch, the "tinny" sound associated with poorly designed parts, strangeness of finish, and difficulty of handling with usual tools (especially in the do-it-yourself market)—all are among the common objections. And no doubt the wide familiarity with automobile construction has instilled doubts about durability. Here is a field in which a thoroughgoing market analysis, not readily available from existing statistics, would be helpful.

A technical problem not solved in many applications is that of heat conductivity. It is not uncommon to find moisture condensing on the inner surfaces of metal windows in cold weather, and complaints that metal windows feel "cold" are widespread. This feeling seems to carry over to the idea that a metal house will necessarily be cold. Technically, of course, this problem can be overcome, but it is a factor to consider.

The fire resistance of metals is better than that of many traditional housing materials, but in actual use they may not perform as well because thin metal parts can easily warp and go out of shape in a hot fire and may lose enough of their strength to allow structural collapse. Nevertheless, the materials are classified as incombustible and should offer no great code problems on that score.

Regarding labor, a principal question is one of jurisdiction and this can become an issue of considerable importance. Should carpenters, sheet metal workers, or structural iron workers handle metal parts, particularly if they perform functions of enclosure and structure simultaneously? If all three crafts must be involved, labor costs might become prohibitively high, and yet if carpenters, who traditionally build the major part of most houses, obtained jurisdiction they would clearly be violating many established crafts lines.

Basic Production Considerations

Advances in housing construction will be small if builders are content merely to substitute new materials and assemblies for old when prices are competitive and local conditions are otherwise favorable. The Realization of the full potentials of new ideas requires a careful determination of each aspect of the over-all design and production approach that would best embody the new ideas. Many of the design considerations involved in such a determination have been brought out in earlier chapters of this book. Here attention is drawn to several considerations more closely related to the production process.

Critically important to a producer's choice of material and method, for example, are the characteristics of distribution systems. He should assess the merits of component construction and those of dimensional coordination, because many of the benefits that he hopes to gain by industrializing his own operations might be equally available through a rationalized distribution of building materials and components, and without the development of a large, integrated house-production organization. The factors involved in these decisions are the subject of the sections which follow.

Distribution System. The channels by which housing products reach the market are highly variable, and they have long had an important influence on the character and the success of new developments. An understanding of these channels and of the problems of the typical building-materials dealer is important to any producer of housing.

For the major conventional housing material, lumber, distribution is traditionally directed through a wholesaler, although the retailer sells to the average builder and, by carrying his account, actually helps to finance his operations. Brick, on the other hand, too heavy a material to be handled often, has long been produced and shipped directly from nearby manufacturer to construction site, with orders taken by manufacturers' associations. For cement, distribution has largely been in the form of ready-mixed concrete, prepared at large local plants; even large builders have preferred to use this rather than set up their own mixing equipment. Gypsum, on the other hand, is warehoused only at the mill and finished products—plaster, lath, wallboard, and sheathing—shipped out on dealer orders.

From the foregoing it is evident that patterns of materials distribution are not uniform. The same situation is found in other materials, such as roofing, flooring, glass, and plumbing and heating supplies. Flow may be from manufacturer to wholesaler to retailer to builder or it may bypass one or more. The manufacturer frequently has no idea where his products eventually arrive after they leave his plant. The situation is sometimes chaotic.

Although distribution practices differ for these building materials, ultimately they all make materials available as needed on the spot to builders in the many local communities. Typically, there is little ordering from far-off plants and waiting for delivery. For dwellings produced by highly localized producers, as in custom and small-scale operative building, the local materials outlet is a logical and efficient means of distribution.

The large development builder, however, purchases in large enough quantities to bypass the local dealer and to buy directly from the wholesaler or the manufacturer; the local dealer is consequently left with the smaller accounts. The prefabricator's requirements also are in sufficient volume to justify direct purchase from the wholesaler if not from the manufacturer.

Hence the role of the local dealer in distribution must increasingly shift. He can attempt to widen the custom market by finding ways of cutting costs for the custom builder, an arrangement that can easily merge into operative building. He can also look for other outlets. A promising market exists in the growing do-it-yourself trend. Dealers have found it advantageous to set up special arrangements to take care of this market, relatively small in individual purchases but in total capable of sustaining an attractive volume. Here a decided sales advantage lies in ease of application and in high material quality. Since the do-it-yourself operator is conscious of his limited labor-time and skill, he will typically pay well for these features.

Repair, rehabilitation, and modernization of existing dwellings also represent an extremely large market, growing continually as the stock of existing houses increases, and aided by FHA guarantees on remodeling loans. For many dealers this supply provides the bulk of their sales and often helps to keep volume more or less steady when new construction diminishes. There is an increasing trend for local dealers and builders to organize specifically to handle the requirements of rehabilitation. For the dealer this means that he will for the most part supply the types of materials found in existing dwellings, as well as such units, assemblies, and components (ready-assembled cabinets, for example), as may fit into the rehabilitation scheme.

Components can become a significant part of the local dealer's business, particularly if he has a small mill in conjunction with his yard. Dealers have found it advantageous to fabricate trussed rafters and to assemble wall and partition panels, all to be delivered to the site where the builder can quickly assemble them. Dump and straddle trucks make it possible for one man to deliver the entire shipment. Precutting and bundling materials for ready assembly at the site are not at all uncommon, especially for delivery to operative builders.

Even within the conventional industry, therefore, changes are in progress; forces exist that tend to further the growth of larger units and more inventive management, both among builders themselves and in the organizations which supply them with building materials.

The producer of a new material or a new building item, particularly if he is not already in the building field and does not have a distribution system organized, is faced with a question of fundamental importance. Should he design his product for distribution through existing channels, or should he attempt to set up new channels of his own?

Distribution through existing channels may require close

involvement with an existing materials producer who, although he may be sympathetic toward the new material, will prefer to fit it into an established pattern. Imaginative ideas are not likely to stem from this arrangement but acceptance of the new product is made easier by the fact that it comes through familiar channels.

Establishing new channels is a slow, arduous process even for the largest producer. Opposition stems from existing dealers, a major obstacle to change for producers of conventional materials. A new product is viewed with double suspicion if it is offered through new and unfamiliar outlets, but on the other hand, the new item does not have to compete with old ones already handled by the dealer, the channels may be set up specifically for the new product, and much of the chaotic condition prevalent in materials distribution may be avoided.

In many ways large-scale building organizations provide the most favorable climate for new products. If a large development builder or a prefabricator finds a new item useful, he at once provides a sizable market, and much of the immense detail necessary to reach the small builder is avoided.

Standardization and Dimensional Coordination. The housing industry is concerned with at least three kinds of standards: (1) social or design standards, such as the requirement of a fixed area or volume for a bedroom; (2) product or industry standards, to assure basic acceptability of units from different manufacturers purporting to perform a specified function, e.g., light bulbs; and (3) standards concerned only with dimensions, to assure ease of application or combination of different products in a building. The first of these is outside the scope of this study; we are here concerned with the second and third.

Product standardization introduces a serious dilemma when it comes to the adoption of new materials and products. On the one hand, manufacturers, builders, designers, and code authorities need a reasonable specification for product performance and a basis on which to judge whether a given material or product is up to specification. On the other hand, standardization tends to freeze materials and products at existing levels of performance, although there may be a real reason for making changes as continuing research and development indicate how performance can be improved and costs reduced. A delicate balance is required. This imposes a heavy responsibility on standardizing agencies like the American Standards Association and the American Society for Testing Materials, on industries drawing up various commercial standards with the cooperation of the Department of Commerce, and on agencies drawing up various Federal and other government specifications. All of these agencies must be ready at all times to revise their standards to take full advantage of new developments, and legal means of incorporating new and changed standards rapidly into regulatory codes are needed.

If the industry is to advance it must produce industrially. Many house components should be truly interchangeable, just as it is possible now to interchange various brands of tires, carburetors, and water pumps for a car. A hopeful small sign is the development of standard "Lu-Re-Co" panels, fabricated by individual lumber dealers all over the country in accordance with uniform designs developed by the Lumber Dealers Research Council. Extending this idea to more and more building components might well simplify a major problem of the manufacturer and of the material distributor and yet retain individuality and variety in home construction.

In some areas product standardization will require technological improvements. For example, it is now generally impossible to use dimension lumber lengths without cutting, when exact dimensions are required. Inaccurate milling makes each piece of lumber slightly different in size, so that it is almost impossible to use studs from the lumber yard without cutting all of them to a uniform length. (Some mills do now cut dimension lumber to exact lengths.) A similar problem exists because of the lack of dimensional stability in concrete blocks and other masonry units.

Dimensional coordination involves a concept quite different from that of product standardization, and it is one that is often misunderstood. Designers frequently use space-planning modules several feet long in two dimensions in order to simplify and expedite the preparation of plans for complex and repetitive buildings, and they are satisfied that this is modular planning. To coordinate the dimensions of building products (plus their required connecting materials), however, we need a smaller, more elastic, three-dimensional module by which *all* product sizes may be guided.

It has long been apparent that much waste of time and materials occurs in every part of building construction because the parts of buildings do not fit together without adjustments. Lumber is produced in one set of sizes, brick in another, windows in still another, and so on for all materials. Cutting and fitting, and the resulting waste, could be avoided by dimensional coordination for all materials.

Less obvious and perhaps more important advantages are the economies of quantity production and of simplified distribution that become possible for many items which otherwise would be custom-built, like staircases, if a general dimensioning system were in force. About the only fairly widespread dimensional standard in conventional construction is 48 inches, a multiple of the widely used stud spacing of 16 inches, used for many wallboards and based originally on the 48-inch wood lath (cut from cordwood) which now has practically disappeared.

The 4-inch cubical module, originally proposed by Albert Farwell Bemis,[7] has had wide acceptance as a basic module to which all building parts may be made to conform. Much study has gone into the applications of this module and many details of design and construction have been worked out.[8] Four

[7] Albert Farwell Bemis, *The Evolving House*, vol. III, *Rational Design*, Technology Press, M.I.T., Cambridge, Mass., 1936.

[8] The promotion of the 4-inch cubical system of dimensional coordination was carried out initially by the Modular Service Association, a Boston

inches is not intended to be the minimum dimension allowable —this would evidently be impractical—but all principal dimensions, including, for example, room dimensions, wall thicknesses, and the spacing and sizes of openings, are expected to conform to some multiple of 4 inches. Modular brick and tile and modular steel windows have been produced to conform to this system.[9]

Objections to the 4-inch cube have been raised on the ground that it is too large a module for small dimensions, and smaller than it need be for large dimensions. The reliance on multiples of 4 inches is objected to as being too inflexible, from the point of view of many large materials manufacturers. Under a recent number pattern proposal,[10] a 3-inch system has been added to simplify the standardization of the many products to which that is particularly suited, and an additive number sequence has been included in line with dimensioning proposals extending from early history to Le Corbusier's *Modulor*, since building design necessarily represents the adding together of many assembled parts.

This proposed number pattern uses three numerical series or progressions. They are

(1) doubling: 1, 2, 4, 8, 16 . . . ;
(2) tripling: 1, 3, 9, 27 . . . ;
(3) adding: 1, 2, 3, 5, 8, 13. . . .

When used together to form a three-dimensional number pattern, the combinations of these three progressions give a series

---

organization subsidized by the Bemis family, and by Committee A62 of the American Standards Association. More recently the work was carried on under a joint committee of the American Institute of Architects and the Producers Council. It is now the function of the recently created Modular Building Standards Association, sponsored by the last two groups and by the Associated General Contractors of America and the National Association of Home Builders.

[9] For window standardization progress, see The Producers Council, Technical Bulletin no. 79, Washington, D.C., March, 1957, p. 107.

[10] Ezra Ehrenkrantz, *The Modular Number Pattern*, Alec Tiranti, Ltd., London, 1956.

of numbers which can be thought of as basic dimensions of products as installed in a building. They provide a large number of basic dimensions in the small-dimension region—fourteen sizes between zero and 2 feet, as against twenty-one between 2 and 12 feet. The 3- and 4-inch modules thus become a part of the number pattern. By judicious use of the three progressions, a large number of dimensional patterns can be worked out. For example, numerous standard sizes can be obtained by cutting a standard sheet of material such as wallboard, with minimum number of cuts and no leftover pieces that do not fit the number pattern. An obvious result is very much simpler distribution and stocking of materials. Furthermore, the greater dimensional elasticity makes it easier for the various elements of the building industry to adjust to the number pattern, and costs of modifying production sizes are less.

It may be argued that dimensional coordination is unnecessary for a prefabricator or for an operative builder who is building a large number of identical or repetitive houses, since these large producers can work out dimensions to suit their own product, and fabricate the parts in quantity. This is true enough, but each part so dimensioned is also inflexible and is limited to one product design. A model change can make it obsolete, and there is little chance of varying the final arrangement to provide freedom in planning. Full benefit cannot be taken of materials, systems, and products devised by others, nor of the possibility of selling products for use in combination with those made by others.

The announcement of a well-worked-out system of dimensions to which components can be designed is not in itself assurance that it will be adopted. It must be made profitable for industry actually to produce according to such a system. This has been and continues to be the crux of the dimensional coordination problem. Not until sufficient volume of demand is generated to make a dimensional changeover worthwhile will it be made. How or even whether that demand will in actuality be generated is by no means clear. It can come about when builder organizations are large enough to order in such volume that it is worthwhile for them to develop their own system of dimensions. Conceivably, if associations of home builders were to adopt component methods of building and to build in sufficient volume, component units would be produced to conform to their requirements. The important point is to generate sufficient volume.

The argument that standardization and industrialization would take the flexibility and ingenuity away from architects and engineers will not stand up to close analysis. Designers call for many different sizes of materials partly because nothing in their current practice encourages the use of a reduced range of products in a more ingenious manner. Architecturally, a vast number of very slightly differing sizes serves no necessary purpose, but it prevents any effective rationalization of production methods. The wastefulness involved in designing and constructing a prodigious variety of sizes is not easily understood at present, for the industry is conditioned to it, tooled up for it, and able to supply it (if quantities are large enough) without extra charge. But, in fact, the merchandising, warehousing, and production of endless variety is a real waste which is multiplied countless times in the industry.

The "pipeline" aspect of the problem is often overlooked when large quantities are involved. For example, in building a 100-family project it might be argued that a few window sections specially designed by the architect could be run off one at a time in the quantity needed for the whole project without raising cost over that of a "standard" section, since the cost of setting up a specialized milling machine could be justified by the quantities involved. However, there are other related problems, including financing the operation, storing the windows after assembly, and rehandling them efficiently. To fit in with the erection schedule, shipments would have to be made for three to five houses at a time, involving every different type of window designed for the project. Therefore, all windows for 100 houses would have to be made at once, stored, sorted, and rehandled for shipment in sets. This would cost more than limited runs on general-purpose machinery for a few houses at a time, even though windows so made are more expensive in actual fabrication cost.

In sum large runs of special shapes can be produced without a premium, but they cannot be specially handled, stored, and rehandled without adding cost. And if the reason for the special shape changes, any accumulated inventory may be a total loss. For most housing conditions, therefore, there are advantages in restricting standard sizes of products to a reasonably small number, produced, stored, and marketed at a minimum cost of lost motion and rehandling. Once a good range of sizes is agreed upon, production by many manufacturers no longer introduces a factor of economic waste and each manufacturer has a much better chance of survival. The present advantage of big producers is simply their ability to handle a large number of models economically; with real standardization, equal efficiency in terms of ultimate use could be obtained with a lower production volume per producer. This should lead to more competition and further cost reduction. The builder's costs then might be reduced still more because of the resulting ready availability of important building components, permitting him to reduce inventory costs and exposure to theft and damage and yet retain flexibility of production.

Progress of this type is difficult to achieve, since many manufacturers are either insufficiently aware of the importance of the final cost of their product "installed in place" or are satisfied to leave things as they are. They tend to leave it to architects and builders to demand standardized sizes, and then, when finally persuaded to produce them, they charge the same price for all sizes. Without a distinct economic incentive, consumers cannot be expected to turn exclusively to standard sizes; mere propaganda in favor of standardization cannot overcome the comfortable habits of years.

Another stumbling block to dimensional coordination is

the difficulty of working out some of the details for combining standard products. An example is the problem of producing interchangeable wood, steel, and aluminum windows to fit into wood, brick, or steel walls without disturbing the spacing of studs in the outside walls and the lintels above. In dimensioning surfacing materials, one soon finds that what is good in utilizing standardized building boards without waste is not necessarily good in producing efficient framing methods. Nevertheless, if components are to be made by a number of manufacturers and assembled in a variety of arrangements, some kind of dimensional coordination is essential. A modular system such as the three-progression system may provide the answer.

Construction by Components. The owner is currently faced with buying from an increasingly broad but fixed choice of quantity-produced houses whose acquisition is made as easy as possible, or of undertaking the more expensive and often nerve-wracking experience of planning and building a custom-built house and attempting within traditional local operations to meet his own needs. Neither alternative may be entirely satisfactory. A middle course between these extremes is being explored by sectors of the building industry. This approach is called "component construction." [11]

In component construction, not the houses but the components of which they are built are the industrial product; the house may be assembled from a standardized catalogue of interchangeable structural and nonstructural units, panels (see photographs 6, 22), bath units, kitchen units, cabinet units, and heating units, all of which can be arranged largely as desired instead of according to a fixed plan.

Many self-evident questions immediately arise. Which are the structural and nonstructural units? What sizes of panels and what kinds? Is the bath a single unit? What about the kitchen? How much of the heating system can be made into a

[11] See "Are Coordinated Components the Site Builder's Answer to Prefabrication?" *House & Home,* vol. 9, no. 6, June, 1956, p. 124.

single unit? Will the mechanical services be combined into one unit, or will they be grouped about a mechanical core? Will the services, especially piping and electrical, be contained within the system of structural units and panels or designed for independent installation?

One principal weakness in component construction lies in planning. How many and what sizes of units composing the shell will give the greatest freedom in space and room arrangement with the smallest number of different production parts? What should be the sizes of mechanical units to fit into the component scheme? A thoroughgoing study of dimensions, combinations, and permutations is needed to establish the optimum combination of number and sizes of production units.

A less conspicuous but more important problem is this: who is the entrepreneur? The organization needed to promote and build houses made from components falls somewhere among the custom builder, the prefabricator, the development builder, and the materials distributor.[12] Competent professional architectural analysis should be the basis of the system for selecting and arranging the available components to fit the needs of potential owners; this kind of planning service benefits from the lessons of custom building. The components must be shop-built, probably in different shops for different units, and a distribution system must be set up to bring them to the site; this phase of the activity resembles the work of the prefabricator and the materials distributor. Maximum efficiency at the site calls for a number of houses to be erected simultaneously instead of one at a time; this calls for the kind of careful advance planning, subdivision of work, and coordination typical of the development builder.

An organization to make maximum use of component construction must be more tightly knit than the contractor-sub-

---

[12] At a different level, components vastly improve the feasibility of do-it-yourself home building. For a good description of a typical case, with photographs, see the real estate section of the *New York Times*, August 11, 1957.

contractor-dealer confederation of the typical custom builder, and it must expect to handle many of the problems that face an industrialized system. Inevitably, conflicts with local codes must arise. The problem of local inspection of mechanical equipment assembled elsewhere must be resolved. Traditional labor practices will be violated. These are the same problems that confront the development builder, the prefabricator, and even the custom builder when he attempts to deviate from traditional practice.

Obviously, the small individual builder, architect, or real estate man cannot handle the tremendous coordinative job of putting together materials, getting them to fit with each other, providing quality control, and interrelating the designs; carrying on the publicity, advertising, public relations, and servicing; and tying in the land purchase and financing with the production of so large a series of operations. This calls for a reconsideration of the organization of industry elements that reflects proportionately their contribution in making the picture complete. The question of building houses of components or building complete systems or selling complete houses then becomes somewhat academic, for all the different approaches become aspects of a single process. Even the trailer, the example of a completely factory-fabricated product, may divide itself into several sets of components—a plumbing assembly, a mechanical core, and related storage units, plus the space to surround all these elements of equipment. Obviously, for a long time to come there will be significant differences in housing accommodation, though the differences even between a trailer and a ranch house may become a great deal less when all are rationally assembled on the basis of factory production.

We may soon see the end of the all-wood, all-steel, all-aluminum, or all-anything house. This development will accompany a real increase in industry-wide standardization. The first basic industries to provide a significant part of the house on a logical standardized basis will force all the collateral materials industries to meet these standards immediately, in order to have their materials usable in the standard structures. Collateral materials and equipment companies are already greatly interested in basing designs on a standardized modular system.

Obviously important to the design of such houses is the principle that the mass-production process is utilized best when a wide variety of designs can be made up from a minimum number of production parts. To carry this principle a little further, the design might work on what might well be called an "additive basis." For instance, an expensive steel rolling machine will work most efficiently if it takes sheet steel in an endless ribbon and processes it in a continuous fashion, performing no specialized intermittent operation on it. The shape coming off the end of the roll can be handled most economically if, instead of undergoing further treatment, it is automatically cut off into pieces of one or more standard lengths for simplified handling in every subsequent step in the construction process.

Design thus would reflect not only the original manufacturing equipment but also the related systems of packing, shipping, inventorying, distribution, and erection. Variation could be achieved through the use of small, inexpensive, easily inventoried fitting pieces which can be combined in any number of ways with the expensive major units that must be produced in much larger quantity. The problem with such a major-parts-and-connectors system is to find a design which makes the field assembly or local fabricating assembly so simple and effective that it compares favorably with the cost of shipping completed panels requiring no field work whatever to be done on them.

To what extent may we expect to see the development of a complete component package of very few different kinds of parts and pieces of equipment but infinite final variation in product? This depends on the level of over-all design quality that may be expected to emerge. If our people could understand and employ a design system based on uniform standards with the sophistication and intelligence displayed by the Japanese in their traditional architecture, it would be easy to develop a standardized production system to supply all the variations of function and use necessary for servicing human shelter requirements.

Hypothetical Illustration: International Homes, Inc. To put all of these considerations in a framework of free speculation, uncluttered by the images of the present production of houses, and to illustrate by what very different paths the virtues of good design and sound technology might reach the public, let us imagine the steps taken by an average couple, Mr. and Mrs. Smith, in getting a new house for their family at a time in the future when a company we shall call "International Homes, Inc.," has grown to its full operating scale.

Then, as now, land will be the first problem—where will the Smiths put their house? It is highly likely that they will be able to choose between single-family house lots with considerably broader community facilities than are now prevalent and multifamily town house or apartment accommodations far better planned than at present. Then having arranged the purchase or long-term lease [13] of a site, they move on to the selection of their house.

From International Homes, the Sears Roebuck of housing, they take a brief but excellent course in house and land design, after which they obtain a catalogue. The selections they make from this catalogue will evolve into the particular kind of house they want. But first a brief lesson in modular design. They learn that, regardless of the wide variety of complete houses shown in the catalogue, all use one system of design dimensions. They can have ells on their house, wings of varying widths and lengths, accessory buildings of different types including separate houses for guests or children, and so on— but in every case the unit will be based on a standard module.

[13] The emergence of large-scale land developers, able to develop large neighborhoods and hold them for appreciation in value, will encourage term-buying and rentals.

From there on, the catalogue offers them a multitude of choices. Their house can be one-story, two-story, or one-story and a half, with a flat roof, a very low sloping pitched roof, or a steep-pitched roof—or under certain conditions a combination. They have the choice of at least a dozen exterior wall material facings—from real brick or stone as little as 1 inch thick, to a considerable variety of plastic, metal, wood, and wood-derivative products. It is suggested tactfully that they keep their choices down to two at the most since they must pay a premium for each additional different material. They note that each has a code number, a price factor, and a color key relating it to trim. The catalogue points out the wisdom and economy of an approved standard combination.

The Smiths next find that there are four types of windows—sliding, casement, fixed, and triple hung—to choose from, all operated either manually or electrically. They check the ones they prefer and the material: aluminum, titanium, pressure-impregnated wood, or plastic. It is pointed out to them that if they wish complete, year-round air conditioning, they will need only one small movable venting section in each room. There is also a gentle reminder at the bottom of each page that for those to whom this multiplicity of choices becomes frightening, the second section of the book contains a series of designer-prepared plans for which, since they are pre-packaged, a discount is offered if they are purchased without change. The Smiths, however, are delighted to continue with the choice procedure.

They learn that International can supply for a small price a complete model kit which contains sufficient plastic parts to plan out, at a quarter-inch to the foot, any house shown in the catalogue or any reasonable variation; the kit also contains parts for kitchen, bathrooms, storage areas, and bedrooms at the scale of 1 inch to the foot, together with all the fittings and equipment that are available from International. Mrs. Smith immediately obtains this kit and they are soon able, by shifting about the parts, to visualize many plans for their house.

Mr. Smith, in the meantime, is interested to note that there is a straightforward and not too complicated method of keeping tabs on the cost of each item selected, from the exterior wall finish through to the number of tie racks selected to fit in his own closet. He keeps a running account of these items, adding the prescribed factor for packing, shipping, site assembly, cost of permits, and all legal and financing expenses.

In laying out their own master bedroom, they find that the closets may be ordered with a choice of plastic accordion doors, plastic-covered folding metal doors, or honeycomb-core thin-wood-veneer sliding doors with drawer faces to match, all drawers having a choice of steel or plastic liners and three alternate types of snap-on hardware in metal, plastic, or lacquered wood. The catalogue gives them an idea of the normal amount of storage space required by various family members, depending on their age, income, and living habits; this is related to the storage units offered—drawers, hangers, various fittings and equipment—so that it is not difficult to fill out an order sheet indicating the amounts of various basic types of storage space they will need. Since all units are designed on the modular system with clearly marked drawings and photographs showing the way the parts fit together and look when assembled, Mrs. Smith can visualize four or five different arrangements for her bedroom and dressing alcove.

Several evenings are spent in figuring the costs of different schemes and coming to a final decision. Mr. Smith notes with pleasure that the catalogue has helped them to cut out $2,000 in all by showing where a simpler, less expensive, and perhaps less pretentious solution could be accomplished. These savings leave the house within the over-all budget—based on Mr. Smith's job, prospects, and the financing available to him—which an early meeting with the International representative had established.

The Smiths have had nearly two weeks of evening entertainment and work and have had to confer with the International representative for a total of only an hour; yet they have finally arrived at a complete design and price for their house, filled in the order forms, and sent them in to International for review. After two days they go again to the company's office, answer two or three additional questions regarding their order, sign a form, pay their deposit, and are promised occupancy of the house in three weeks' time.

Mr. Smith begins to worry when the first week goes by and nothing happens on his lot, but then things begin to move. He is asked to check a set of marking stakes against the house location previously spotted on an isometric map of his property showing trees, slope of the land, and relationship to the adjacent houses. The next day a small bulldozer carefully scrapes all the topsoil off the area to be covered by the house itself and a distance of two feet outside it; the driveway is put in, and surface laid on it. The third day a load of gravel is spread over the whole foundation area of the house. Early on the fourth day a shipment of packages arrives, all on one truck. Three men start to work at once, and by noon the house is completely under roof, all exterior and interior partitions are in with their final paint on, and from the street the house appears to be finished. No foundations have been poured, no water has been used, nor has any tool been required other than an electric wrench and a small portable crane for the roof members.

Mr. Smith is so impressed with the ease of assembly that he quickly calls his International representative to ask if he can change his mind and take the option of doing all the interior work himself at a saving of $200. This is agreed to, and the following weekend the Smith family move in to do all their interior planning and layout. Packages are piled neatly in the living room with complete directions at hand, including a bill of particulars stenciled on the face of each package. By Sunday night they have finished the house to the last curtain, kitchen utensil, shoe rack, and toothbrush holder, using only tools supplied free by International: a small wrench, a screwdriver, and a pair of rubber-nosed pliers.

Mr. Smith remarks that for the first time in his life he has been involved in a do-it-yourself project which really saved him money and gave him a feeling of accomplishment at the end. Inasmuch as he has had no training in the arts and crafts he is particularly grateful to International for working out a system requiring only simple tools for each operation. Moreover, all the electrical and electronic equipment they bought is made up in sealed operating-equipment packages, so that he need no longer depend for maintenance on a service company with the human element in it; a complete set of spares is available, designed with a visible fuse in each pack to indicate clearly just which part needs replacing. Mrs. Smith adds, as she surveys the house with extreme satisfaction, that she feels she has been given the opportunity to design her own house to her own tastes and select every single thing in it, and still she finds that it fits perfectly in the neighborhood of other International houses.

Chapter 7

HOUSING INDUSTRY RESEARCH

In this chapter, Albert G. H. Dietz discusses the types of organizations carrying on housing industry research and summarizes research and information needs in the field, concerning himself primarily with aspects of building materials and construction systems.

It comes as no surprise to learn that the builders of houses are not research-oriented. Few organizations in the industry are large enough and strong enough to be able to invest money in research and then wait until it pays off, and these few rarely concern themselves with problems extending beyond the narrow group of building materials which constitutes the basis for their product line. Even the background on the economics and social science aspects of housing is sparse, considering the importance of such study to so complex a field.

To illustrate by way of contrast, the Department of Agriculture spends more money on housing research for 6 million farm families than the Housing and Home Finance Agency spends on housing research for 55 million nonfarm families.[1] In this effort, so important to the welfare of its citizens, it is hard to explain why the United States should be significantly behind nearly every country in the world.

[1] W. L. C. Wheaton in *Urban Renewal in Selected Cities, Hearings Before a Subcommittee of the Committee on Banking and Currency*, U.S. Senate, 85th Cong., 1st Sess. November–December, 1957, p. 896.

Types of Research Organizations

Research in the United States is spread over many segments of housing and related industries and agencies. There is no central organization to point up and coordinate research—such as is commonly found in other countries. Industries, trade associations, foundations, governmental and academic institutions, private research organizations, and professional societies carry on a wide variety of unrelated research activities, each emphasizing those aspects of housing which are of particular concern to it.

Industry. Industrial research is largely devoted to materials and equipment and to the development of plant processes for their fabrication. Manufacturers tend to concentrate on products rather than to analyze their potential contribution to the house as a whole. It is usually assumed that product improvements will be applied to a structure which is otherwise traditional in construction. New combinations of widely divergent materials, even though such combinations might be highly efficient, have thus tended to get little study unless one manufacturer happened to make all of the materials in his own plants. This viewpoint is changing and major manufacturers are beginning to look seriously into the development of composites.

Patent protection often is a major consideration. Few manufacturers can be expected to spend considerable amounts of money and time on developments which can be copied immediately by competitors, who may indeed cheapen the product and undersell the manufacturer who first organized it. With some notable exceptions, industrial research consequently tends to concentrate on research which can be shown to bear directly upon the company's market position; indeed, market research is one kind that is rapidly growing.

Industry would do well to look hard at the house as a whole and to address itself to the production of specialized units combining materials, units, components, and equipment to perform multiple functions with greater efficiency and at less cost than at present; larger industries not traditionally or exclusively associated with housing have already entered this field and have found it lucrative.

The builders themselves are rarely able to carry on research. Though they have an obvious concern for the house as a whole, they have neither the capital nor the stability to undertake research and wait for the answers. Since they must depend on product manufacturers to do their development work for them, they suffer from the limited perspective of most such manufacturers. Only when building in large quantity are they able to analyze their special needs and impose them on their suppliers, and on occasion they have made real advances for the industry in so doing, as when Levitt started Johns-Manville making larger and integrally colored asbestos-cement shingles. Most individual builders are too small to generate such an effective demand, but close-knit associations of builders could provide both the ideas and the market.

Associations. Industrial associations are common, and a number of them undertake studies broader than those of the manufacturers and expect to benefit all members rather than a selected few.

Yet with few expections these are sharply focused on the products of the members. In some instances the associations maintain their own laboratories; in others, they take their problems to existing laboratories in private research organizations, academic institutions, or government agencies. A few examples may be used to illustrate these activities:

1. Structural Clay Products Institute. This research organization has promoted the adoption of new types of brick, including those dimensioned to coordinate with the basic 4-inch module. It has also made an intensive study of bricklaying methods; and it has developed procedures which greatly increase the output of the bricklayer without increasing fatigue.

2. Douglas Fir Plywood Association. This association maintains a central laboratory in which problems of durability,

strength, and related characteristics of plywood are constantly being studied. Improved adhesives and improved engineering utilization of plywood resulting from the laboratory's efforts are useful to all producers of Douglas fir plywood.

3. National Association of Home Builders. Although the Association does not maintain a research laboratory in the generally accepted sense of the term, its Research Institute does sponsor, among other things, Research Houses which are designed to try out the latest techniques and advances in construction materials and construction methods. A favorable climate is provided to encourage manufacturers to take up the new ideas and translate them into products for the housing industry.

Other associations make a valuable research contribution in the course of their normal activities by assembling industry data and statistics. An organization of this kind is the Home Manufacturers Association. Such associations may undertake other activities of a general nature to promote the interests of their members. The Manufacturing Chemists Association and the Society of the Plastics Industry have groups studying building applications of plastics and formulating suggested provisions for incorporation into building codes. Although these activities are not research in the technical sense, they are designed to bring about greater use of plastics in building.

Government. Research carried on in government agencies can be and often is of broader range and more basic nature than the type likely to be found in industrial laboratories.

The HHFA, in its various branches, carries on a large amount of study and analysis of great value to the housing industry. For a few years following World War II, it had a Research Division with appropriate funds, and a number of reports were prepared on aspects of the industry, many of them of broad economic orientation. The Federal Housing Administration, in addition to its development of standards for houses and housing projects, surveys research needs and likely projects. Several have been carried out for FHA by the Building Research Advisory Board.[2] A recent FHA listing of important research projects was estimated to require a budget of $1 million, or about $1 per new house. Research funds in this amount were then appropriated to FHA, but it should be noted that the Central Mortgage and Housing Corporation, FHA's opposite number in Canada, spends almost $5 per new house on research.

Typical research conducted by government laboratories includes studies of basic properties of materials, methods of construction, the properties of structures and components, and engineering design. Two examples may be cited.

The U.S. Forest Products Laboratory carries on research in wood and wood products as well as methods of constructing with wood. It has also recently become involved in research in plastics, metals, and other materials combined with adhesives and wood into sandwiches and building components. Out of this has come, for example, the development of the stressed-skin construction now commonly employed by prefabricators and the more recent work on structural sandwich constructions.

The National Bureau of Standards conducts basic research in materials of construction and also such studies as that on the performance of heating and air-conditioning equipment under closely controlled conditions in a research house. It also tests components and construction methods at the request of industry.

A curious situation respecting patents sometimes arises from government research. In order to prevent the monopolization of methods and devices stemming from government research, it is standard practice for government agencies to apply for patents and then to make the patents freely available to the public. This may actually defer technical advance, for it may

[2] The Building Research Advisory Board has a Technical Studies Advisory Committee which examines numerous technical problems confronting the FHA and recommends courses of action which frequently lead to the establishment of research projects to furnish the answers.

result in a situation in which no one takes up the patent, because the further cost of development into a commercially usable product cannot be adequately protected, and consequently competitors could come into the field and reap the benefit without the costs of development.

Other research organizations may be quasi-governmental, in the sense that they are set up and authorized by government to carry on research but not intended to have support from directly appropriated government funds. For example, the Building Research Advisory Board and the Building Research Institute are branches of the National Academy of Science—National Research Council—chartered by Congress. These agencies depend for their funds on private sources and on contracts with government agencies. They operate largely through boards and committees whose members serve on a voluntary basis without remuneration. The members of the Building Research Advisory Board, drawn from industry, academic institutions, and government agencies, serve to advise the government and the public on problems involving housing and other kinds of building. The Building Research Institute draws its membership from industries involved in building and includes private individuals and others who are interested in the housing field. Conferences and study groups are organized on a wide variety of building subjects and the results are made available in the form of publications. Currently of great interest is the plan of these agencies to undertake a broad analysis and coordination of research activity in the building industry.

Research may be supported by government agencies and placed in academic and other laboratories, or one government agency may place a project with another government agency. For example, projects have been undertaken by the Building Research Advisory Board for FHA and by the Forest Products Laboratory for the National Advisory Committee for Aeronautics.

Research undertaken by or for government and quasi-governmental agencies is necessarily of a general character. It is not concerned with the detailed type of problem that industry can and should solve for itself, but with more general studies of social, economic, and design factors affecting housing.

Private Agencies. Endowed foundations are in a position to conduct research in a wide field, but they rarely study materials, methods of construction, equipment, structure, or arrangement of component parts of buildings. Because of their broad charters and the availability of largely unrestricted funds, they tend to address themselves to social, economic, and broad design aspects of housing dealing with families and their requirements, the interrelationships of housing and communities, the economic aspects of the housing industry, and the relationship of the industry to the economy of the country.

When producers need specific research performed but do not have the facilities to undertake it, they may take their problems to private research organizations as sponsored projects. A wide variety of problems may be undertaken by such organizations. When research is conducted for industry, it is likely to be quite specific, but occasionally there are broad surveys of likely uses for new developments, or market surveys to establish demand. If the sponsoring agent is a government organization the problems may be very broad, e.g., forecasts of materials requirements in building for periods of years ahead. Seldom does the private organization have the resources to undertake broad-scale projects of its own.

Academic institutions also conduct research in the general field of housing. Strictly academic research projects may be carried on by the academic staff. Designed primarily to contribute to the educational process, they may or may not be directly useful to industry. Problems chosen tend to be broad and general and exploratory in nature, involving architectural or sociological concepts, engineering approaches, economics, or marketing methods. Private financial backing for this kind of research is rarely extensive if present at all.

Research foundations or institutes associated with universities are likely to undertake more specific problems. Generally speaking, the universities prefer to undertake projects the results of which can be freely published. Specialized agencies have occasionally been created to focus university attention on the housing field. Examples are the Small Homes Council of the University of Illinois and the Housing Research Center of Cornell University. Agencies of this type may carry on their work with their own funds, or with funds provided by outside sponsoring agencies, or both. The university atmosphere and facilities are better suited to long-range research than to developmental work. Because university research is not directed toward immediate ends, support is seldom on more than a modest scale.

Professional Societies. Some professional societies maintain their own laboratories to carry on research in fields of direct interest to their members, generally aimed at the advancement of knowledge and technology, whether it has any commercial bearing or not. An example is the work of the laboratory of the American Society of Heating and Air-Conditioning Engineers on the control of environment within buildings. Professional societies also do useful work in the promotion of standards, in education in new methods, and in similar fields of general interest.

The American Institute of Architects has, for example, undertaken the promotion of modular coordination, the registration of building products to give orderly performance information, a service to improve the quality of specifications, and a number of conferences on the fundamental problems of human environment and other neglected areas of basic research in architecture. The AIA Committee on Research, however, emphasizes that architectural research is different from building research, calling for more general sharing of experience and the creation of a bridge between the social and physical sciences.

Although among them the many organizations and agencies

enumerated in this chapter carry on extensive research, the spread is uneven. Certain aspects of building are intensively studied whereas others are covered sketchily at best. Materials and equipment are given the most attention because these are of direct concern to the industrial laboratories which are the largest participants in the entire research picture. Furthermore, materials and equipment find extensive markets outside of the dwelling-producing industry. Methods of construction are subjected to less intensive research because they are not so directly related to the large producers. Still less attention is paid to research into the house as a whole, its basic functions, and the best and most efficient ways of accommodating those functions. Because research into the house as a whole cuts across all lines and presumably calls for cooperation by all research organizations, few actually concern themselves with it. Since this type of study involves architecture, economics, and sociology and appears to be highly affected by intangible elements, the researcher accustomed to working with tangible and reasonably exact entities is likely to be at a loss as to how to approach it. Perhaps quantitative conclusions are impossible; yet, the study of the optimum functioning of the house as a whole is of fundamental importance to the industry.

Construction Research Needs

Information and Research Coordination. Despite the weak and scattered character of much housing industry research, substantial benefits could be obtained if the research information and experience were gathered together and put to work in practical demonstrations and tests. Many information sources on building construction already exist. These include the architectural catalogue services, the various trade associations, and the publications of the Bureau of Standards and the Building Research Institute. Architectural and building periodicals also summarize and distribute information on new developments. However, neither these nor other sources provide complete coverage of research and development activities.

It seems undeniable that a thorough coverage of current research and development, broadly disseminated throughout the dwelling-producing industry, would be of considerable benefit and would help to hasten the practical use of new developments as they occur.

One of the most important results of the gathering and dissemination of information would be the emergence of a clear picture of the status of research itself: which areas are strong and which are weak and where added effort is most needed. If over-all aims and potentials were more clearly defined, more fruitful programs of research in the deficient areas could be undertaken. If for no other reason, therefore, we need to gather and disseminate information in order to obtain a balanced program of research.

A single central research organization conducting a coordinated and well-rounded program of research into housing might at first glance appear to be the most effective way to open the way for optimum housing at minimum cost. In such a facility, duplication of effort could be avoided, no essential facets of housing would be omitted or slighted, and all necessary resources could be directed toward the solution of any problem that might arise. The history of progress in research and discovery shows, however, that greatest originality in the finding of new solutions occurs when many minds, working independently, approach problems from widely different starting points. The atmosphere of independence and complete freedom and the sharpening effect of competition are likely to be lacking in a large central organization, especially if research projects are assigned by a central administrative staff. Even though highly competent research is carried out, the all-important original ideas that could start progress in completely new directions may not be forthcoming.

On the other hand, research can be so fragmentary and scattered that broad trends are lost sight of, and a general advance is not made. In many ways this is true of building at the present time.

A middle ground between highly centralized research and the scattered type of research currently typical of housing is needed. Some agency should be able to gain a view of the field as a whole together with the means of encouraging and fostering research both in neglected areas and on a broad front.

The logical agency to perform this coordinating function is neither narrowly private nor completely governmental. A completely governmental agency would be subject to congressional whims and controls that could well be stultifying, and many private agencies could not gain broad industry confidence. But the coordinating function might be performed by a respected private research organization, an association or professional organization, an educational institution, or an agency occupying a position midway between private and public, such as the Building Research Advisory Board.

The principal coordination activities of such an organization are visualized as follows:

1. Keeping in touch with research projects under way in various laboratories and organizations of the types enumerated above. It is recognized that much research, especially that conducted by industry, is not likely to be disclosed in detail until it has been completed and protected by patents if necessary. Nevertheless, the general fields and trends of research can be known.

2. Determining trends in dwelling construction and the areas that appear to be most in need of research and development.

3. Encouraging appropriate groups to undertake research and development in the promising and the neglected areas. In many instances it would be sufficient to call attention to these areas and their potentialities to get the research under way by industrial, association, and similar laboratories.

4. Providing or obtaining financial support for research in areas deemed important in providing optimum shelter at minimum cost but of such a nature that industrial and association laboratories, for example, might not find them appropriate to

undertake and that other research organizations might not otherwise have the funds to support.

5. Giving the widest possible publicity to the results of research of all kinds, whether directly supported by the agency or not.

Activities such as these are aimed at making most effective use of the many research agencies that already exist in the United States, rather than creating a new one. In this respect the course of action would be similar to that of the National Science Foundation and of the Social Science Research Council.

A dynamic operation to coordinate information and research in building in the United States might model itself upon *Bouwcentrum* in Holland, adding another important function of *Bouwcentrum* which is barely touched upon in a few places like the National Housing Center of the National Association of Home Builders: the full-scale, three-dimensional demonstration of materials and systems as they actually are used, complete with reports and evaluations on performance in practice. In *Bouwcentrum*, information is made available to all concerned, stripped of advertising phraseology and containing all data necessary for incorporation of the product into building design and specifications. The Dutch center further serves as repository of technological information on construction methods, equipment, and materials. The basic information comes in part from a program of study and testing of full-scale mockups of building assemblies that are built and paid for under contract with interested designers and builders. In this country, several such centers would in all likelihood be required to serve the industry adequately, and they might appropriately be located where major research institutions already exist. The financing of such an information and research coordinating agency should be the responsibility primarily of industry itself, or of industry and public agencies combined. It should not be the sole responsibility of public agencies. The industry could easily provide the necessary funds. A contribution of $1 for each dwelling unit produced, for example, would raise more than $1 million annually at current levels of building. Such a sum would be a significant contribution toward the research and information activities envisioned.

Analysis of Existing Housing. It is shocking that practically nothing has been done to make use of the rich source of information about the behavior of materials and equipment that is available in the millions of houses already in existence. No better laboratory can be found than actual performance under exposure to the wide range of climatic and use conditions found in this country. The FHA should be given every support in its desire to undertake this kind of study on sufficient scale to be significant. Insurance groups also could well undertake such examinations with profitable results to the entire housebuilding industry.

Weathering Behavior. In order to predict the durability of materials in actual use, an intensive and detailed study of weather itself and the intricate interactions of chemical and physical phenomena that cause weathering is needed. Even a cursory examination of gross weather data shows that year-to-year variations from the average are marked, and a given ten-year period of weather may be quite different from another ten-year period. Within any given region, the microclimate may fluctuate even more broadly; i.e., the climate found in one area of a city may be substantially different from another and certainly will be different from a nearby rural area. The confusing and markedly different behavior of apparently identical materials in these different areas may in part be explained by these differences in weather and highly local climate. The effects of combinations of rain, temperature fluctuations, freezing and thawing, sunlight (from ultraviolet to infrared), and atmospheric constituents, such as gases and dust, need intensive study in the laboratory. They must be correlated with detailed weather data and with observations of the behavior of materials exposed in the areas where such detailed data are taken. Chemical and physical examination of the exposed materials must determine the kinds of changes that have occurred. From such comprehensive and detailed studies by a wide range of research organizations can come the necessary basis for improved laboratory predictions of weathering behavior.

Meanwhile, lack of information on long-term performance is a serious technological block in the way of the ready acceptance of new materials or products. Housing is expected to last at least for the life of the mortgage, and preferably far longer, and so it is necessary to predict the fate of a material or product with inadequate or partial information.

This difficulty can be minimized by careful and imaginative design so that building elements which are constructed of new products can easily and inexpensively be removed and replaced if necessary. Few designers and engineers take the precaution to make allowances for such subsequent corrective measures, and so costly and time-consuming replacement, involving extensive damage and reconstruction of the building, may be required, if a component does not stand up for the entire life of the building.

Performance Testing. A further block to the application of new materials and products in building is the fact that they may require new methods of evaluation. Too often they are required to pass tests and evaluations originally developed for completely different products and not applicable to those under consideration. This unrealistic procedure may even result in the passing of inferior and the rejecting of superior new building elements. For example, the short-time strength test, which may be perfectly adequate for existing materials, may completely overlook the effect of long-time creep and the accompanying deformation and possible failure of a new material. Evaluating agencies must always be alert to the necessity of developing new procedures.

Judgment based on engineering and research experience must play a large part in the setting up of tests suitable to new materials and other end results of the new technologies. No set rules for such tests can be laid down. Each development must be evaluated in its own terms but at the same time it is most desirable, for comparative purposes, to subject components intended for similar purposes to similar tests.

Examples of Research Opportunities. A few examples may illustrate the kind of research program that might be undertaken as the result of a coordinated program and could well prove very helpful to the industry.

1. *Foundations.* Relatively little study appears to have been made of the possibilities of building foundations other than by essentially on-site procedures.

Level terrain and good soil in many areas are becoming difficult to find and correspondingly expensive; poorer terrain, often irregular, must be utilized. The less site preparation such land requires, the more economical its use becomes. Pier-and-beam construction, for example, becomes attractive. If the essential foundation elements can be prefabricated and assembled with minimum labor at the site, perhaps with power lifting equipment, economies are indicated. With the trend toward component construction, the desirability increases of foundation components such as piers and grillages to support the components of the superstructure.

2. *Heating and cooling.* Year-round performance at minimum fuel consumption is the common aspiration of modern heating and cooling systems and much is to be gained by considering the problem in broad terms. In many ways the solar collector and the heat pump can supplement each other, with the solar collector employed in its most efficient temperature range to raise the source of heat for the heat pump, such as water, to the temperature at which the heat pump operates most efficiently. However, widespread adoption of the heat pump, solar energy, or both, would have considerable repercussions on the fuels picture. The heat pump in essence shifts the fuel consumption to the power station; solar energy reduces the over-all fuel requirement. To the extent that a practicable solar installation probably would require a stand-by heating plant to handle unusually long sunless periods, some

domestic fuel supply system would still be needed. A broad research opportunity exists in this area.

3. *The autonomous house.* As residential areas become more widespread and scattered, the extension of utilities, including sewers, water supply, and fuel distribution systems, becomes more difficult and costly. To the degree that a house can be made independent of such utility networks, this problem can be reduced. Sewers are in many ways the most complex networks of all, and septic tanks cannot be employed in crowded areas or in unfavorable soils; therefore chemical and mechanical treatment of wastes, resulting in simplified disposal or even a usable end product, is being explored. Similarly, recovering waste water for reuse, so that water stores need be supplied only in the amount required to replace that unavoidably consumed or lost, may make it possible to do without piping. To the extent that such developments emerge, areas once considered unavailable can be developed for housing, and a major change in outlying development patterns may be on the way.[3] A broad field for research is involved in such a possibility.

Economic and Social Factors

Economic and social research needs in many respects are of considerably greater magnitude than the construction research needs already touched upon. A summary can no more than indicate their nature.

Considering its size and importance there is a surprising lack of detailed facts and figures concerning the housebuilding industry. National, regional, and local figures concerning types of houses built are available but the categories are frequently too broad to be of use to a prospective producer.

Good detailed figures are lacking on the costs of different construction methods as practiced in different parts of the country under differing local conditions. The relative merits

[3] See *House & Home,* vol. 9, no. 6, June, 1956, p. 162.

of prefabrication versus site fabrication often cannot be determined because of lack of detailed facts and figures. The same is true of standardization, components, and the many units being developed for house construction. To what degree and under what conditions these are superior to, and more economical than, traditional construction methods is difficult to determine.

More refined techniques for market analyses are required to give insight into the relationship between demand and supply on one hand and price and vacancies on the other. A trend toward higher-priced houses may occur just at the time that lower-cost housing is needed. Builders frequently make their plans for construction on the basis of incomplete or contradictory figures which they must interpret as best they can. Better techniques for market analyses might lead to better short-term market predictions and to the production of housing more nearly suited to the actual demand.

Short- and long-term trends in the mortgage market require more intensive and refined analysis. Information is needed respecting the mortgage-to-value ratio, value trends in housing, and such items as the ratio of debt service to family income. This information needs to be broken down according to income levels, trends in different regions of the United States, and trends among different lending institutions.

There is little doubt that national fiscal policy has a strong effect on housing and housing production, particularly as it relates to prefabricators and to development builders. A clear understanding of these interrelationships is required. The effect of taxes, both direct and hidden, needs thorough study to determine how they influence the patterns of house production and purchase.

In materials distribution, profitable studies could be made of the various kinds of distribution channels, how they operate, to what extent they fit into the changing patterns of house production, and how distribution could be made more efficient and less costly than it now is.

The effect of housing regulations, including building codes and the minimum standards of such agencies as the FHA and the VA would be fruitful subjects for research. From this should stem a better realization of what is required to solve the pressing problem of building codes and their effects on costs and on the introduction of new materials and new methods.

Much more needs to be known about family activities in the house, with different values emphasized, so that a better and more fundamental basis for the design of houses can be developed. Better arrangement of space within the house can come from study of such questions as under what conditions open plans are desirable, when privacy is needed, how desirable the separation or the grouping of activities is, and what are the causes of satisfactions and irritations in the house.

Family requirements change with time as the family goes through the stages of family formation, the birth of children, the growth of children to the point where they leave the family home, and the subsequent shrinkage of the family to the parents alone. Needed is research not only in living patterns but also in design and construction proposals for providing the necessary flexibility in the house and in the community.

Role of Management

Because of the preponderant position of industrial research, industrial management carries a heavy responsibility for the initiation and conduct of balanced and sustained research in the broad problems of housing. Skilled managers understand that sporadic research may be only partially effective and is likely to be totally unproductive. By its very nature, research requires continuing patient effort, free from interruptions and distractions. The typical research program in housing is either narrow or sporadic. Too often, when economic conditions become slack, this is the first budget area to be cut, with the result that promising developments are dropped and the industry has no advances to offer when the economy moves ahead again. The coming surge in housing construction will find many industries unprepared.

One way of disclosing the special problems in the housing industry would be to conduct research into the very process by which research proposals are adopted—or rejected. In few industries are the possible slips between a sound research man and a profitable product so many and complex. Even the crucial first step—bringing a significant new idea to management attention—often is not accomplished, for lack of a broad basis of research and information coordination. Should such an idea come before an appropriate management, it often is dropped at once, because the management believes that the chances of clearing all the later hurdles in the way of actual use in the field are too slim to warrant the broad effort that appears to be required. In large part, such a decision must rest at present on inadequate or inaccurate information regarding consumer preferences, labor or community restrictions, banking requirements, building trends, materials performance, distribution costs, or market analysis; thus it stands a good chance of being wrong.

If the decision is made to go ahead, the stages through which development must proceed form a kind of hierarchy of potential dangers, and the idea can die at any stage because of management fear of the uncertain path ahead. A review of this decision process would cast useful light on the nature and strength of impediments in the field, and it might give a sharpened sense of the potentials that may be realized when the impediments are removed.

Often the process of removal of impediments is beyond the control of any single management; this is true, for example, of the attempt to modernize building codes. Collective effort is then required, with all segments of the industry working together to open the gate beyond which each company may pursue a different path to success.

Chapter 8

LABOR-MANAGEMENT RELATIONS

This chapter, written by John T. Dunlop, is concerned with labor-management relations in the construction industry generally, in building construction, and especially in residential construction; and it explores the manner in which conditions existing in the first two of these categories help to determine patterns in the third. The discussion assumes no great change between the organization of present housing operations and those likely to prevail in the next five or ten years; it is not concerned with more long-run and radical innovations in the organization of labor-management relations.

The Nature of Construction Employment

The nature of on-site work operations and the contractor system decisively affects the labor force and the patterns of labor-management relations in the housing industry; as a consequence the labor picture is markedly different from that of industry generally. Place of employment continually shifts, with no two situations identical. Jobs at any one site are usually of quite limited duration. Contractors are continuously in the process of creating or liquidating job organizations and working crews, except for a limited number of key personnel. Job opportunities vary a great deal both seasonally and geographically, and large parts of the work force are able to move about within localities and even between areas. Compared to other industries, workers in housebuilding tend to have less strong ties to particular employers and also less permanent attachments to work groups.

The work force is not only in flux geographically and among contractors, but the individual worker may alternate fairly readily between being a foreman and a journeyman and even between being a contractor working at times with the tools and being an employee. There is also a fair degree of mobility, on the part of both contractors and workers, among the various sectors of the larger construction industry. A contractor may build churches or commercial buildings as well as homes, and craft workers may shift from one to another of such building types. The seasonal nature of large segments of the industry accentuates the variability of the employment relationship.[1]

The work force of the construction industry in general is comprised of an extraordinarily high proportion of skilled workers, reflecting the character of on-site operations. There are slightly more than twice as many skilled manual workers engaged on typical construction sites as there are helpers and laborers. The craft composition of a work force varies with the type of construction and the characteristics of the particular project. Residential work employs a large proportion of carpenters and laborers, and numbers of bricklayers, plumbers, electricians, and painters. Moreover, the craft composition of the work force on a single project varies substantially during the course of construction. Engineers, carpenters, iron workers, and laborers may be used extensively for foundation work whereas painters and roofers may appear only toward the end of work operations.

The high proportion of skilled craftsmen in the work force of the construction industry is associated with emphasis on apprenticeship programs. In mid-1956 there were 103,612 reg-

---

[1] Emphasis upon this relatively high degree of flux and mobility should not obscure the fact that in the over-all construction industry there are situations where labor has a relatively stable employment attachment to a particular contractor in a single locality.

istered building-trade apprentices, comprising nearly 60 per
cent of the registered apprentices in all occupations in the
country. The crafts with the largest number of registered apprentices are the carpenters, plumbers and steamfitters, electricians, and the trowel trades. A number of the crafts—bricklayers, electricians, sheet metal workers, roofers and plumbers
and steamfitters—are training apprentices at a fast enough rate
to replace depletions in the work force caused by death, retirement, or disability. Carpenters and painters, on the other hand,
have had fewer apprentice completions than retirements; in the
case of the carpenters eight apprentice completions for each
eighteen journeymen lost to the trade and in the case of the
painters, six apprentice completions for each eighteen lost. As
might be expected, carpenters and painters are more frequently
recruited without benefit of formal apprenticeship programs
than are the mechanical and trowel trades.

Contractors range from large enterprises doing world-wide
business to self-employed workers using the tools in one
locality. It is conventional to classify contractors as general
or specialty according to whether they accept a contract for
a full project or take a subcontract or separate prime contract
for a part of the operation. Subcontracting is prevalent in the
housing field. Carpenters may be employed on subcontract by
contractors for many separate types of jobs—doing concrete
foundations, framing, roofing, flooring, dry wall, interior trim,
insulation, acoustical tile ceilings, or weatherstripping. At
times a contractor or builder may himself do work which at
other times he may subcontract as a consequence of price or
bids, specialized equipment, amount of work, location of the
project, or other factors. There is therefore keen competition
between general contractors and specialty contractors, and
among the various types of specialty contractors; although
contractors tend to concentrate in a specialized field, competitive opportunities or pressures may lead them to shift or to
overlap fields.

The typical building construction project involves a general contractor with a number of subcontractors, or perhaps with separate prime contractors engaging specialty contractors. The same crafts may be employed by a number of separate contractors on a single project, although ordinarily a specialty contractor tends to hire only one craft. Employment relations among the various contractors and their employees are therefore highly interdependent; labor difficulties which originate with respect to a single specialty contractor may affect all contractors on the job.

Contractors, whether general or specialty, may operate under a variety of contract arrangements. Some have a continuing relationship with clients and may do work on a cost plus percentage basis; others submit bids to an owner, to another contractor, or to an awarding government authority. In the housing field, however, so-called speculative or operative builders typically erect homes on their own account and then sell to the public or to dealers, and bidding is not involved.

The characteristics of the work force and the contractor system briefly outlined above have decisive consequences for labor-management relations.

1. The need for a mobile and flexible work force and the variation in place of work combine to focus attention on procedures for recruitment and hiring.

2. The lack of attachment of individual workers to particular employers means that the work force may be regarded as a variable pool available to all sorts of contractors. The unions in this industry in the United States, in contrast to construction practices in any other country, have long served as a source of labor supply, as an agency to furnish men of an established skill on request of the contractor, and as a means of moving labor away from areas of surplus to areas in short supply.

3. The keen competition among skilled workers and between highly specialized contractors over job opportunities each of limited duration help to give birth to the jurisdictional dispute and work stoppage.

4. The need for constant assembling and reassembling of work crews for projects places a premium on organizing ability in contractor management, since each job and location is to a degree unique.

5. The standards of labor productivity and pace offer a special problem to construction because they cannot be established once and then maintained, as in industries with a relatively stable work force, but must in a sense be faced anew on each project.

6. The ease with which new firms can enter the industry and the consequent very large number of small firms result in keen competition among contractors and builders, a high turnover among firms, and considerable administrative difficulties for both unions and contractor associations in the policing of agreements.

7. The area-wide determination of wages and other conditions of employment, normally for specified periods into the future, is rooted in the necessity felt by workers, contractors, and owners alike to place competing contractors, be they local or from other areas, on an equal basis as regards wage rates and other conditions of work.

These distinctive features of the employment picture in the construction industry are no accident, nor were they imposed from outside arbitrarily by union or contractor organizations. They evolved over time as reflections of the nature of construction operations, the characteristics of the work force, and the competitive character of on-site construction. These and other features of labor-management relations have been formalized by the system of collective bargaining long established in the industry.[2]

[2] For more detail on the structure of the industry, see Miles L. Colean and Robinson Newcomb, *Stabilizing Construction*, McGraw-Hill Book Company, Inc., New York, 1952; Sherman J. Maisel, *Housebuilding in Transition*, University of California Press, Berkeley, Calif., 1953; *Construction during Five Decades*, U.S. Bureau of Labor Statistics Bulletin 1146, 1954; John T. Dunlop, *Industrial Relations Systems*, Henry Holt and Company, Inc., New York, 1958, pp. 198–263.

Collective Bargaining

The building trades unions are among the oldest in the country; indeed, the strike of the carpenters in Philadelphia for the ten-hour day in 1828 is ordinarily used to date the beginnings of the American labor movement. The present national unions of the bricklayers and the plasterers, reflecting the migratory character of the work force, were founded in 1865. The carpenters' national union established in 1881 antedated the AFL. The AFL Building and Construction Trades Department was formed in 1908 to settle jurisdictional problems and to coordinate the activities of the various national unions in the industry.

Affiliated with the Building and Construction Trades Department are nineteen national unions.[3] These unions have organized approximately 2.5 million workers in the construction industry; their total membership, including workers in other industries, is approximately 4.5 million. Despite exceptions in certain segments and in some localities (home building is such an exception), the construction industry as a whole is highly organized—approximately 80 per cent of the potential membership are in the unions.

The Department is a loose federation, with the locus of union control in the national unions. National officers are loathe to interfere in local problems, but the constitutions of the building trades unions permit strong action, and on certain matters, such as jurisdiction, the national offices exercise a good deal of authority. Although collective bargaining agreements must typically be approved by national headquarters, considerable local autonomy for settlement remains in most cases.

For the purpose of dealing with labor, the contractors are typically organized into local associations, many of which in turn are affiliated with national associations. The Associated General Contractors of America, Inc., with over one hundred

---

[3] Eighteen, since the expulsion of the teamsters in early 1958.

chapters is composed largely of commercial, heavy, and high-way contractors. The National Constructors Association is composed of approximately twenty-five of the largest industrial contractors. National associations of specialty contractors include the electrical, heating and piping, plumbing, sheet metal, painting and decorating, tile, masonry, insulating, acoustical, boiler erecting, and pipeline contractors. Recently, the National Association of Home Builders has also become active in labor relations matters.

Collective bargaining typically takes place at the local or regional level between local unions and a local association of contractors. Negotiations are conducted separately by each of the crafts, although in a few localities, the basic crafts (carpenters, laborers, cement finishers, engineers, iron workers, and teamsters) may join together in negotiations with the general contractors. Occasionally, different kinds of management associations may join together for the purpose of bargaining with a single craft, as, for example, in Detroit, where the general contractors and home builders worked out an agreement with the carpenters. The specialty crafts negotiate separate contracts with their specialty contractors. From all of these negotiations come local or regional agreements which establish the area wage rates, fringe benefits, and conditions of work for unionized workers. These contract terms are conformed to not only by the local contractors who originally participated in the agreement but also by "foreign contractors" from other localities who enter the area to perform work.

In recent years, the "national agreement" has become prominent with contractors doing business on a regional or national basis. Such an agreement is between a national union and a contractor; it is usually simple, providing that the contractor conform to the conditions of employment called for in the applicable local agreements of each area in which he does work. For the national union, this arrangement makes it unnecessary to organize each of the contractor's projects, the national contractor in turn secures a source of local labor supply and access to the national office of the union in the event of difficulties with a local union. In recent years, many locality agreements have been consolidated into state-wide or regional agreements, particularly outside of the East.

On three occasions, the Building and Construction Trades Department has negotiated agreements covering all affiliated member unions. Two of these agreements concerned conditions of work on wartime construction jobs. The third, made with national contractor groups after the passage of the Taft-Hartley Act in 1947, set up private machinery to settle jurisdictional disputes in the industry: the National Joint Board for the Settlement of Jurisdictional Disputes, which has been in operation since April, 1948.

In the past, these national, regional, and special agreements have had little or no application to housebuilding, very little of which is done on a regional—let alone a national—basis. They are likely to be applied to housebuilding more frequently in the future, however, as size and scope of housebuilding organizations increase.

Collective bargaining was a firmly established procedure in many sectors of the industry and in many localities long before passage of the Wagner Act in 1935. The Act's procedures for holding elections were not well adapted to an industry with projects of relatively short duration and shifting craft composition; as a consequence, these provisions of the Wagner Act were simply not applied, and the organization of nonunion or new contractors is carried on by strike or by persuading contractors and workers without benefit of elections. The Taft-Hartley Act (1947) contained certain provisions, such as limitations on secondary boycotts and jurisdictional disputes, which were intended to deal with construction conditions. It, like the Wagner Act, however, set up procedures that are effective primarily in industrial plant conditions and consequently are not well suited to construction conditions.

It is widely recognized that the current labor relations law is ill-adapted to this industry in a number of respects. In the construction field, collective bargaining contracts must be negotiated before employees are hired so that contractors will know what wage rates to use; by contrast, in industry generally, no agreement is legal prior to the hiring of a substantial number of employees and the determination of the bargaining representative. The union security provisions of the statute are impractical in the construction field where the union serves as a source of skilled labor supply for migratory contractors. As a consequence of such factors the large majority of union contractors probably have been in continuous violation of the law.[4]

No entirely satisfactory survey exists of the extent of union organization in the home-building branch of the construction industry but unionization has been increasing in the past decade. Although estimates of this growth are most difficult to make, a survey by the National Association of Home Builders in 1955 revealed that associations in eighteen of the thirty largest United States cities, producing 77 per cent of the units built in their areas, operated under agreements with building trades unions. The fifty largest cities produced almost 60 per cent of the total number of houses built in 1955; two-thirds of the houses, it was estimated, were built in cities operating under union conditions. Although this survey probably overstates the proportion of all houses produced completely under union conditions, no doubt in many major cities collective bargaining has become an established feature of home building, particularly among larger builders.[5] An informed guess sug-

[4] Early in 1958, under the threat of heavy penalties, the National Labor Relations Board instructed the construction industry to put an end to the closed shop and discriminatory hiring halls. Extensive revisions are being made in the hiring provisions of collective bargaining agreements, but it is doubtful that there will be very much change in other than form. See Louis Sherman, "Legal Status of the Building and Construction Trades Unions in the Hiring Process," *The Georgetown Law Journal,* Winter, 1958, pp. 203–223.

[5] For more detail on the collective bargaining system, see Gordon W. Bertram and Sherman J. Maisel, *Industrial Relations in the Construction Industry,* University of California Press, Berkeley, Calif., 1955; John T.

gests that 50 to 60 per cent of all new housing construction is built under union conditions; in most major metropolitan centers union organization is a factor in the home-building industry which cannot be ignored.

An Analysis of Labor Problems in Home Building

Many home builders seem to think of labor problems primarily in terms of union resistance to technological advances that tend to reduce labor costs. Indeed, long lists of such "cost-inflationary practices" with "horrible" examples have frequently been compiled. Such an approach to the problem has not been particularly fruitful for a number of reasons: trivial and isolated instances are not separated from practices that raise issues of widespread or national significance; as is only human, builders tend to blame high costs, delays, and failures in planning on the other fellow; performance of labor is compared with some ideal norm, whereas difficulties associated with land acquisition, design, municipal services, building codes, materials, financing, and builder management are appraised against a more realistic test of men and organizations. Some complaints merely represent a desire for lower wages or conditions more favorable to the builder than those granted in other sectors of the construction industry or in industry generally; others arise when work agreements specifically designed to favor larger-scale and more efficient operations are applied to uneconomically operated small-sized projects.

Consideration of these and other reasons may not excuse unwise labor restrictions, but it does suggest that the mere listing of practices condemned by builders is not likely to bring improvements. An attempt must be made to analyze the underlying problem that is expressed in the disliked symptom. Moreover, as will be seen, many of the most serious problems

Dunlop and Arthur D. Hill, *The Wage Adjustment Board*, Harvard University Press, Cambridge, Mass., 1950; William Haber, *Industrial Relations in the Building Industry*, Harvard University Press, Cambridge, Mass., 1930.

have no grotesque exterior symptoms and therefore escape the lists; hence it is important to identify and to analyze the more widespread and fundamental labor problems of the industry.

Representation of Home Builders in Labor Negotiations. The relationship of home building to other sectors of the construction industry in the determination of wages and conditions of employment is the source of many questions. In highly unionized localities, the question arises whether home builders are to negotiate separately and apart from other general contractors whose interests and ability to pay may be quite different, to follow abjectly the pattern of settlements made by these others, or to participate in negotiations jointly with them. In nonunion or poorly organized localities the question is how to establish levels and forms of compensation in home building relative to those prevailing in other types of construction.

In many localities substantial sections of the home-building field were not organized until after World War II, and bargaining arrangements in the field are still somewhat in flux. It has not always been easy for contractors or unions to work out relationships between a newly organized home-building group and the well-established commercial and industrial groups. Frequently, when home builders have not taken part in the negotiation of commercial and industrial contracts, they have been confronted by settlements on a take-it-or-strike basis. These settlements may call for increases larger than the home builders—faced with keen competition or different conditions of demand—feel they can afford. Moreover, the general working rules or conditions set forth in the settlements may not be entirely suitable to home building. For a time, attempts to negotiate separate and lower wage scales for housing construction were successful in some localities, but the tight labor market of the post-Korean period tended to eliminate these differentials. Regular construction wages had to be paid if home building was to attract qualified labor from alternative employment in other branches of the industry. Joint negotiations by representatives of both home builders and commercial and industrial contractors present internal difficulties for the contractors' negotiating committee. Home builders may request special provisions as to size of crews or other conditions for the presence of foremen and special rules regarding loss of tools, whereas other contractors may find acceptable rules regarding apprenticeship, grievance procedures, and stewards which are onerous to home builders. Divergent interests may enable the unions to split up the contractors during negotiations or in a strike. Thus, whether they negotiate separately, strictly follow patterns established by others, or negotiate jointly with other contractors, home builders are confronted with real bargaining problems.

The simple fact is that home builders often have interests or economic positions quite different from those of other groups of contractors. In times of construction booms, home builders may be content to pay the wages prevailing in other branches of the industry or even to exceed these levels in order to attract men. But when business declines, home builders are likely to be under greater competitive pressures than other contractors and thus to request a relatively lower wage scale or working rules more adapted to their type of construction. Union-organized home builders face competition not only from nonunion builders but also from small self-employed builders and from do-it-yourself addicts. Furthermore, home building may be slack when other branches of construction are booming and a tight labor market has been created. But once a policy of equality with other sectors of the industry has been established in a locality, parity cannot readily or lightly be abandoned.

In the past decade, the growth of fringe benefits, such as health and welfare plans, holiday and vacation pay, and pensions, in the construction industry underlies the basic dilemma of the home-building sector. Joint negotiations probably tend to accentuate the introduction or expansion of such benefits in home building; but the levels of these payments may be raised higher without the restraining influence of home builders in joint negotiations. There are special problems of administering such funds in the home-building field where contractors tend to be smaller, turnover among contractors is greater, and many have limited credit rating. Fringe benefits more readily apply to other branches of construction; they may place the unionized sector of home building at a disadvantage (save in tight labor markets) in competing with nonunion builders.

Contractor associations and union representatives do not always welcome the participation of home builders in joint negotiations. There are rivalries among the associations; local associations of general contractors or master builders may feel that a separate home-builder group is not warranted in the negotiation sessions. The older-established associations include some home builders among their members. In the absence of elections and certifications required by law, there is no government intervention in the determination of authorized bargaining spokesmen, and so a good deal of jockeying may take place among rival associations for the prestige of negotiating the master area agreement which others are then expected to follow. Associations of home builders, having only lately come into existence, are finding it necessary to overcome a natural resistance to newcomers.

There is another reason why bargaining arrangements affecting home building have been in flux. Although home builders do employ labor directly, they also employ a wide range of carpentry subcontractors to perform specialized operations such as forming concrete foundations, framing, or flooring. These subcontractors may be organized into employer associations of their own. The issue immediately arises whether collective bargaining with the carpenters' union should be conducted by these subcontractors or by the builders, or whether the various groups concerned should be affiliated in a single home-building association. The builders and these subcontractors have some elements of conflicting interests; as a result of bidding and financial transactions, the subcontractors may distrust the builders and not wish to be represented by them in dealings with the union. The builders, on the other hand, may feel that they should be the ones to negotiate with the union because they are stronger than the subcontractors and more able to keep costs down. The subcontractors may invoke the union against the builders on such matters as nonpayment of accounts. The union in turn may regard the subcontractors as direct employers with more understanding—and weakness—than the builders, but the latter may be better organized and administratively more convenient for the union to do business with. Obviously such conflicting and competing interests between the builders and their carpentry subcontractors may complicate both relations with the general contractors dealing in commercial and heavy construction and negotiations with the union.

With home building showing signs, as now seems to be the case, of changing from an industry subject to considerable ups and downs to one giving promise of a more stable high volume of activity over a period of years, its relationships in the bargaining area are apt to change. Home-builder associations may be expected to achieve stability and develop skilled professional staffs able to negotiate with unions and with other associations and to administer labor relations on a par with representatives of commercial and industrial construction.

The home builder, like the general contractor, however, has no means of participation in the negotiations between the specialty contractors in the electrical, plumbing, painting, and roofing fields and their specialized craft unions. He often feels that the special problems of home construction receive little attention in such negotiations, which are dominated by commercial and industrial work, and yet he is compelled in practice to accept the working rules and cost consequences of these specialty agreements whenever he subcontracts, as he typically must do, heating, plumbing, electrical, and other work. The greater volume of mechanical work in modern housing may be expected eventually to create an interest in this problem among the specialized contractors and the unions with which they bargain, much as has been the case with carpentry work. But the problem is a difficult one, particularly since there is no current forum in which it can be directly considered.

In summary, the form of bargaining relationships has not been long established in most of the union-organized sectors of home building; there is much experimentation and flux. Only in a minority of union-organized cities have joint bargaining relationships been established between home builders and other groups of contractors. Divergent and competing interests among general contractor groups have not been resolved. The need for special provisions in labor agreements to take care of special home-building problems has not often been recognized. Fluctuations in demand are likely to affect housing contractors more severely than many others, particularly in newly organized localities. Builders have problems in connection with representing their subcontractors in dealings with the unions. Although housebuilding is part of the larger construction industry, the relationship of builders to other contractors in collective bargaining has not been settled in many localities. Changing business and competitive conditions affect these interrelations very substantially. In any particular locality, the unionized builder cannot escape the effects of other organized branches of the construction industry, on the one hand, and of nonunion builders on the other. Conditions in the other branches of construction affect his labor supply and costs; the nonunion and self-employed builders affect his demand and market position.

Piecework and Lumping. One of the most persistent labor problems in home building in this country is the legitimacy and extent of piecework, incentive, lump-sum, or other bonus arrangements. Unlike other countries of the world, in the United States the straight hourly or day rate is the only method of wage payment recognized in commercial, industrial, or heavy construction. Elimination of other methods has almost always been a labor objective in unionized cities. "No lump or piecework shall be permitted" is a fairly standard contract clause. Despite such prohibitions the practice persists, to some degree, in most communities even among unionized groups. For instance, shinglers may be paid so much a bundle for installing a roof, or a rough-carpenter crew may split a lump sum for putting up the frame of a house. In nonunion cities piecework and lumping exist side by side with extensive use of hourly or daily rates.

It is important to analyze the factors creating these different methods of wage payment, the reasons why both unions and contractors' associations oppose piecework and lumping, and the implications for labor costs. For the incidence of piecework and lumping is a symptom of a group of significant problems.

Systems of payment by results are extensively used in the building industries of other countries, particularly in Sweden, Denmark, Norway, Finland, and a number of countries in the Russian orbit. Piecework is practiced to a smaller extent in England, France, Germany, Italy, and Switzerland.[6] In Scandinavia, the parties concerned have built up over the years elaborate books showing piece rates for a wide variety of building operations and conditions. Although such an arrangement may be difficult to visualize from an American background, the systems have operated in these countries to the satisfaction of union and contractor groups.

A number of the characteristics of home building both stimulate and are congenial to piecework and lumping. Individual projects may be scattered, making close supervision by one contractor difficult; payment by results relieves him from having to pay constant attention in order to reduce idle time. Considerable labor turnover and a high proportion of new recruits on jobs of short duration make for wide disparity in the quality and speed of workers; payment by results provides a way of paying new recruits less than experienced skilled

[6] See International Labor Office, *Payments by Results*, 1951, pp. 75–78; "Payment by Results in the Building Industry," *International Labour Review*, vol. 63, no. 1, January, 1951, pp. 64–78.

workers. The flat hourly rate tends to create dissatisfactions in a work crew composed of men of varying skill, experience, and pace of work because the lower productivity of the newer or less skilled group limits the earnings of the more experienced. As in other industries, payment by results is designed to compensate workers for skill and output above some implied standard, thereby increasing earnings and reducing per-unit costs.

Lumping develops from the competitive character of the new housing market and is essentially a form of bid peddling or "labor-only" subcontracting to a work crew. A builder estimates what a particular operation such as flooring or framing may be expected to cost; he may compare this figure with bids he has been able to get from a recognized subcontractor; he then may offer the job at a lower figure, in a lump sum, to a work crew. This crew is said to "lump" the job. If the crew works faster than it would under an hourly rate, it can take on another job in the same work week and thus achieve higher-than-standard earnings. For all these reasons, both piecework and lumping persist on some jobs in many localities, and some individual workers and contractors would appear to prefer it.

Nevertheless, contractors' associations and unions alike have offered reasons for opposing the recognition of piecework and lumping. Setting piecework rates is technically difficult when the product is not highly standardized, and at the present time housing units and conditions of construction are seldom standardized. The quality of materials, the weather and other site conditions, and the coordination of work flows all affect production and are beyond the control of individual workers. Moreover, in the absence of careful supervision, piecework and lumping can have very adverse effects upon quality of the house. Varying piece rates to accommodate a variety of construction projects and conditions would impose a difficult administrative problem for contractors' associations and union business agents. On scattered projects the system cannot be policed to assure all workers the same incentive opportunities.

From the union viewpoint, piecework is not consonant with skilled craftsmen who perform a variety of operations; payment by results tends to create groups of narrow specialists whose livelihood is threatened by small changes in technology or competitive forces among contractors. For the contractors, lumping and piecework create uncertain competitive conditions as regards labor rates.

If all work operations in housing were standardized and uniform pieces rates were established as in the clothing industry, then labor costs could be standardized. But piece rates are not market-wide, and probably cannot be so long as present interrelations persist between home building and the rest of the construction industry. Piecework arrangements also make it difficult to know whether earnings vary because of performance or because of differences in the wage rate. In competitive markets, there has always been a concern under collective bargaining to put firms on an "equal basis" as regards rates, and the piecework or lumping arrangements of the housing industry in this country at the present time do not appear to meet this crucial objective. The hourly rate basis of payment is believed to place all firms on a more nearly equal basis. The labor costs per house will then clearly vary among contractors with the same hourly rate depending upon the quality and speed of workers and the ability of management. The more efficient firms should have the lower labor costs and should be able to expand relative to the less efficient.

The attempt to suppress or control the use of piecework and lumping practices in home building may be understood as a surface symptom of two fundamental labor problems in the industry.

First, how are contractors to obtain a well-trained labor force, supervise its work, secure a high quality of performance, and establish a pace of work that approaches reasonable potentials? Piecework or lumping has frequently developed as a short-cut solution. But in the current American construction industry such practices persist only in the underground; they are not likely to be stable methods of wage payment unless a large percentage of housing labor is transferred to more typically industrial conditions and unless site operations are more fully standardized. The problems of planning, supervision, quality, and pace of work must be faced more directly as a function of better-organized management and a forward look on the part of the union in collective bargaining.

Second, how are competing builders and their subcontractors to be placed on an equal basis with respect to labor rates and conditions? Piecework or lumping frequently has developed as a symptom of inequality between specialized operations or branches. Confronted with keen competition from the self-employed, from do-it-yourself methods, or from larger or more efficient builders, or threatened by a decline in demand, builders or subcontractors may resort to piecework or lumping practices as a way of reducing production costs. The spread of such practices in a locality indicates that all contractors are not on an equal competitive basis—a condition which is of concern both to contractor associations and to the union. The problem remains of how in the future to place producers of housing on an equal basis with regard to labor rates and conditions and yet to encourage a healthy degree of competition among these employers and a high level of productivity on the part of labor.

The Economic Organization of Home Building. Labor problems associated with changing technology have attracted a great deal of attention, and a later section will explore some of them in detail. But less prominence has been given to the relatively more significant labor problems associated with the economic organization of the industry: the number and size of firms, the distribution of work operations between the building site and the fabrication plant, and the distribution of operations between builders and subcontractors.

Compared with other basic industries entrance into the home-building field is found to be easy; capital costs are small and the minimum-sized firm is one man working for himself, even on a part-time basis. It is difficult to find a field of economic activity which may be entered so easily. Hence, the number of business units is very large and the rate of business births and deaths very high. Such entry conditions keep home building highly competitive and make the standardization of wages and work conditions a difficult undertaking. Since the smaller firms tend to be less efficient, their labor conditions are frequently below those prevailing among larger operators. Technological and market developments favoring larger building operations would reduce the number of business births of the smallest firms and lead the way to greater standardization of labor conditions.

Labor factors in turn help to influence the size of operations. In unionized areas, contract provisions or working rules may help to determine the size or scale of operation that is economically most feasible. A few trades seek, for example, to limit the employer's working with the tools himself. When there are more than six, eight, or some higher number of workers in their craft on the project, they prohibit a foreman from working with the tools and require that he devote full time to supervision, or, under certain conditions, they require a general foreman in addition to a foreman or specify certain transportation expenses or gasoline allowances for a steward traveling between the contractor's projects. Such rules bear more heavily on the smaller firms; they tend to discourage the very smallest, for which turnover is no doubt greatest, and to encourage a larger minimum size for which the chance of success is greater. It is not clear that union rules affecting the scale of operations are economically undesirable or that their impact has raised costs in the industry. Actually, we know too little about the consequences of current or alternative union rules as they may affect the size of home builders. We do know that the sum of many factors appears to favor a continuing increase in average size of builder organization.

A number of such factors, quite apart from labor costs or

industrial relations considerations, tend to encourage the trend toward the performance of work operations before delivery to the site. The growth in the differential expressed in dollars and cents between factory wages and construction wages has added incentive to this development. In 1939, average hourly earnings were 23 cents an hour higher in construction than in durable goods manufacturing (93 cents per hour in construction compared with 70 cents per hour in durable goods); in 1956, average hourly earnings were almost 70 cents higher in construction ($2.80 per hour compared with $2.10 per hour in durable goods). Although the percentage rise in hourly earnings in the two sectors was almost identical, the increasing dollar differential provides a strong incentive for the housing industry to experiment with ways of transferring work operations from the job site to the factory.

The relative shift of activity from construction site to factory is a significant development for construction labor, because only a minority of construction materials, in terms of dollar volume, are fabricated in shops or factories organized by construction unions. Bricklayers have not typically organized brick factories, and basic steel mills are not organized by structural iron workers. When building-materials factories have been organized by building trades unions, in most instances the unions act with regard to these factories much as though they were industrial unions. To what extent do the unions combat the trend to off-site labor?

On-site construction workers sometimes boycott and refuse to install a material or piece of equipment coming from a factory not organized by their union. This occurs when the union has long organized a significant sector of shops fabricating the product involved and it has become traditional to use the products only of the organized shops. For example, in most localities the carpenters' union has organized millwork plants, and the carpenters' label, dating back to the 1880s, has customarily appeared on all products. Carpenters may refuse to install millwork that does not carry the label, although the practice varies substantially from locality to locality and is much more entrenched in the North and West than in the South. On the other hand, carpenters would normally not raise a question about installing a wide range of other materials —metal forms, metal windows, acoustical tile ceilings, asphalt tile, or insulation—manufactured in a former CIO or even an unorganized plant.

A full review of practice would reveal that some unions, such as the bricklayers, have seldom adopted a policy of refusal to install products fabricated outside of the union. Although some of the other unions seek to enforce such a policy in the case of certain items which they have traditionally fabricated and controlled, such items constitute only a small minority of materials used in home building. As for the motive, it may be not only the desire to protect fabricating job opportunities from competition, but also the intent to maintain the competitive position of the production plants.

Boycott policy questions raise understandable complications for a unified labor movement where the products involved are fabricated in a plant organized by a former CIO affiliate. They also raise problems under provisions of the Taft-Hartley Act prohibiting secondary boycotts. The unions feel they can avoid legal penalties by refusing to furnish men at the outset of a job using controversial material instead of furnishing men and then pulling them off the job. Moreover, designers and builders, despite the statute, will tend to avoid materials regarding which there are likely to be project delays. Resort to job action of various sorts is another way to enforce union policy; as one contractor has put it, "Somehow doors without the label never seem to be hung properly."

Except for a relatively few items, on which there is great feeling, apparently the unions are not now making any substantial effort to prevent the shift of operations away from the site as builders pursue technological changes and market economies.

Distribution of operations between builders and subcontractors is a feature of the economic organization of home building which can have important effects on labor costs and labor relations. As has been noted earlier in this chapter, the question is: To what extent are builders to determine and be responsible for costs and policies in relation to labor directly employed by their subcontractors? Builders and subcontractors have a common interest in keeping wage rates as low as possible consistent with the recruitment of an adequate labor supply; subcontractors and the unions have a common interest in placing all subcontractors and all builders on the same competitive basis as far as labor rates and conditions are concerned and in seeing that builders do not take advantage of a strong buyer's position to depress the bids of subcontractors and thereby the wages of their employees.

Builders find themselves with conflicting objectives. They subcontract operations and act as brokers to escape some of the problems of supervision and management. But subcontractors frequently operate on a small scale and cannot deal effectively with the unions; separately the subcontractors do not have bargaining power, staff, or organization to match the union. Moreover, union problems are created by the variety of subcontractors on a single project, even among those dealing with the same union. The situation is further confused when the builders both accept and refuse responsibility for labor policy and its coordination on a project or in a locality. This state of affairs, until clearly resolved in a locality, is the source of many labor problems in home building.

Training and Allocation of Labor. The training and allocation of a skilled labor force comprise another major problem area. Except in periods of labor shortage the issue is not conspicuous and receives almost no attention; yet few questions are more central at all times to labor efficiency and labor costs. And a labor shortage may be on the way.

By and large, home builders have done little to train workers in any formal sense; in this respect it might be said that the home-building industry has been parasitic. In localities where collective bargaining prevails, the union has served to some degree as an employment exchange, providing information on job opportunities and reducing the frictions of movement in the labor market. For the large part of the home-building labor market which is unorganized, however, there are very large personal, social, and business costs in the form of turnover, lack of training, and underemployment.

Home builders find it hard to develop a highly trained labor force because organizations are small, jobs are of short duration, and operations are subcontracted on a very narrow and specialized basis, down to the installation of weatherstripping or counter-tops. There is an understandable inclination to draw labor from a skilled pool and to avoid if possible the costs of training; each builder realizes that the workers he trains might soon be working for a competitor. But such a course, motivated by immediate competitive conditions, neither brings new additions to the pool of skilled labor nor raises the standards of training. In the construction industry generally, on the other hand, collective bargaining agreements tend increasingly to provide for an educational fund, financed by a cents-per-hour levy on all contractors and jointly administered, for the purpose of apprenticeship and journeyman training.

An understandable and ancient conflict of interest exists between the desire of the unions for broadly trained journeymen and the preference of some contractors for narrow specialists and of many others for operations requiring a minimum of site labor and calling for a minimum of skill. The broad training of formal apprenticeship programs is designed as a form of security or insurance against changes in job opportunities in a labor market characterized by frequent changes of jobs on projects of short duration. A broadly trained journeyman can more adequately protect himself against changes in technology and shifting job opportunities, whereas the unskilled laborer has little job security.

This conflict of interest is not readily resolved, and the

actual range of skills among journeymen is in fact widely variable. Thus, some operating engineers can operate a long list of equipment; others are competent with only one machine. Some bricklayers are also plasterers, tile setters, marble setters, stone setters, cement finishers, and competent in a wide range of trowel-trade skills; others can perform only one of these skills. Within any one such craft there may also be specialization by type of work; for instance, bricklayers may specialize in chimneys, furnaces, arches, or types of walls. The number of such specialties appears to be growing among all crafts and within all unions in the building industry.

The different specialties and ranges of skill are significant to the allocation and referral of the labor force to various jobs. It is not enough to refer bricklayers and engineers since not all are in fact interchangeable. In unionized sectors the range of a member's specialties is typically recorded with the local union and taken into account in the allocation of workers to available job opportunities and in filling contractor requests for men. No systematic study has been made, however, of the actual range of specialties in either the home-building work force or construction generally, or of the manner in which these different ranges of skill and specialization affect work opportunities, turnover, and labor costs. The operation of the construction labor market is a rich field for potential research.

Jurisdictional Disputes. The labor problems treated in the previous four sections have not ordinarily been included in popular discussions of "cost-inflationary practices" in construction and home building. In fact, however, they have a significant impact upon construction costs. The problem area taken up here, however, has been more generally discussed, and accordingly may be considered in less detail. Furthermore, although there is no statistical basis for estimating, it may be said that this area is quantitatively less important in its impact on labor costs than those already discussed. The popular presentation of labor problems in home building has been thrown considerably out of focus by failure to take these factors into account.

Jurisdictional disputes and work stoppages have been persistent and hardy problems in the construction industry, although their significance in home building has been relatively minor compared to commercial and industrial construction. Jurisdictional disputes are complex and varied, and they arise from a number of industry features,[7] frequently as a symptom of other conflicts—the part of the iceberg above the surface which masks the larger reality. They may stem from rivalries and conflicting interests of competing local unions, each anxious to preserve or gain demarcations of work opportunities, or from similar rivalries among national unions in the industry. Contractors may transport work assignments from one locality to another where different customs prevail, thereby creating disputes. Superintendents and supervisors frequently have strong craft and union attachments, and they may be influenced by such personal factors in making work assignments. Small volume of work or a contractor's desire to maintain a stable crew in the face of reduced work requirements may lead to deviations from strict craft lines and to disputes. Rapid technological changes and new methods of construction involve problems when the attempt is made to apply old jurisdictional lines to new situations. The subcontracting system creates a special bond between the subcontractor and the craft he normally employs; in making assignments, the subcontractor tends to favor this craft over others. In many disputes, one contractor and the union predominately employed by him are arrayed against, and in competition with, another contractor and the union normally working in that specialty. Troubled labor relations or morale in a particular area may cause jurisdictional disputes, or they may grow out of normal problems of adjustment in a small community suddenly deluged with a large volume of work, as in Paducah,

[7] See John T. Dunlop, "Jurisdictional Disputes: 10 Types," *The Constructor*, July, 1953, pp. 165–173.

Kentucky, when construction of a gaseous diffusion plant for the Atomic Energy Commission was begun. Indeed, there are few conflicts affecting workers, their unions, and contractor organizations which may not at some time break out in the form of a jurisdictional dispute on a construction site.

These conflicts tend to result in work stoppages more frequently in the construction industry than in other industries, not merely because of the craft labor organization and the subcontracting system, but basically because of the short duration of each project and the even shorter duration of specific work operations. The natural tendency in a controversy is to shut down the work; otherwise it may be completed. Unlike normal industrial expectation, settlement reached on one project does not necessarily apply to the next project. The time pressure and contract penalties on construction jobs encourage the resort to strike threat as a means of securing favorable assignments of work.

For practical purposes, the machinery for the settlement of jurisdictional disputes is the National Joint Board, established in 1948 by agreement between representatives of the Associated General Contractors of America, Inc., of national specialty contractor associations, and of the Building and Construction Trades Department of the American Federation of Labor. The scope of the Board's work is indicated by the fact that in 1956 it handled over 800 work stoppages, took action in almost 700 cases, and adjusted under its procedural rules a great many other disputes. However, only a very small proportion, probably less than 5 per cent, of these work stoppages and decisions occurred in home building.

Although numerous jurisdictional disputes in home building undoubtedly are not reported to the National Joint Board, those most frequently reported have been between the carpenters and roofers over the application of composition or asphalt shingles, between the carpenters and cement finishers over screeds or forms, and between the carpenters and plumbers over the placing of wood backing for plumbing fixtures.

These jurisdictional problems are less serious than formerly because established machinery, representing both contractor and union, is constantly at work on the problems. Although disputes and work stoppages probably will not soon be eliminated since they are rooted in the current structure and economic organization of the construction industry, through the use of this machinery they can be contained within tolerable limits.

Restrictive Practices. Restrictive practices by workers and unions have frequently been cited as a major labor problem in construction and home building.[8] The usual list includes such oft-repeated instances as limitations on spray painting, and on the width of paint brushes, and on the number of bricks laid per day; refusal to install factory-cut bridging or factory-glazed sash, and to handle ready-mixed concrete; and requirement of a minimum number of men per crew and of various forms of stand-by labor. That such practices have existed to some degree in the past in certain localities and some such practices are currently operative is beyond dispute. But we have very little systematic comprehensive information on the subject; there have been few, if any, objective surveys of the actual extent of such practices throughout the country and their effect according to locality.

Collective bargaining agreements may contain provisions prohibiting restrictive practices, but such practices may nonetheless be operative; on the other hand, agreements may contain restrictive clauses which are not actually enforced. Moreover, these practices are peculiarly a local matter, varying from one locality to another, and they may even be enforced differently among different branches of construction and among individual contractors in a given locality. Their ap-

[8] See William Haber and Harold M. Levinson, *Labor Relations and Productivity in the Building Trades,* University of Michigan, Bureau of Industrial Relations, Ann Arbor, Mich., 1956, pp. 103–203. This discussion is the most comprehensive recent review of the problem and includes the results of field work in sixteen cities in 1952.

plication may also vary—usually inversely—with the volume of construction activity.

Like other labor problems, so-called restrictive practices represent a large cluster of interrelated issues, each of which requires a separate approach. Certainly, any policy program to deal with this range of questions must be detailed and selective; there is no such single problem as "restrictive practices," and there certainly is no single solution or formula. A number of individual problems may be distinguished, such as resistance to use of machinery and new methods, pace of work operations including any limitations on output, manning requirements for equipment, performance of work operations considered unnecessary by the contractor, requirements of work assignments to higher-paid crafts.

To give an illustration, building operations are man-paced rather than machine-paced; the pace of work, the skill of the work force, and its distribution among the different skills and rates of work comprise a significant determinant of productivity and labor costs. Bricklaying is a case in point. There is wide agreement that the average pace of this work was raised substantially during the Depression of the 1930s, when individual workers competed for limited jobs and the small volume of output was concentrated in the most able and fastest group. A variety of factors is said to have reduced average performance during and immediately after the war: surplus of jobs and shortage of labor, cost-plus government work, a relatively older work force, the influx of many new workers of lower quality, considerable overtime, and the generally lowered morale and discipline of the work community. Since the late 1940s conditions have improved because of a very considerable number of new apprentices, keener competition among contractors, and a better balance between labor supply and demand. This postwar cycle of worker efficiency has been observed in most industries. The unions appear to have had relatively little direct and independent influence either on the deterioration or on the improvement.

The complexities of craft jurisdiction and of the subcontracting system make it difficult to deal with this group of problems in a simple and direct way, but as both the extent and the skill of site labor are changed in the future, the importance of a simple solution will grow, and the nature of the problems will change. New materials and methods are in fairly wide use and their benefits are increasingly well understood. As in other industries the role of the international unions has been to stress the necessity of mechanization to the long-range health of the industry as a whole, its inevitability, and the futility of a policy of opposition, but in many situations, the national union has chosen to keep hands off, leaving these issues entirely to local unions and contractors in the area. The program announced early in 1958 by the Building and Construction Department in cooperation with several national contractors' associations is an encouraging indication of the possibilities of dealing with work practices on a national basis.

Although the issues discussed under the six headings in this section undoubtedly have an important impact on productivity and labor costs in home building, there is no way to assign precisely the relative weight of each factor. Some indication of the total differentials in costs between localities is provided by data on the comparative construction costs of standardized houses, excluding lot or land development. For example, FHA data [9] for a three-bedroom frame house show a cost of $13,181 for Cleveland and $9,343 for Los Angeles. But both of these cities have highly organized home-building industries. What accounts for this difference? To what extent is it attributable to the labor factor? To what extent may differences within this factor be attributed to bargaining procedures, to methods of wage payment, to the local economic organization of the industry including scale of operations and extent of subcontracting, to the skill and training and alloca-

[9] "Comparative Construction Costs—Three-bedroom Frame House," August 12, 1956.

tion of the labor force, to differences in work practices? Careful research would be required to develop informed judgments as to the basis for these cost differentials and the relative role of the various elements discussed in this chapter.

The Future of the Labor Factor in Home Building

To a large degree, the pattern of an industry's labor relations reflects the technological character and economic organization of that industry, even though labor factors may independently have an effect on developments. Elsewhere in this book it has been predicted that the construction industry generally, and home building as a part of it, will become more and more an assembly operation and that the proportion of fabrication performed at the site will continue to decline. Houses will continue to be constructed, however, under a wide variety of economic organizations. Owner-builders will remain a major factor, particularly in non-metropolitan areas, and the prospects for substantial increases in economic efficiency in this area are small. The small-scale operative builder will still do without many of the economies of scale. The larger-scale builders and prefabricators constructing several hundred houses a year, frequently including community developments around metropolitan areas, will continue to offer the greatest early prospects for increases in efficiency. Trailers, with no on-site construction costs at all, are also expected to expand their share of the housing market. The proportion of homes constructed under each of these types of economic organization will have a significant impact on average efficiencies, labor costs, and labor problems. Partly as a result, the major innovations in the industry may be expected to be introduced by elements not engaged in construction operations; materials suppliers and community developers rather than typical builders will probably be the principal instigators of change in construction methods and operating efficiencies. And consumers will tend on the whole to choose increased levels of performance rather than lower costs. In this developing technological and economic context, a number of labor changes may be expected.

A smaller proportion of the total man-hours of labor input will be performed at the site and a larger proportion in factories and plants where wage rates are lower. Construction labor will lose employment relatively, but this tendency has prevailed for a number of years, and the concern of the building trades is for total employment rather than employment per house. The increase in factory fabrication may be expected to create problems in some unionized areas where the work involved has customarily been performed in construction-union shops. As has been noted earlier, this problem is likely to be encountered in connection with only a small proportion of materials, and these can be readily identified. In the main, the development of larger units and more completely finished preassemblies will encounter less resistance from labor than ordinarily presumed.

The growth in the scale of operative builders and the tendency to develop small communities as a whole carry a significant potential not only for increased efficiencies but also for labor organization. Generally, it is easier for the union to organize when operations are large in scale. But small-scale operations are likely to continue to be an important factor in the assembly of houses on scattered plots. As a consequence the home-building industry may well become more generally unionized, but it is likely to continue to have important unorganized segments, particularly outside metropolitan areas. The larger-scale operations will tend to bring international union officers more into house construction problems which have thus far been left largely to the local unions.

The changing nature of home construction—new processes and materials—will alter the work operations at the site, but the craft structure of building labor is not likely to be radically altered. Operations in all branches of construction have changed substantially over the years, but the craft structure has been pliable, seeking to preserve some balance between narrow specialists and broadly trained craftsmen. The shift toward factory fabrication should raise relatively few jurisdictional problems for a broad area of home building since a high proportion of housing work is likely to continue to be carpenters' work, and the operations of the electricians, plumbers, painters, and other specialty groups are relatively clearly specified.

A heavy volume of construction steadily maintained—the figure currently is over a million housing units a year and is expected to grow to a million and a half in the next decade—will go a long way toward stabilizing employer-employee relations in home building. Builders in most areas, however, have still to gain a voice and to participate with other contractor groups in the determination of wages and other terms of area-wide collective bargaining agreements. Opposition has come not so much from unions as from the longer-established groups of general contractors who contend they represent home builders and too often regard home builders' associations as unimportant and unreliable allies. In the course of time, as the latter become better established, and better staffed, they will be recognized as parties to the negotiation of the area-wide contracts, leaving a few specific contract provisions, not including wage rates, to be negotiated for distinctive homebuilding conditions.

On the union side, it is reasonable to envisage the six or eight national unions within the Building and Construction Trades Department which are particularly interested in home building joining together in a special operating committee for the purpose of organizing and establishing a stronger union position in home building as the nature of the industry changes. The pattern for this type of joint action has already been set by the "Pact of Four" (laborers, engineers, teamsters, and carpenters) in heavy and highway construction and the joint committee (laborers, engineers, plumbers, and teamsters) which has fully organized pipeline construction in recent years. In similar fashion there could be, within the framework of

the eighteen national unions currently comprising the Department, an operating machinery concerned with and responsive
to the special problems of labor in home building.

The growth in size of home-building firms will not necessarily bring wage rates or methods of wage payment unique
to this branch of construction; wage rates will tend to be the
same as in other branches, except for the possibility of some
specialized job classifications with special rates. The method
of piece rate or lumping is not likely to grow or become
recognized as proper unless operations are standardized and
to a large degree performed away from the site. So long as
the highly interdependent character of all branches of the construction industry persists, it is not likely that wage rates,
methods of compensation, fringe benefits, or industrial relations practices substantially different from the rest of the
industry can be maintained in home building, particularly
among large-scale builders in metropolitan areas. Therefore,
wage rates and labor costs may on occasion rise in home
building, not because of developments in this field, but as a
consequence of actions in other branches of construction.

The prospects are for a continuation of the rising level of
money wage rates and fringe benefits, which has characterized
construction in the past decade. There are sound reasons for
believing that construction wages and benefits may advance
faster than in industry generally. As a consequence of population changes in the Depression of the 1930s, there will be no
increase in the number of men in the labor force in the vital
twenty-five-to-forty-four-year age group until after 1970,
despite substantial increases in the total labor force in the
form of women and older men. Moreover, industrial technology seems to be increasing the demands for skilled craftsmen in factories. These pressures are likely to find building
craftsmen, including those in housebuilding, in short supply,
with consequent increased pressure on wage rates.[10]

[10] See John T. Dunlop, *The Secular Outlook: Wages and Prices*, University of California, Institute of Industrial Relations, Berkeley, Calif., 1957.

Whether these higher money wage rates and benefits will correspondingly affect labor costs depends upon what happens to the agglomerate called "labor productivity." In the past decade labor productivity has increased in construction, but not as fast as in industry generally. Although a wide variety of factors, such as increased mechanization, improved designs, larger-scale operations, more prefabrication, and improved training, may be expected to increase labor productivity, the prospects on balance must appear to be a continued rise in labor costs per unit.

Some Suggestions and Alternative Approaches

No attempt is made here to lay out a blueprint for "solving" the labor problems of home building in the light of the projections made above; any detailed program, even if there were a way to get it accepted, would probably be out of date before it could be adopted. The following suggestions, partly procedural partly substantive, constitute lines or directions along which some headway may be made in dealing with the basic problems outlined above.

1. There is as yet no procedure by which these problems may be systematically and regularly considered by the groups in a position to do most about them, namely, the labor unions and the home builders. A prime requisite is a national forum where the responsible leaders of the national unions most affected may regularly meet with the responsible leaders of the NAHB and other national contractor groups concerned with home building. It would be a grave error here to prescribe the form of such a forum or organization, since to be effective it should grow and take its shape from discussion. But solely for the purposes of illustration and to convey the potentialities of the idea, a day-long session could be held every two or three months at which the top officers of the six or eight most affected national unions, or specialized representatives designated by them, would meet with a like group of contractors and builders drawn from unionized localities and rep-

resenting the affected national builder and contractor associations. This group could hear and discuss staff reports which spell out the basic problems in more detail, marshal the available information, receive reports from both sides on problems in particular localities, and then discuss methods of doing something about these issues, general and specific.

At the beginning, each representative in such a forum necessarily would have only a partial view of the home-building industry and its problems, derived from his experience. It would first be essential, therefore, for the members to become acquainted with each other's view of the problems at hand. Staff reports and research papers on problems and impending developments would have a role to play in such a forum. It is important, however, that the forum itself be comprised of responsible union officers or their representatives and of contractors representing unionized building operations or localities; staff or research representatives cannot develop a broad interest and concern with problems among those in a position to take action at a national level and to affect attitudes and policies in local communities.

The number of published research reports on some of the labor problems of home building prepared by government agencies and universities may be increased, but many of the officers of labor and builder organizations are not conscious of material of this kind. A way must be found of competing with other urgent problems for the attention of these responsible leaders, of regularly bringing information and developments to their notice, and of affecting attitudes and policies through an exchange of ideas. It would be better to make use of the demonstrated potentialities of solving problems through informal discussion among leaders than to resort to further legislation, congressional investigations, publicity campaigns, or gimmicks.

The proportion of homes, particularly in larger cities, now constructed under union conditions is sufficiently large to warrant the regular forum proposed. On behalf of its members employing union labor, the NAHB may well want to take an interest in such a development although in an earlier period this might have been precluded by the opposition or hostility of nonunionized members. The general contractors' associations should also be interested in participating on behalf of their members in the home-building field. The volume of unionized home building is so large that responsible officers of national unions would have to take a genuine interest in so large a part of their constituency. Both sides evidently have a stake in the potentialities of joint consultation for the future. The recent action of placing health and welfare funds of national building trades unions in the home-building mortgage market of unionized cities illustrates the wide scope of common interests and the possibilities inherent in joint consultation.

The establishment of a forum should be undertaken directly between the parties concerned without the sponsorship of any government agency or officer. Government departments might be asked to secure information or their representatives invited to attend sessions and discuss problems, such as apprenticeship, but the forum would be more effective if it arose directly from the enlightened self-interest of the parties involved. Some outside private research assistance might be usefully provided at the outset, but otherwise the individual unions and associations should bear the costs of meetings and transportation. In the traditions of the industry, such a forum should under no circumstances be launched with a fanfare of publicity.

The fundamental point is that the basic labor problems in home building outlined in this chapter can be most effectively approached only when there is a forum or mechanism for their regular and systematic consideration by the responsible representatives of organizations which are in a position to take action. Labor-contractor relations to date have only adapted slowly, and frequently with some difficulty and some time lag, to changes in technology and market conditions; the need is for labor-management cooperation to lead events rather than to follow them.

2. Experience in a number of cities—Los Angeles and Detroit among them—seems to indicate that stable bargaining relationships in union-organized communities are established and maintained only when home builders and their subcontractors join with the associations of general or specialty contractors from other branches of construction in negotiating area agreements with each craft or labor organization. Entirely separate negotiations, with the hope of securing advantageous contract terms, or the policy of abjectly following the settlements developed by other general contractors, does not seem to lead to satisfactory results in home building. Joint negotiations do not preclude the development in any branch of the industry of a limited number of contract clauses which are tailor-made to the special problems of that branch.

Joint negotiations are suggested in recognition of the fact that for some time to come wages and labor conditions in other branches of construction are likely to have significant effects on home building. A symbol of the growing maturity of labor relations in this sector of construction, joint negotiations afford home builders and their subcontractors an opportunity to have a more effective voice in decisions certain to affect the wage rates of their labor and the working rules of their operations. True, joint negotiations may be more cumbersome; the contractor group becomes less homogeneous and perhaps easier for the union to split up should there be a strike. These objections cannot alter the central fact that, under conditions of a reasonably high volume of home building in a union-organized community, either the home builders participate in joint local negotiations with other contractors employing the craft, or for practical purposes, they will have to follow the settlements made by others.

There is no feasible way in which collective bargaining in unionizing centers can be reorganized by edict or pronouncement. But it should be possible to marshal the experience gained in various forms of local bargaining affecting home builders and to persuade national leaders of the forms which should be encouraged and stimulated. A careful report of the forms in use and some analysis of experience, dispatched to various local communities by national leaders, would in itself be likely to have significant effects. The point is that changes in bargaining arrangements which affect home building are in process, and it would seem that national leaders could, to a degree, speed up and channel these changes.

3. The status of subcontractors in relation to the builder, particularly in carpentry, raises significant questions concerning collective bargaining in home building. (Ordinarily the plumbing, electrical, painting, excavating, and roofing subcontractors in home building are parties to the established area-wide associations and agreements in these specialties.) In the case of carpentry subcontractors—who do foundation forms, framing, dry wall, flooring, roofing, weatherstripping, etc.—the question is whether they shall conduct their own separate negotiations or whether the home builders as general contractors shall carry the ball. Ambiguity or divided responsibility will not contribute to stability or to the solution of labor relations problems.

In general, these specialty subcontractors cannot effectively bargain with the carpenters' union; they are too small and divided to coordinate with contractors employing carpenters and laborers in other branches of construction and conduct joint negotiations as proposed above. Only the builders can perform this coordination function. It is imperative that home builders form associations which can effectively and fairly resolve any conflicts with their carpentry subcontractors if the home builders are to represent both themselves and these subcontractors in negotiations and other labor relations.

4. Probably in larger communities, where the use of subcontractors for some types of carpentry work persists, the union will sooner or later seek to regulate the extent and the

"blocks" in which carpentry work is subcontracted. Thus, home builders may be permitted to elect to perform work themselves, or they may choose to subcontract certain specified work operations which are within a range of related operations. As an illustration, subcontracts might be let in blocks for foundation forms, exterior framing, interior finish, flooring, insulation, or roofing but not in smaller segments such as weatherstripping, window installation, or cabinetwork alone. Such provisions would be designed to stabilize competition among sectors of subcontractors and to assure larger-scale operations. In effect, the contracts would limit the degree of contractor specialization. In highly competitive markets in other industries with subcontracting problems, such as the ladies' garment, millinery, and men's clothing industries, collective bargaining has developed either comparable limitations on subcontracting or a standardization of the product.

5. The economic organization of the housing industry—the number and size of contractors, the scale of operations, the distribution of operations between builders and subcontractors and between off-site and on-site work—has most important effects on the labor factor and labor costs. Probably here lies the greatest possibility for cost reduction, elimination of inefficiencies, and rationalization of home construction. Although the basic organizational decisions involved are affected to a degree by the policies and practices of workers and their unions, this aspect of the industry is peculiarly the responsibility of management. That is why we have managers and that is why we compensate them.

It is incumbent upon contractors, builders, and manufacturers considering decisions which will affect the economic organization of the industry to explore the consequences for labor of alternative courses. For example, minimum manning requirements, although not immutable, should be considered early when a course of action will result in alteration of the size and scale of operations. Far too frequently a decision is made without regard to the labor factor, and then the problem is revealed in a rude awakening on the site. With forethought, the decision might equally well have been different, or through collective bargaining, working conditions might well have been adapted to the new method. Thus, as has been observed, the use of some prefabrication techniques may cause no difficulties, whereas others may be the source of considerable conflict. Just as industrial managements have come to consider the labor factor in making a wide range of business decisions, so must manufacturers of building materials, designers, and builders. A little foresight in this respect is usually to be preferred to a great deal of experience.

Organization in the service, repair, and remodeling field is another facet of the housing industry needing attention. The house has an increasing amount of equipment which requires expert attention, and full use must be made of the existing stock of houses to meet developing demand. It would appear there is a significant market for firms to service, remodel, and repair homes, calling for skilled mechanics to do a variety of operations. Such a development raises difficult labor problems, since the maintenance of craft lines would often be inappropriate and impractical.

6. The home-building industry has not trained its share of apprentices, and in the past, it has paid little attention to modern methods of job training. With a larger scale of operations and greater responsibility for labor policies, builders as a group might show greater interest in the further development of a skilled labor force and might share in the costs of apprenticeship in proportion to man-hours of work, rather than let the burden fall on a few large local builders.

In organized areas, local unions could be encouraged to keep more formal and detailed records of the specialization of their members in the home-building field so that less time would be required in the referral of men. Thus men and jobs could be more effectively matched and steadier employment for the work force secured.

As housing standards rise with higher income levels and improved technology and materials, it will be effective to report new work methods in union journals and in reports distributed to workers and to local unions. In these reports attention should be paid to inspection standards and to the problems of quality control. A work force kept abreast of developments can be expected to adapt more readily to the technological, economic, and organizational changes in store for home building.

There is room for considerable research on training methods and first-line supervision. In the absence of piecework, particularly, it is a most important and difficult task to develop a high standard of performance and pace of work in local home building. A series of comparative studies along these lines, among localities and among builders, should be fruitful.

7. An earlier analysis of cost-inflationary practices attributed to workers and unions suggested that each such practice must be approached separately; there can be no single policy or formula to reduce their impact. These practices vary widely from locality to locality, and their significance also probably varies with the level of unemployment over the long run.

Such practices must be confronted in the locality in which they arise, but a significant contribution can be made by officers of national unions and national leaders of the contractors and builders. National union officers have typically opposed such practices, although they have not ordinarily taken full measures to implement this judgment, preferring not to take an active part in so local an issue. Their judgments have been based less on altruism than on interest in the long-run welfare of the national union. In a competitive industry, high-cost practices may cut employment and union membership, surrender work opportunities to substitute materials or methods falling under the jurisdiction of other unions, create serious nonunion competition, and otherwise impair the position of the national union. Many demonstrations of the long-term negative effects of restrictive local practices come readily to the minds of national officers with a lifetime of experience. In housing as in other fields, the leadership takes the view that you cannot long stand in the way of machines, technological change, or progress. In a sense this view, placed against the natural response of individual workers affected by changes, may well be one of the most basic contributions of the labor movement to the American economy.

The forum of national leaders outlined above would afford a place where specific local situations could be reviewed, the facts gathered, and attempts made to secure adjustments by the local groups involved. It would be unrealistic to hope for strong action by national leaders in many such local situations, but a great deal can be accomplished by persuasion and factual reports initiated by responsible national officers.

This chapter has sought to outline the structure of labor-builder relations and the collective bargaining system in home building. A number of major labor problems have been identified, and some suggestions have been offered which may make a contribution toward their mitigation or resolution. The chapter has sought to place the labor problems of the industry in perspective or focus: too often issues of greatest significance are overlooked, whereas others of lesser importance receive major public prominence.

Chapter 9

BUILDING AND LAND USE CONTROLS

In this chapter, Burnham Kelly considers the most common controls over building and land use development, direct and indirect, public and private; he suggests interrelationships between them, and brings out a number of points that may require changes in order to reflect the needs of large-scale producers seeking to introduce significant housing innovations.

A major consideration in the production of houses, particularly for those who seek to introduce new materials or methods of construction, is the network of controls that has grown up over the years to assure public health and safety, fire protection, structural strength, investment security, and balanced community relationships in housing. No one doubts that these are appropriate subjects for regulation, or that the public benefits to be expected from such regulation amply justify a reasonable degree of added complication and cost for producers. Despite obvious flaws in the actual operation of controls over so vast an area of enterprise, the general situation in the housing field is perhaps not worse than that in many other areas of public regulation.

Yet certain current aspects of building and land use control need review and consideration if design and production potentials are to be realized. This chapter will seek to identify problem areas and to suggest possible solutions. For convenience in discussion, the controls are divided into four groups. Most of the chapter is devoted to the direct municipal regulations dealing with land and building development (building codes, housing codes, zoning ordinances, subdivision regulations, and various engineering specifications). Second are the indirect public controls, such as the imposition of taxes, the location of major roads and extension of municipal services, the power to take land by eminent domain, and the power to add land to a municipal corporation by annexation. Third are the private controls such as deed restrictions and the lending regulations of financial institutions. Last are the Federal regulations that affect the lending process, in particular those of the Federal Housing Administration.

The effects of many broader forces, particularly those of over-all government fiscal policy and of the manipulation of money and credit to combat inflation or depression, are beyond the scope of this study; they are covered elsewhere in the ACTION series.[1] It is worth noting, however, that although these may have greater over-all effect than any of the more specific controls discussed in this chapter, since they can determine the total housing industry volume, they have little direct effect on housing design and technology. The controls which are the subject of this chapter, on the other hand, have an often crucial effect on the use of new methods, even though, in many cases, those who establish and administer the controls do not understand this.

Building Codes

Direct public regulation of land and of the construction of buildings is carried on under the so-called police power, through which a government exercises its function of assuring the health, safety, and general welfare of its citizens. Generally speaking, the courts have determined that such regulation is a

[1] Charles M. Haar, *Federal Credit and Private Housing: The Mass Financing Dilemma*, McGraw-Hill Book Company, Inc., New York, 1959.

matter of state rather than Federal police power under our Constitution, and in the states this power has been delegated within specified statutory limits to local municipal governments. Local building codes are the most direct and obvious example of local police power regulation in the housing field.

Building codes have been generating heat for years. The building industry regularly claims that prevailing codes are obsolete or arbitrary. Typically a magazine speaking for the industry asks the editorial question, *does code Babel add $1,000 to small house building cost?* and gives this answer:

> The most expensive thing about today's house is the local building code under which it has to be erected, with its countless unpredictable and often senseless variances from sound national standards. The variances cost the home-buyer (and the homebuilder) a lot more than it would cost to make all the living rooms and all the bedrooms 20% larger—more than wall-to-wall carpeting, more than complete insulation and double glazing, more than an extra bathroom.[2]

The article calls upon the strengthened and organized home builders to fight these cost increases rather than have them offset by special fiscal arrangements or passed on directly to the public.

Undoubtedly many building codes call for exaggerated standards of public safety; such standards are far easier to put into effect than they are to remove from the books. In part this difficulty stems from the natural tendency of many local building officials to favor the most conservative practices of the conventional system under which they have developed their experience; in part, it stems from the very real difficulty of defining public safety in such a way as to assure protection without penalizing innovation and advance. A major factor is the autonomy of local government, which tends to encourage a wide divergence of local standards and to put many difficulties in the way of broad definition of national or state stand-

[2] *House & Home*, vol. 2, no. 3, September, 1952, p. 108.

ards. It is in our tradition to leave it to local communities to determine for themselves the level of standards they will require. A magazine speaking for the building officials put the argument in its purest form:

> It is about time the critics of the codes recalled a fundamental of government. Building regulations are a legislative problem subject to local legislative choice. City councils are free to choose a building code consistent with their ideas of local needs. If they wish, they are free to provide protection ranging from no code at all to one that is highly restrictive and which would provide complete protection. Most cities select a reasonable building code which will provide a reasonable degree of protection.[3]

Cities decide for themselves the level of water and sewer service they wish to provide, so long as they exceed minimum state regulations. They provide wide variation in quality of streets, of protection services, and of public education. Why should they not set their own levels of fire and structural safety?

The answer is that new elements of public policy must enter the picture when the question is one of encouraging the rational development of a top national industry supplying the most expensive product purchased by the average family. Clearly building regulation requires a broader view, but as clearly this is hard to obtain. The average voter is no more aware of the potential benefits to him of a modernized building industry than the average builder is aware of the long-range effect on the community of the subdivision and construction decisions he makes on the basis of small points of convenience and profit.

Students of building codes generally agree that local excesses and variations are usually the result of honest intentions but inadequate knowledge and that difficulties would be sharply reduced if codes were based on performance standards, that

[3] *Building Standards Monthly*, March, 1957.

is, if the objective were stated, but not the specific means of complying with it. Legislation which spells out the specifications of technical details and requirements quickly becomes antiquated and restrictive, for the tremendous scope of progress in the building field makes it impossible to encompass all acceptable variations. Since it is humanly impossible for enforcement officers to be acquainted with all the variations, they hesitate to use discretion and tend to enforce the law to the letter.

One method of keeping up to date employed by many local communities is the adoption of the national model code provisions of some public or private code-drafting organization. The situation with respect to code restrictions and inspections in one group of such communities (in the San Francisco Bay area) has been described by Maisel in these terms:

> In houses built in the localities where the uniform codes applied without changes—some 33 per cent of the total number built in the area—no inefficiency could be charged to the restriction of codes. Fifty per cent had their costs raised less than 1 per cent for the typical house through code alterations. Even in the case of the final 15 to 20 per cent, where greater code restrictions were in force, the increased costs did not run more than 3 per cent above the uniform code areas. . . .
>
> Although some instances of delays and arbitrary rulings were reported, most builders in the area stated that neither was of any consequence in the total cost of the building. Between 5 and 10 per cent of the builders reported that they had occasional difficulties in obtaining inspections on time or in having their plans approved, but the remainder said any delays or problems were unusual.[4]

If the difficulties are small, why do building industry spokesmen complain about codes? First, because adoption of the national model codes is not common. A recent report indicated that fewer than 10 per cent of the 37,400 municipalities in the

---

[4] Sherman J. Maisel, *Housebuilding in Transition*, University of California Press, Berkeley, Calif., 1953, p. 249.

country have taken this step.[5] Second, the national codes are not uniform, even in their relatively simple residential construction provisions, and there are many of them. Even within the government, the Army, Navy, and public building agencies all have their own separate codes. Furthermore, the national model codes can hardly be accused of throwing off all restraint. They tend to be the guardians of good standard practice.

Maisel suggests that the observed lack of builder complaints in San Francisco stems from the fact that the average builder is not an innovator, but is content to build a house in a traditional manner, familiar both to him and to the building inspector. Many of the ablest producers, on the other hand, are deeply aware of the importance of innovation, both technological and entrepreneurial, if significant progress is to be made in the provision of housing and if real value is to be offered to the public. The codes may be criticized for unnecessarily delaying or even prohibiting significant progress in building, yet there are difficulties with most of the suggested approaches to this problem.

Performance Standards. To have only objectives in engineering terms stated, rather than detailed specifications of materials and methods of construction, is not in itself the complete answer, for such standards require a level of administration higher than the average community can afford. Systems that aim to take full design advantage of the potentialities of

[5] *House & Home*, vol. 13, no. 6, June, 1958, p. 61, gives the following claimed figures for adoptions of the four largest, noting that there is probably overlap:

Building Officials Conference of America	300
International Conference of Building Officials	1,167
National Board of Fire Underwriters	1,100
Southern Building Code Congress	712

The national electric code may be adopted by as many as 70 per cent of United States communities, at least in part, but only about three hundred have adopted the national plumbing code.

new approaches are not subject to easy calculation. It may take a man with skill equal to that of the innovator and the testing facilities of an industrial laboratory to decide whether a reinforced plastic panel can handle the required loads. For the large-scale builder, the expense and delay of submitting a full portfolio of test results to every local board of appeals constitutes a severe penalty whatever the final decisions.

Furthermore, local inspectors may insist that inspections be locally made. A panel assembly may have to be torn apart, inspected, and then reassembled at the site, even though many identical assemblies have previously been given the same treatment and all have passed. In this way a principal advantage of producing such assemblies is lost. Often the men concerned with the regulation of local building tend to work together to preserve conventional methods. The local builder, laborer, materials supplier, and inspector have all gone through the same background of experience. They have long relied on the same techniques, and to some extent, individuals have exchanged roles from builder to inspector on the local scene. In the case of a complex innovation, their firm and outspoken doubts and fears can give pause to the most enlightened banker, government appraiser, or prospective purchaser. Needless to say their practical judgment has often averted trouble. But the reassurance offered by local inspection may be too high a price to pay if it destroys the opportunity for significant production advances. Furthermore, localism may be motivated primarily by the desire to block further housing development by any means easily available. Such an environment is obviously not one in which the new is encouraged and the efficient is praised.

Model Codes. Even when they make use of such national model codes as those developed by the Building Officials Conference of America, the International Conference of Building Officials, the National Board of Fire Underwriters, or the Southern Building Code Congress, local communities can and frequently do add extra and purely local requirements to the carefully standardized provisions. True, education on the value to community and to builder of genuine uniformity is spreading; progress may be illustrated by the New York State Building Code, adopted by 33 of 62 cities and by 250 of 1,500 communities through mid-1958, and with a high degree of uniformity among these communities. This code itself is short. A separate booklet lists the standards of national organizations, like the American Concrete Institute, that may be used. A code manual indicates in specification form the materials and methods that represent acceptable versions of the code provisions. Most important of all, perhaps, a central testing and approval body is staffed and supplied with state funds [6] to keep the code up to date and to issue certificates of acceptability for new ideas and combinations. Although these certificates are passed along to the adopting communities for information only, and have no legally binding local effect, they have had good local acceptance, and many of the nation's largest prefabricators have taken advantage of the system to speed approvals in the large and lucrative New York market. Like all state-wide uniform codes, however, this has one important defect: concentration is on state-wide minimum requirements and no ceiling is placed over locally enacted variants.

Broad Area Controls and Maximum Requirements. Sound engineering principles do not change at community boundaries, and the public has much to gain by the administrative recognition of this simple fact in the form of a single code setting maximum as well as minimum provisions over a wide area. Public attention tends, perhaps naturally enough, to dwell on negative arguments such as the threat of invasion by millions of cheap, look-alike houses that will clutter the land and inflate the cost of education. For the most part, these negative arguments have little or nothing to do with the public

[6] Other model code organizations depend on memberships, fees, and contributions for their expenses, and operations are considerably less expeditious as a result.

health, safety, and welfare considerations which form the basis for police power controls over building, but they are very clear and real to the public. The positive arguments are more abstract because they deal mostly with potentials—with estimates and projections of what the building industry might be able to provide if it were free to innovate and to recoup the necessary development costs by sales over broad market areas.

It would seem to be highly desirable to assure the prospective manufacturer of a new product or process that, if his research men work out a good idea and his development men get it into production, he can pass a single series of extensive tests and then distribute without further local approvals throughout an area at least as large as a metropolis, preferably as large as a state, and potentially even throughout the whole nation. There are climatic variations and other differences from region to region, but these need offer no serious obstacle. FHA's proposed new Minimum Property Standards use simplified maps to reflect regional differences affecting factors like earthquake resistance, wind loading, and insulation. In view of the long legal tradition putting controls over local property in state hands, however, it is probably advisable to attempt national uniformity not through direct regulation, but rather through the device of uniform state laws.

If building approval agencies were set up to cover very large areas, it would be administratively justifiable to bring into play extensive testing facilities and expert officials, whose contributions could even include significant improvements in the original design ideas. Under these circumstances, performance standards could actually be made to perform for the benefit of innovator and public alike. Even if margins of safety were made conservatively high, many producers would be glad to comply in return for the assurance that they could then concentrate on sales over a broad area.

Revision Procedure. It will be generally conceded that many building codes are sadly out of date, remaining operative only because able inspecting staffs are making extensive use of the discretion granted to them. Even the best need frequent revision to reflect advances in building technology, but this can be a costly, complex, and frustrating experience; hence many small communities give up and make do with adaptations of the codes of other communities thought to be suited to their purposes.

The typical revision procedure starts with a conference of technical experts seeking to set the character of technical requirements. Since there is no sharp line dividing reasonable from unreasonable, and since only judgment can set levels for fire safety and public health or mediate between low initial cost and low maintenance, the process becomes one of broad-front negotiation wherein a small but determined group insisting upon a single vested interest generally can force a compromise in its favor. In the next stage, the operational and administrative form for the execution of these technical requirements is under consideration, and the same process occurs. It is worth noting that loosely phrased technical requirements call for extra specification in administrative requirements, and vice versa. Finally, the code draft goes to the legislative body, and the process of logrolling starts in earnest. In the end, despite expert help and extensive effort, the community may have a code that holds little practical advantage over the outdated one that provoked the drive for revision.[7]

In short, any procedure by which code revision may be simplified and new ideas introduced without arousing all the forces of traditional resistance must be welcomed. One solution would be to bypass the usual process entirely, perhaps through a procedure for revision by the accumulation of a series of individual decisions on specific new methods and materials over a period of time. A key element here would be the creation at metropolitan or state level of a review board like that of New York, with a budget sufficient to provide

[7] Even the adoption of a standard code may be a major effort. Many committees, several years, and thousands of dollars were required in St. Louis for the local adoption of the national electrical code.

well-qualified personnel and full testing resources. To this board would come designers, builders, or fabricators for decisions on new materials and methods. Implementation of the decisions would take the form of certificates of approval, supplemented by detailed description of the new material and by a careful analysis of the conditions of its use. Such certificates would by statute be legally established as acceptable alternatives to local code provisions. They would be sent to all code jurisdictions which would then be obliged to give a local permit to any application embodying the approved system. It is on this last vital point only that the procedure differs significantly from that of New York.

A procedure of this sort would guarantee each innovator a full and fair hearing directed at the merits of his proposal and a chance at a large market if he obtains approval. From the community's point of view there would be a gradual modernization of building regulations by a procedure that tends to bring up most-needed changes first and never involves the expense and frustrations of a full-scale code revision. Meanwhile local regulations and code officials could continue to handle traditional problems in the time-honored manner, supplying the detailed specifications of conventional construction which often serve as a sort of construction manual for local small builders. Local authority in building matters would not be rudely uprooted, and since most of the proposals seeking the advantage of the new procedure would involve structures regarding which the local inspector would have little opportunity for effective judgment because of his limited experience and resources, his objections would tend to be reduced. Furthermore, the principal underlying this system—that of referring new and complex technical decisions to a specially qualified central review board—should not prove politically unpalatable in the state legislature. Such a procedure warrants further consideration.

Incorporation by Reference. A simpler proposal to the same end is the extension among the states of the grant of power to local communities to incorporate by reference the provisions of codes worked out by independent experts. If all states would grant this power, any community could accept for local building-control purposes the appropriate code of a major code-drafting group, in its latest amended form. Currently in many states, such a model code must be adopted word for word in the local ordinance; if it is later amended, the community must also amend its ordinance.[8] This becomes too complex to warrant the trouble.

If the power to incorporate by reference were granted for this purpose, the model code might well be that of a central state agency, like the one in New York, which could also serve as an appeal board for matters of interpretation, analysis, and testing. It is important to repeat, however, that the significant gain for the innovator is not mere uniformity among communities of similar requirements, nor uniformity plus minimum state-wide standards. More important for the stimulation of new production ideas and of over-all advance in the housing industry is the insistence that there be a maximum level of building-code requirements throughout the state, above which individual communities will not be permitted to establish their own special regulations.

Action on Codes. Experience indicates that the public is not likely to take the initiative in improving the building-code situation, and in any case progress is likely to be greatest when those who understand the complex problems involved are brought together.[9] An important resource would be the participation of producers who see and can explain the general

[8] A possible way around this roadblock, at least in some states, would be the incorporation of a provision that conformance to provisions of nationally accepted standards shall constitute adequate performance under the local code.

[9] In 1958, Henry Luce of Time, Inc., ACTION, and fourteen trade and professional associations asked the American Standards Association to consolidate the residential provisions of the major national codes into a single set of construction requirements for one- and two-family dwellings, and then to set up a procedure for annual review. Because a number of other code interests objected, ASA declined.

benefits that will result when localized conventions have been removed from the control system. Equally important (and often overlooked) would be the active participation of those who understand the emerging patterns of housing design and construction and will insist that advances be made in the procedural and administrative as well as the technical provisions. Only when all aspects move forward together may major innovations be fairly reviewed, tested, and put into practice. Only a broad approach can set the groundwork for advances in the whole pattern of living, as opposed to making a few detailed corrections in provisions regarding materials and systems of construction.

In many ways the building-code situation has already improved during the 1950s. Large builders operating across community and even state lines have tended to break down extremes of localism. The increasing mobility of the people is tending to reduce regional differences in design and in the regulations that go with them. And the increasingly national approach to financing is a powerful standardizing influence. Nevertheless the vast majority of communities retain individual local codes, most of which pay little attention to the future of housing.

Coordination of Regulatory Measures. The discussion of building codes would not be complete without calling attention to the need for coordination among the various police power control measures used by a community to regulate building development. To require high standards of fire resistance in panel-wall structures, when the major part—if not all—of the wall may be simple sheets of glass, is clearly illogical. Panelized and component approaches that offer considerable design and production innovations may be blocked by minor points in the plumbing or electrical codes. Many such conflicts and cross-purposes may be weeded out by the use of performance standards in the legislative language adopted by the community, leaving interpretation and application to the innovator and the administrator. But constant attention must be focused on the final result to be obtained by the interplay of all the various police power tools. Although the application of such tools as zoning and subdivision control must remain essentially local because of the need for detailed familiarity with local conditions, this is not true of building codes, and the combined effect upon the larger community over the long haul increasingly calls for review at a higher level than the local one.

Housing and Health Codes are focused on maintaining minimum standards of fitness for human occupancy in old as well as new structures, and in units that may have been remodeled and subdivided many times in their long history.[10] The major concern of such controls is the up-grading of the existing stock of housing or, where this proves to be out of the question, its elimination.

Similar tools are found in laws providing for the compulsory vacation of deficient structures, in compulsory repair and lien laws, and in laws assessing fines for a variety of health and safety offenses. Although this sort of local provision is aimed essentially at the opposite end of the housing-supply picture from that with which this book is concerned and serves to stimulate mostly the repair and rehabilitation organizations, it is still important to builders because aggressive use of such provisions enlarges the market for new housing. Currently, new housing costs are relatively so high and the need for inexpensive housing is so great that communities hesitate to eliminate existing units or—by requiring extensive repairs—to put them out of reach of families now able to afford them. Major innovations could alter this situation considerably, by bringing down the costs of remodeling or of new units so that the enforcement of reasonable housing standards would not

---

[10] This is a subject to which ACTION has devoted a good deal of attention, as may be seen from *Reports from ACTION*, nos. 2, 11, 15, 1956, dealing respectively with the Housing Court in Baltimore, the court decisions on municipal housing codes, and a reference guide to housing-code provisions for citizen organizations.

work a social hardship. Clearly, therefore, all aspects of public control are related parts of a single picture, with which builders should be more familiar than they are.

Zoning

In 1916, zoning was first applied in the United States to assure light and air in city streets and to avoid incompatible land use mixtures. Soon zoning was embraced by development interests as a means of avoiding the worst effects of hit-and-run speculative building and of protecting sound neighborhoods, maintaining real estate values, and guiding extensions of existing urban patterns. City growth had become so chaotic that almost any orderly control system would be an improvement, and the choice naturally fell upon a system which was relatively simple to define, understand, follow, and enforce.[11] Potential land uses were listed, graded according to intensity and unpleasantness, and allocated to carefully mapped zones ranging from high-priced and well-protected residential areas at one extreme to nuisance industry at the other. Building permits were granted only for uses permitted within the zone affected.

Urban growth has accelerated in recent years, and it has become clear that the simple hierarchy of zones which was the model during the 1920s is not suited to the kind of metropolitan and suburban pattern being created today. Thus a great outcry has developed in design and building circles against zoning as a crystallization of outmoded needs, desires, and patterns. Because the old ordinances were inelastic, many would like to do away with zoning itself; others, including the city planners, argue rather for adaptation of the tool to

[11] No doubt the simplicity and orderliness of the concept was of great importance (together with its thoroughly demonstrated acceptance by communities throughout the land) in convincing the Supreme Court in the case of *Euclid v. Ambler* 272 U.S. 365 (1926) that the Constitution was not violated when similar parcels of land were governed by the same regulations within a carefully defined zone, usually large in size and homogeneous in character, but smaller than the legal boundaries of the community.

modern needs, pointing out that potentially this extension of the basic police power is a control of very great importance [12] and one capable of a much higher degree of subtlety in reflecting the interests of both community and building industry than is usually provided.

A principal difficulty in zoning has been the familiar one of poor education. Those most eager for land controls had little knowledge of the future potentials in building and land development and tended to establish control patterns based on the assumption of conventional practices. Those most interested in new design, building, and land-development ideas, on the other hand, tended to dismiss zoning as dull administrative routine until they ran afoul of its provisions. It is a rare designer who has taken the trouble to suggest how zoning provisions might be effectively modified to handle his new ideas.[13] Especially in dealing with multifamily construction have the provisions and principles of zoning tended to be behind the designers, though perhaps this reflects a general backwardness in this country regarding the design potentials of multifamily construction.

The typical builder's attack on zoning in recent years, however, is probably focused elsewhere. He suspects that the community is indirectly trying to run up his costs or keep him out of town, and he has little patience with the city planners' talk of elastic guidance for new types of urban growth.

Housing developments are far more extensive than in the past, however; they tend to take the form of entire neighborhoods and even communities designed and built at one time for which an over-all plan is needed from the start. The com-

[12] The British were considered radical when they condemned private development rights, though the original act provided for a token payment in compensation. The zoning concept allows control of development under the police power, without compensation of any sort, if private rights are not unreasonably restricted and if a suitable background in public benefit and development policy has been created.

[13] There are exceptions. See Charles K. Agle, "A New Kind of Zoning," *Architectural Forum*, vol. 95, no. 1, July, 1951, p. 175.

munity is suddenly confronted with the need for miles of streets, water mains, and sewers and—dominating all other considerations—a skyrocketing demand for new schools. The typical voter, thoroughly frightened, supports the use of any tactic that will stem the flood of houses.

The Builder's View. Community design opportunities are of little concern to the typical builder. His main interest is to find buildable land and get construction under way. In many cases, however, he finds himself faced with a zoning plan devised to delay or even prohibit growth. There has been a trend toward requiring ever-larger house lots, up to several acres in the most restrictive zones,[14] on the assumption that larger lots require more expensive houses and thus create a better tax base for the community, tend to slow down development, or (preferably) both.[15] The fear motive is made perfectly clear when a Westchester town attempts to ration building permits according to average numbers granted over previous years, or when one on Long Island defines the speculative building of houses as a business use, not permitted in residential areas except by special permit from the town. When communities go too far, the courts intervene,[16] but recently the courts have extended the benefit of doubt when a provision shows evidence

[14] A zoning requirement of five acres was upheld in the case of *Fischer v. Bedminster Township*, 11 New Jersey 194, 93 A.2d 378 (1952).

[15] A study based on communities in the Boston area found no evidence of a correlation between increased lot size and deferred development. See *The Effects of Large Lot Size on Residential Development*, Urban Land Institute, Technical Bulletin no. 32, Washington, July, 1958. Indeed, if the community sets high general standards of development, it may make itself only more attractive to builders and purchasers. Of course, if lots are large, fewer total families can be placed on available building land, and the expected urban growth must take over proportionately more land and extend proportionately farther out. On the other hand, evidence from all sources is clear that average lot size is going up as much from consumer demand as from zoning requirement. If the consumer had his way, there is little doubt that outlying raw land would be turned into larger lots, and the study suggests that, with appropriately reduced subdivision standards, this could be done at relatively little added cost to builder and community.

[16] In New York, both the devices cited have been ruled unconstitutional.

of careful study and seems to be in the broad interests of the community.

The advantage to the community of new building designs and methods tends to be little understood and sought at the local level. Indeed, far more study is needed on the effects on home building of zoning and other land-development controls. The relations and linkages, the accessibility requirements of different types of activities, and many other aspects of these controls should be the subject of research studies.[17] More than study is needed, however. Builders must find a way to make clear to the voters that tangible benefits can be gained by permitting the use of new methods and designs. Demonstrations and illustrations and sound examples will help to stir interest, but something must be done at the same time to counter fear. The National Association of Home Builders could provide few more useful services to its members than the stimulation of a full-dress reconsideration of the allocation of school costs among forms of taxation and levels of government.

Project Development Provisions. In view of the increasing trend toward rapid, planned construction of large-scale developments, interest has been growing in special zoning provisions that allow builder and community to sidestep the conventional lot-by-lot approach and consider the plan of the project as a whole. Under many of these provisions, which represent one type of "special exception" in zoning, it is possible to vary bulk and density of individual units within a project in order to achieve design improvements and land use economies, so long as the average over the project as a whole is up to requirements and the general aims of the ordinance are observed. Under others, dwelling type as well as bulk and

[17] An example of such a study is Shirley Adelson Siegel, "Relation of Planning and Zoning to Housing Policy and Law," *Law and Contemporary Problems*, vol. 20, no. 3, Summer, 1955, in which zoning was found inadequate in many respects in its handling of public housing projects. Articles like Charles M. Haar "The Wayne Township Case," *Harvard Law Review*, vol. 66, no. 6, April, 1953, raise basic issues regarding the aims and objectives of local zoning control.

density may vary. Under a few, it is even possible to introduce different land uses—a shopping center or possibly a small light industrial enterprise—where they will appropriately serve the project. Provisions authorizing these special projects are typically spelled out in the initial zoning ordinance, but the area so to be zoned is actually shown on the map only when the owner of a specified minimum acreage in a specified general area comes in and requests planning-board permission to undertake such a development, subject to a review of details of design and planning before the board gives its approval.[18]

Such special-exception procedures are of considerable importance today, and likely to be even more so in the future. They also represent a considerable extension of the original theory of zoning control, including as they do many of the characteristics of subdivision regulation. This is a development that offers hope of providing the environment in which innovation in housing and site-planning design may flourish, and designer and builders should find it very much in their interests to encourage its extension.

Flexible Controls. Experimentation in all aspects of zoning is needed in order to develop means of assuring community objectives without needlessly restricting design and construction innovation. Those who draft and enact zoning ordinances are often unfamiliar with new ideas in design and building and therefore tend to devise regulations which perpetuate conventional practices and requirements. Furthermore, administrative officers have a natural and reasonable tendency to prefer provisions that are simple to understand and express as well as to enforce. Unfortunately, such provisions, although working well for conventional builders, may constitute a block against the inventive designer or builder who is willing to deal with a

[18] See Fred W. Tuemmler, "Zoning for the Planned Community," *Urban Land,* vol. 13, no. 4, April, 1954, for a discussion of a number of the recent provisions of this kind. Also, William C. Vladeck, "Large-scale Developments and One-house Zoning Controls," *Law and Contemporary Problems,* vol. 20, no. 2, Spring, 1955.

complex formula or a subtle series of checks and balances so long as he gains thereby the chance to innovate. Every encouragement should be offered to the development of elastic controls which will permit both the conventional and the creative approaches without lowering the standards of public benefit and protection. Builders must find ways of identifying the major paths of innovation developed by designers and producers, getting this information into the hands of administrative officers, and helping to make sure that control systems will provide the needed elasticity.

Much progress has been made along these lines in recent years. To an increasing degree the method of regulating bulk and density in zoning has moved away from the requirement of specific yards and heights and toward the setting of ratios of floor area to lot area. Provision for light and air in dense development areas may be made through formulas dealing with the amount of sky area that must be visible from each window, rather than through the conventional routines of setting buildings back from the street at various distances according to height. Such provisions require more explanation and consequently appear more complex to the average person, but they offer the prospective designer little difficulty and a tremendously broadened range of freedom. Other examples of elasticity are the zoning of industry by the use of performance standards [19] instead of by oversimplified listings according to nuisance level and the use of special-exception provisions to permit certain unusual but necessary land uses in specified zones—for example the construction of hospitals in the most restrictive residential areas.

At the present time, the general public is alarmed at growth problems and local officials are sharply aware of the need for development planning. Trained planners are much in demand, have good local support, and generally receive the benefit of every doubt in case of judicial review. In some cases, these

[19] This idea has been given wide attention by city planners; it is far more difficult to apply the idea to the zoning of residential development.

factors have induced a tendency to plunge into bold experiments and to authorize a great deal of discretionary power in watching over the public interests. This growing civic zeal has to be balanced with a sharper recognition of the needs of private development. One decided advantage of the observed increase in builder size is the resulting builder ability to make certain that zoning regulations reflect his interests adequately. The large builder can afford the time to clear away improper restrictions, and he has the resources to do so, both in money and in practical experience and test results.

Other Zoning Problems. Brief mention may be made of several other items in the zoning field which are of general concern to the builder. One of these is the common complaint of poor and occasionally high-handed administration in the processing of variances, special exceptions, and appeals. To this, the best solution is to encourage the builder to stand upon his rights, in court if necessary, and through the medium of his association if he dares not risk local retaliation following individual action.

In general, zoning controls are too often treated as isolated matters and not adequately related to the other means of local building control: building codes, subdivision regulations, and general planning provisions. In some states, Massachusetts, for example, zoning and subdivision control must be absolutely separate, although they deal with different aspects of a single problem. True, zoning generally was introduced into most communities years in advance of subdivision control, and often in advance of planning regulations having any aspect of effective local control.[20] This does not prohibit the designer and

[20] Consequently, requirements in state enabling acts that local zoning shall be "in accordance with a comprehensive plan" have in the past been assumed to mean only that the zoning shall not be trivial, arbitrary, or partial, but shall represent a considered scheme for the entire community. Recent years have seen a significant advance in other local controls, however, and the courts are beginning to see to it that there is in fact a relationship between these tools. See Charles M. Haar, "In Accordance with a Comprehensive Plan," *Harvard Law Review,* vol. 68, no. 7, May, 1955.

builder from insisting that the various regulations be reasonably related to each other and to a master plan.

From the designer's point of view as well as the community's, there is reason for concern that measures of local regulation may tend to put an unnecessary strait jacket on innovation. Careful attention should be paid to the recent expansion of municipal regulation of aesthetic qualities in building development. In upholding the District of Columbia in its redevelopment activities, Mr. Justice Douglas of the Supreme Court recently commented that nothing in the Constitution stands in the way if the District seeks to make areas of Washington beautiful, as well as efficient.[21] From this and from other developments in the states (historical districts, for example, and measures to preserve breathing spaces and sky lines), planners have been given a boost in what may prove to be a dangerous direction. For there are significant difficulties in regulating aesthetics; average public tastes are not sophisticated, and over time they change. To be required to adhere in the future to a current common denominator of design taste is not only to face frighteningly dreary prospects in terms of visual pleasure (as anyone may observe for himself if he will but check back through magazine illustrations of buildings of a generation ago), but also to put a tremendous barrier in the path of innovation in design and construction. Yet just such a trend appears to be in the air at the present time. A specific zoning illustration may be found in an ordinance adopted in 1951 by Rye, New York, which set up a five-member Board of Review instructed to disapprove projected house plans of excessive similarity or dissimilarity. One can sympathize with the emotions behind such a regulation, but it is only too clear that in ordinary administration, the device was expected to keep out unconventional houses, and very likely also to keep out any large-scale merchant builder.

So long as the general public regards such a provision as

---

[21] *Berman v. Parker,* 348 U.S. 26 (1954).

nothing more than a convenient way to avoid the shocking modern and the crass speculative, there is little chance of arousing opinion against it. Yet the chances are substantial that it will also bar sensible and cost-saving innovations of all sorts and generally present just such a block to the advance of the housing industry as we seek to identify and remove.

The general experience of this country has been that the public welfare is advanced, rather than injured, by encouraging experimentation of all sorts, even though the initial form may seem strange and may be very different from the one finally accepted by the mass market. The "picture window" is a commonplace variation by conventional builders on a theme developed by a small number of very advanced designs in exploring the free use of glass areas. The ranch house with its outdoor sitting areas and cooking facilities is a popular adaptation of free-flowing housing designs once considered dangerously radical, and the carport and breezeway would have caused serious problems under the zoning yard requirements of a very few years ago. The public likes and benefits from these developments; it should not let itself be persuaded to cut off the sources from which they spring.

Subdivision Control

It was early recognized as an important function of local government to review the proposals of land developers for the creation of new streets. The importance of guiding the street pattern became evident in the nineteenth century when the outskirts of many cities were becoming a patchwork of subdivisions, patterned by the accident of landholdings and the speculative interests of the developer more than by any concern for the resulting effect on public circulation throughout subsequent decades of service. Boards of survey and comparable official community bodies undertook to designate the location and design as well as the character and quality of street pavement.

In the building boom following World War I, however,

new problems made their appearance. Speculative land developers subdivided hundreds of square miles of outlying land, had streets and services put in at municipal expense, and then found themselves unable to sell their lots. As a result of this experience, municipal governments sought a way of checking more closely the developer's plans, and requiring him to put enough capital into land development so that his calculation of market possibilities would be sharpened by the concrete dimensions of his own potential loss. It came to be generally understood that the level and expense of normal municipal services are such that the government can no longer provide them without cost to new development lots; municipal tax returns from residential development are not enough to warrant such an outlay, and long-range cost to the community of poor design is far too great to encourage it by municipal assumption of risk. Hence today the developer, who plans to make a profit from converting undeveloped local land into lots and houses, is generally required to pay most or all of the costs associated with streets, drains, and other required municipal services, and his plans are typically made to conform to over-all community development plans and standards.

As a result, normal development costs can be high; in some rapidly growing areas of the country additional charges are made: a pro rata contribution to school construction cost in California communities,[22] for instance, or a fee in lieu of dedication of land for public purposes within the development. Although in some cases the corrective action may have gone too far, the public objective has been to find the level of regulation that will assure high-grade development and at the same time equitably allocate its over-all costs among purchaser, developer, and community.[23]

[22] Attacked in recent court tests.

[23] See J. Ross McKeever, "Utilities and Facilities for New Residential Construction," Urban Land Institute, Technical Bulletin no. 27, Washington, D.C., December, 1955, which notes that progress is being made in the equitable sharing of costs. For example, there is increasing agreement that developers should not be charged the full price of utility installations de-

The Builder's View. Subdivision control is under heavy fire from builders all over the country; they call it extreme and arbitrary and say it is being used in many communities to raise costs artificially in order to stop or hinder development.[24] On the other side, planners claim that in too many cases effective controls become politically acceptable only after major damage has been done. These claims and counterclaims have brought the matter to a head, particularly in view of the proclaimed shortage of prime development land in the outskirts of many of our metropolitan areas.

It is significant that in their general objections to subdivision regulations, builders frequently confuse the issue with complaints about lot size, yards, and other requirements established by the zoning ordinance rather than the subdivision regulations, and occasionally an argument is raised that stems in fact from the building code. This underlines the point that for the builder a control is a control. Even though he is cur-

---

signed for extra capacity in order to serve areas beyond the current development. There remains, however, the likelihood that adjoining communities will have different specifications governing land development within the same region. Summarizing the regulations of 114 cities:

1. One hundred and two had subdivision regulations.
2. Fifty-three extended subdivision controls beyond the city limits. (On this, and subsequent, questions, some did not answer.)
3. Developers must pay for improvements as follows:
    a. Street grading: all 95, part 3
    b. Street paving: all 80, part 9
    c. Curbs and gutters: all 79, part 7
    d. Sidewalks: all 75, part 4
    e. Water mains: all 61, part 13
    f. Sanitary sewers: all 81, part 9
    g. Storm sewers: all 71, part 7
4. Completion guaranteed by bond or otherwise: 81.
5. Developer reimbursed for one or more items: 36.
6. City pays additional cost of larger installations needed to serve areas outside subdivision: all 43, part 40.

[24] A typical extra cost per lot of $1,500 might include $600 for concrete streets, $400 for lots an extra 10 feet in width, and $500 for curbs, sidewalks, and storm sewers.

rently required to make separate visits to different people at City Hall to handle each of these requirements, in his mind these are all part of a single municipal control system.

Administration. For both builder and community, increased time and expense are required as a result of recent refinements in subdivision control. As the procedure has grown in effectiveness, title companies and conveyancers have been shocked to discover the possibility of hidden title defects stemming from the subdivider's failure to get the required approvals before filing a subdivision plat with the recorder of deeds; [25] they have promoted laws requiring the municipalities to put on record at the recorders' offices all the details of the local regulatory structure and, for each subdivision plat, a full certification of acceptability or nonacceptability by the approving agency.[26]

In addition, builders have called for the holding of open meetings and the maintenance of complex records. As a result of all these demands, many a suburban planning commission finds itself swamped by the administrative aspects of subdivision control and unable to keep up with its other work. Many have been forced to charge filing and examination fees, thus to reimburse the costs of trained review personnel and so both speed and strengthen the approval process.

Relationship to Zoning. In the discussion of zoning we noted a trend in the direction of flexible controls, designed more to guide rapid new development than to preserve the *status quo* in settled communities. Subdivision control has the

[25] In several states the sensible provision has been adopted that the innocent purchaser of a lot in an unapproved subdivision may, if he wishes, void the purchase and sue his seller.

[26] This illustrates the effectiveness of private enforcement methods as contrasted with reliance on reviews and inspections by public officials. Since every banker will insist on clear title, the public may be sure that every subdivision approval formality is observed without spending a cent for enforcement. If failure to comply with other community controls should result in a prior lien or a title defect on the property, compliance with controls might become all but automatic.

same objective and tends to rely on the same principles. The time has come to undertake a combined approach to these two control measures. If our level of skill warrants the use of performance standards and of community guidance on specific aspects of large-project design, then it is only causing confusion to call part of this activity "zoning" and the rest of it "subdivision control." No administrative realist lightly throws away an established body of legislation and decision as well tested as that on zoning, but up-to-date lawyers, planners, and builders can quickly agree that the time has come for simplification and improvement. It is not necessary to know the exact steps a new joint approach might take in order to underline the importance of starting discussions on the subject.

An illustration is the common failure to adjust subdivision improvement standards to zoning lot size. Since improvement standards are a reflection of the contemplated character and intensity of land use, it is only reasonable to expect them to bear some relationship to the permitted intensities. It is patently foolish for a community to require, in an area that is zoned to permit only 1 family to the acre, a level of improvement and development engineering designed to serve a density of 100 families to the acre. Yet upper-income suburbs sometimes do just this. The resulting development costs may be such that no one can afford to develop his land at the permitted density, and in the end the community is compelled to permit development at a density better suited to the required standards. On the other hand, it can be expected [27] that if, as lot size increases, the standards of improvement are reduced to reflect the reduction in requirements for drainage, traffic, and other service loads that is inherent in such an increase, the land-development costs may be reduced enough so that the larger, less-engineered lot will cost the developer and community

[27] Borne out in a study of selected Boston area communities by the Massachusetts Department of Commerce, *The Effects of Large-Lot Size on Residential Development*, Urban Land Institute, Technical Bulletin no. 32, Washington, D.C., July, 1958.

little if any more than the smaller, more highly engineered lot. Under such circumstances, the builder can afford to give the homeowner the larger lot which he seems to prefer. Thus large-lot zoning requirements need not necessarily raise land-development costs and so reduce the output of lower-priced houses, as is sometimes alleged by builders. Adjustment of sub-division improvement standards to suit permitted development density is nowhere near common enough, however, and when it is found it typically is granted at local official discretion and not as a matter of right. This is one aspect of the relationship between zoning and subdivision control on which builders could call for immediate action.

Yet in the few cases where such adjustments in standards have been put into effect, builders tend to misunderstand the purpose and enter loud complaints. They feel it is unreasonable that in the large-lot areas, which they regard as suited to high-priced houses, few improvements are required, while in the congested small-lot areas, "the bus driver, who is trying to buy a $10,000 house, must pay for all the excessive requirements." In fact, of course, the smaller lots mean more families; hence they require full streets, sidewalks, curbs, sewerage, and other engineering services, and as a result, far higher development cost per acre. The low-cost builder uses small lots because they spread these costs and thus offer the best per-lot price within the area of high accessibility that has been considered essential for low-income families.[28]

Other Subdivision Control Problems. What is the fair method of getting from the builder the land areas required for schools, parks, and other community purposes? In some states he may simply be required to convey such areas, on the assumption that his abutting land gets the benefit from the

[28] High accessibility to jobs and urban facilities may no longer be essential for such families. Inexpensive houses often go up on good-sized lots that are far out in the suburbs, with low sales prices reflecting freedom from codes (and so construction-cost savings) as much as reduction in improvement standards.

subsequent community development of the public areas and so he suffers no real loss. This is particularly true where the facility provided is required to serve his development. In others he may be required to hold the land available for the community when it wants it, and increasingly a time limit is being placed on the period within which the community must act. Some developers still argue that the community should pay for such land areas at the start if it wants to reserve rights over them. This issue calls for more detailed information concerning real costs and benefits accruing to both sides than is now available.

From time to time communities explore procedures by which a subdivision may be prevented on the ground, not that it is poorly designed or below development standards, but only that it is premature. Experts often note a need for such procedures, and there persists in many areas of the country a sharp memory of the waste, cost, and subsequent legal tangles attending the flood of premature subdivision during the boom of the 1920s. A continued rise in the basic knowledge and understanding of over-all planning agencies may one day make it possible to determine without a doubt the full extent of needed development, but for the present it seems clear that the best defense against premature subdivision is the general requirement that the subdivider invest substantial amounts of development money, so that he does not dare move too far ahead of market demand. Since development land tends to be sold today in the form not of building lots but of completed speculative houses, the required investment is very high indeed, and the developer moves with caution unless special programs and policies of the FHA or VA allow him in effect to speculate without personal risk.

But development may still be premature in terms of community facilities: schools, major utilities, etc. City planners are sympathetic to attempts to control the *pace* of development on the theory that smoother social, technical, and economic adjustments to new needs can be made when rates of growth are moderate than in periods of violent changes. Recognition of this fact has led large builders like Levitt to take the sting out of rapid community growth by building the required schools and turning them over to the community.

The Larger View

Many difficulties arise for both builder and community from the failure to see the system of building and land use controls as a comprehensive whole, rather than a collection of independent pieces, and to consider the operation of this system of controls as one having definite objectives and applying over a broad geographical area. The building-code discussion brought out the importance to a would-be innovator of obtaining uniform treatment from many communities. The interdependence of zoning and subdivision control measures has just been demonstrated. Needed as the indispensable foundation upon which all the applications of individual police power tools must rest is a continuing program of comprehensive community analysis and planning. For the essence of the problem is to find out what really needs to be controlled, and to control only that, by as simple and as direct means as possible, while allowing a maximum degree of freedom elsewhere.

Community Planning. At the present time most communities have established programs of community planning, and some have made a considerable effort in this direction, with a trained staff, a system of referring proposed public improvements for report, a capital budget procedure, and a series of published and approved reports on elements of the general plan for the community.

Programs of Federal assistance have placed a growing importance on local planning. Highway programs give recognition to local plans if they can. Public housing requires consideration of local plans. And the urban renewal program not only calls for specific reference to local plans but also, in specifying the preparation of a municipal "workable program" for long-range planning development on the part of any community seeking Federal assistance, requires that there be an effective planning agency with a full range of basic planning tools and controls. Federal funds are granted specifically for the advance planning of public works. And for smaller communities, Federal grants-in-aid share the cost of initiating planning studies beyond the resources of the community.

From the point of view of the average builder, these planning tools and controls are often exercised in an arbitrary manner because the planners either do not understand the facts of life in building development or are content to take a narrowly local view of the matter. Yet he typically does little about it, other than become intimate with key local officials in order to be in line for the benefit of a friendly doubt. He rarely seeks direct legal recourse for alleged injustices. In the first place, this procedure takes time, which he cannot afford.[29] In the second place, he suspects that the local officials will all support one another, and that if he should succeed in upsetting one ruling, he would find himself subjected to constant harassing technicalities that would make it almost impossible for him to go about his normal business. In any case, the average builder is not an innovator. He is usually concerned not with removing blocks to new methods, but only with getting red tape cleared away so that he may move ahead with his building operations. And he readily adjusts details of his designs to local preferences, in order to eliminate a major source of trouble.

If his building volume grows, his point of view changes, as does his relative ability to do something about it. The medium-sized builder may be perfectly willing to follow local regulations so far as materials and methods of construction are concerned, but he must have development land ready in advance of need in order to operate efficiently. On a few structural points he may argue with the local building inspector. But

[29] Priority on the docket, or other means of expediting court review, can be important to the builder. In some states this has been specifically granted by statute. It is a measure that deserves broader consideration.

typically he is much more concerned with the restrictions covering available land, the cost involved in providing the lot frontages and yards required under the zoning ordinance, and the general engineering layout and site design called for under the subdivision regulations. In recent years his complaints about land-planning controls have become louder and clearer whenever the mortgage-money pinch is not the overriding concern. These problems are still regarded by the National Association of Home Builders as major fighting issues for the industry.

The medium-sized builder tends to feel, and with some justification, that local control devices are being exercised for the purpose of excluding him from the community, or failing that, of forcing up his costs and prices until local tax assessments will balance rising municipal costs. Even so, he prefers not to take a case to court, for he, too, must keep going at full steam during the building season in order to make profits.

The large builder frequently solves the problem of land-planning controls by staying clear of the regulatory structure. He buys outlying land, where community controls are either nonexistent or weak, or else he operates in a community where his size, power, and experience give him a great deal of local influence. He is able to invest time and effort in clearing away local difficulties, because he will have a large and continuing operation in one place after the way has been cleared.

Thus one way for the builder to deal with the problems of local control is to grow large. Not all builders can achieve such a solution, however; many would prefer in any case not to become so large as to alter their basic pattern of operations. All are glad to benefit from such liberalization of building and planning controls as may be brought about by the efforts of some of their larger brothers, but relatively few are inclined to band together and present a united front on this problem or to use local associations as negotiating or fighting instruments. The independent builder is simply too independent a personality, on the one hand and, on the other, too thoroughly imbued with the short-range view that all profit lies in expedition and compromise. Still, the benefits of size are rapidly becoming clear and the undoubted trend of local building in this direction may be credited in part to the growing complexity and breadth of planning controls.

Larger Geographic Areas. It is increasingly clear that urban growth problems cannot be understood or solved if they are cut up and treated within the boundaries of individual small communities. As metropolitan area population pours into the outlying suburbs and as residential, industrial, and commercial developments extend along new highway systems, it becomes increasingly evident that reasonableness of development regulations and characteristics of the public interest must be considered in terms of larger development areas, probably the entire metropolitan area.

In most communities, for example, the purposes of zoning are formulated on a local basis, and it is the traditional view that the citizens of an independent municipality should guard jealously the power to determine their own goals and standards.

The courts have made it clear from the very start in the Euclid [30] case that extreme local zoning disregard of the needs of the larger community would be corrected, and in several recent cases they have specifically taken account of developments outside of the municipal jurisdiction in judging the reasonableness of local provisions.[31] The courts are not intended, qualified, or staffed to work out metropolitan development plans, however; they cannot supply an efficient building program for a multitude of independent local governments or see that maximum public benefit is gained from the use of productive resources. Indeed, as a matter of policy, they will uphold a local determination unless it is invalid beyond a reasonable doubt.

[30] *Op. cit.,* p. 316*n.*
[31] See, for example, *Cresskill v. Dumont,* 15 New Jersey 238, 104 A.2d 441, 1954.

In general, therefore, there is merit to the claim that the broad public interest is not adequately identified and protected in current zoning. A sound builder may be prevented by the concerted action of a whole ring of suburbs from providing housing that offers hope of advanced standards at reduced cost. Or on the other hand, an outlying piece of raw land may be purchased, incorporated as a municipality, and ruined by a speculative developer before any effective representation of the future public interest can be brought to bear. Such factors are increasingly recognized by planners, and metropolitan groups frequently offer guidance and advice to local communities regarding their development problems and the implications of their control proposals. It will soon be necessary to go further, however, and to formalize the means by which local zoning controls may be checked against the basic interests of the larger community.

An additional point should be made regarding enforcement of zoning. The courts called on to settle disputes in this field are less concerned with creating a structure of principles and precedents than with identifying the nature and extent of the conflicting interests of the general public and of the individual landowner or developer. They need some frame of reference in policies and facts within which to compare costs and benefits. Local control systems often fail to provide a suitable frame of reference, and in defending local provisions, individual communities often fail to supply the background of information and evidence required by the court. Similarly, builders tend to limit their presentations to the narrowest details, with no united effort to show the broad public benefits to be gained from a healthy industry. Under the circumstances, zoning decisions may be expected to be unpredictable.

As in the case of zoning, it is important under subdivision control to recognize the needs of an entire metropolitan area as well as those of the immediate community. These two types of control differ in this respect from building codes, where the concern is for the design and construction of a building rather than the use of local land, and where such regional variations as may be required—for example, by temperature and precipitation—can be reflected as factors to be read from generalized maps so that uniform regulations may be applied over very extensive areas. In zoning and subdivision control, it is important not only that detailed recognition be given to the characteristics of the local community and the land on which it lies, but also that underlying the regulations there be a basic understanding of the structure, functioning, and growth potentials of the broader area of which the community is a part. Thus, for subdivision control as for zoning, consideration should be given to setting up a review and analysis function on at least a metropolitan scale.

Such a review function might be exercised by a variety of agencies, from an unofficial committee to a formal department at a higher level of government, with a variety of areas of concern, from the metropolitan area to the county, state, or region. An unofficial metropolitan planning agency with power only to advise would perform this function better than no agency at all. The exact form and authority are less important than the fact of such an agency, provided that it has an adequate budget and a skilled staff. Such an agency could serve this purpose far better than the courts and indeed would soon find itself swamped with local requests for background analysis and professional guidance. Should matters finally require formal adjudication, the courts would be considerably aided by having before them a clear record and a well-considered frame of reference within which to judge it.[32]

Although a check on the operational practices and procedures of local communities would weed out many problems, the important element in the review procedure would be the creation of a framework of policy and planning assumptions against which the reasonableness of local programs could be checked. Population forecasts, economic base determinations,

[32] See Charles M. Haar, "The Master Plan, an Impermanent Constitution," in *Law and Contemporary Problems*, vol. 20, no. 3, Summer, 1955, p. 353.

and the locations of major transportation lines are typical elements of such a framework, and they are elements essentially beyond the determination of a single local community. In the final analysis, many of these elements may have to be determined at the state level, and since they are questions of policy, they should be considered by a body politic that is directly responsive to an electorate.

From the builder's point of view, there is much to recommend the creation of some sort of higher review function or trained appeals board. If the mechanism were easy to use and could reach rapid decisions in an emergency, the builder might more often challenge the local regulations, and the over-all result might be beneficial to all concerned.

Such an appeal mechanism could also be used by local citizens or bodies to protect the public against inadequate local administration or against the pressures that can be brought to bear on small communities by large and aggressive developers.[33]

This is not the place to discuss the formal governmental alternatives for dealing with metropolitan problems,[34] but it may be urged that a review mechanism be considered, and a few extreme possibilities may be noted to illustrate the implications of the proposal. The higher policy body might spell out over-all development goals and determinants, leaving the entire structure of local controls to be freely established by local communities within these limits. Or it might work out the general nature and extent of certain uses (housing, industry, etc.) that each local community must provide, and let the community arrange these uses much as it pleased, so long as

[33] An appeals proposal of this sort in Massachusetts in 1955 was resoundingly opposed by towns as an invasion of local liberty. There are many problems to be solved, for example, the pressures by vested interests who can afford to concentrate efforts on a board with such great potential influence.

[34] See Edward C. Banfield and Morton Grodzins, *Government and Housing in Metropolitan Areas,* McGraw-Hill Book Company, Inc., New York, 1958.

adjacent communities harmonize at mutual boundaries. Or it might spell out standardized zone descriptions and provisions, with the decision left to the local community whether and where to use them but with the benefits of standardization assured to builders. Eventually, there might be a large-scale, highly flexible "design plan" with a schedule of related provisions regarding zoning, subdivision control, and other development regulations.

However far along this line the builder and the public may be prepared to go, it is to their interests to recognize that the different kinds of municipal regulation and the different individual communities within a metropolitan area are all parts of a whole and that improved operation of the parts can come only from a closer study of the whole.

Indirect Municipal Regulations

A number of municipal actions have an indirect impact on home building, the effect of which in some cases may be greater than that of the direct controls. Some of these indirect controls are briefly noted here as a reminder of the wide range of factors that must be kept in mind if there is to be a rationally planned system of guiding residential development.

The character of local government and its wealth, as reflected in assessed valuation and tax rate, are a major determinant of development. Many communities and states have used exemption or partial exemption from taxes as a means of encouraging development, usually of industrial property, but sometimes of commercial or residential. Long before the time of Henry George, arguments were made in favor of differentiating in rate or assessment basis between taxes on the land and those on improvements, or between different classes of property, in order to encourage or even compel development. Planners have proposed the deferment of increases in the local assessments on open land (under compact on the part of the owner to pay at what would have been normal rates all the way back to date of initial agreement, should he ever decide to develop) as an efficient method of retaining selected metropolitan land areas in low intensity of use as breathing spaces without requiring public expenditures.

Equitable distribution of taxes on industrial and commercial land, to cover the costs of education and other municipal services in the area where workers live, is one of the undoubted benefits of adopting some form of metropolitan equalization or tax system. And there is a wide range of real estate taxes, personal property taxes, income taxes, and sales or business taxes. Yet taxes are of only indirect importance to the builder in determining design and construction, though he takes whatever steps he can to minimize them.[35]

Eminent domain, or the right to condemn private property for public purposes in return for just compensation, is another local power that may have an effect on builders, but it is a power usually exercised in the central-city areas where the objective is urban renewal rather than the construction of new houses. It can be used to clear away title and tax encumbrances on undeveloped land and to obtain roadways and public building sites; otherwise it is of less interest to builders than most of the other controls in current use. Planners occasionally suggest the creation of a public or semipublic land agency to take land and hold it for development purposes in order to lift the standards and check the speculative profits of private land development. Usually suggested for industrial development purposes, it may be considered also for residential development, although builder resistance and basic legal complications are sure to be very great. Probably more acceptable is the proposal that the public condemn development rights in order to preserve open spaces in the urban structure.

Annexation procedures are coming back into use. In the

---

[35] For one special kind of building—the mobile home—the problems implicit in finding an appropriate method of local taxation and a fair level of municipal services are more important, because many a community will continue to fight trailers and trailer parks until it has been convinced that these problems as well as the related social problems can be solved.

nineteenth century, adding to municipal land through annexation of outlying areas was a common and important aspect of municipal growth. During the current century, legislative requirements (in most states, majority vote of both the annexing and annexed areas) for a time made it almost a dead issue, since outlying areas almost universally feared the consequences of being added to the central city with its higher taxes and greater economic and social problems. Today, outlying areas are under a serious handicap in many parts of the country unless they can obtain the benefits of municipal water supply and sewage disposal, and frequently they want to use municipal schools and other facilities as well. As a result, not only are there more cases of annexation, but also special assessments are charged by the central city to cover the pro rata share of the capital cost of services.

The granting of extensions of municipal services may in itself be used very effectively to control outlying residential development, entirely aside from questions of annexation.[36] Until the day of the autonomous (fully self-contained) house arrives, it will be essential for builders to have water piped in, sewage piped out, and access to the city provided by good roads. One of the main determinants of urban development patterns in the future, for example, is likely to be the access provided to new areas of raw land by the extensive program of new Federal highways for which initial appropriations were made in 1956.

Recently, builders have devoted a good deal of attention to the possibilities of private project systems for the supply of water and the disposal of wastes, and the pressure for such developments has increased with the realization that extensive areas of the country have soil conditions unsuited to the use of septic tanks. Furthermore, communities have deliberately re-

[36] The courts will intercede if the community goes too far. See *Reid Development Corp. v. Township of Parsippany-Troy Hills,* 10 New Jersey 229, 89 A.2d 667 (1952).

fused water and sewer extensions, or have asked exorbitant prices for these services, as a means of blocking development. In some cases, the service extensions have even been used as a club to force major concessions in development design—larger lot sizes, for example.

There has also been a good deal of interest recently in the design and production of chemical and mechanical toilets that can considerably simplify the job of waste disposal. In the long run, it is conceivable that technological developments of this sort may make largely obsolete many of the fundamental principles upon which rest modern municipal requirements regarding subdivision design. It is also possible that other lines of technological development may completely undermine the requirements based on a need for light and air in many zoning provisions. A high standard of human environment can be provided by artificial means. These and other possibilities will have a decided influence on the level and characteristics of municipal services in the future, and so on their effectiveness as a device for development control.

Private Controls

Of great importance to builder and community alike is the structure of private controls on the land built up through the use of deed restrictions and covenants. The courts have long recognized a high degree of freedom for these private contractual agreements, and developers and government agencies have long understood their importance in securing certain major aspects of development value: cost level of houses, for instance, or architectural style and major materials. Using deed restrictions together with flexible zoning and subdivision controls, it becomes possible to regulate community design in considerable detail. This combination is at present more closely studied for redevelopment and renewal applications than for outlying residential development, but it has been a common element of subdivision practice, and as such is recommended in detail by the FHA for projects that it insures.[37] That the courts will maintain a check on the abuse of private covenants has been illustrated by the refusal of the Supreme Court to permit use of the courts to enforce race-restrictive covenants. For the most part, however, the courts will sustain the major positive elements of a structure of covenants.

In the future, communities may have to find ways of reviewing the reasonableness of this sort of control, perhaps even by some special review body at the metropolitan level. The basic planning objectives would be the same as for review of public controls, though, of course, legal difficulties would be vastly greater.

Also significant as controls on building development are a number of local institutional forces: the real estate fraternity, the unions, the local tradesmen and building-supply channels, and most of all, the banking fraternity with its procedures and policies concerning the making of construction and mortgage loans and its estimate of the local market preferences and demands. A brilliant innovator may occasionally wonder, like "The Man in the White Suit," [38] whether all these people really want him to bring out a substantially better product at a sharply reduced price.

Specifically, attention needs to be drawn to closing costs, now running as much as $500 per house (or in the same order of magnitude as the average plumbing contract) and representing a contribution to an archaic legal and administrative system. Operations research methods and the recording of title data on business machines should substantially cut the cost of title search and insurance and might eliminate the need for a separate fee for each lot in a major development. Legal re-

[37] Charles S. Ascher in Coleman Woodbury (ed.), *Urban Redevelopment: Problems and Practices,* University of Chicago Press, Chicago, 1953, pp. 223ff., offers an interesting study of the use of private covenants in the development of a new community.

[38] A British motion picture of the 1950s in which the inventor of an indestructible, nonsoiling cloth sees every faction of industry and labor try to suppress the idea.

search should make major simplifications in the costly closing process.

Federal Mortgage Guarantees

No discussion of local controls would be complete if it did not underline the tremendous significance to the builder of FHA and VA guarantee of mortgages on his houses. In some areas of the country, New England and many small Middle Western towns, for example, major reliance is placed on the regular operations of local commercial and savings banks and savings and loan associations. In most of the country, however, the government mortgage guarantee is a major factor in home building. For many a large-scale builder or prefabricator, advance commitments on mortgages insured under FHA or VA have been almost a requirement of volume production.

The regulations of these agencies are constantly under fire by builders for adding needless and occasionally indefensible costs and complications to the building process. Maisel in his study of housebuilding in the San Francisco Bay area [39] substantiates the frequency of builder allegations of difficulties both in processing procedures and in substantive rulings and interpretations. It takes time, skill, and experience to handle FHA and VA smoothly—an advantage to the larger builders.

FHA has recently taken a number of steps to deal with the most frequent complaints. Appraisals now may make allowance for increases in cost that will yield increases in value. The income formula of FHA has been adjusted to encourage greater expenditures for housing as family income rises. But builders still feel that fair allowance is not made in appraisals for the cost of borrowing money or for sales costs, and they would like mortgage rates freed from control to stimulate the flow of investment money into housebuilding. FHA is also criticized for not easing the financing of trade-in deals and for the autonomy of its local offices, but underneath all this, builders

[39] Sherman J. Maisel, *Housebuilding in Transition*, University of California Press, Berkeley, Calif., 1953, pp. 250ff.

recognize that FHA has been an important ally and a major factor in the rapid rise of home ownership and suburban growth.

Perhaps the basic question to be asked is one rarely raised by builders: what is the long-range purpose of Federal mortgage insurance? The government has consistently followed the view that the purpose is one of spreading the benefits and building the security of conventional consumer financing, and its actions have been based upon policies appropriate to a conservative local banking institution. However, some within the government and many outside believe that a major purpose should be to maximize both the output and the quality of housing production—to improve the health of the industry. In this view, conservatism regarding design and construction, and the retention of extensive powers in local offices to judge local marketability, must necessarily and irrevocably interfere with innovation and tie producers to the standards of today.

Government mortgage insurance conservatism does not affect the many builders who are content to follow any regulation so long as it is clear, predictable, easy to follow, and sure to result in good valuations and easy sales. Nor does it eliminate dedicated innovators or powerful operators. For many intelligent builders (and, as important, might-have-been builders) however, conservatism in the fiscal control system means that the new cannot be tried, and thus a major opportunity to improve the manner of doing things is rejected. The broad competitive position of an industry so "supported" may in the long run be weakened as a result of government intervention.

Other industries know that to survive means to encourage innovation, for the best security lies in seeding, nourishing, and cultivating the ability to improve designs and production methods. The housing agency should be as well qualified as any in the country to check out new ideas in a climate of change. It could be thorough and hardheaded in selecting experimental projects and in keeping records on new systems, so that the broadest possible advantage would be taken of our vast laboratory of building experience.

It may be argued that the creation by government assistance programs of the low-risk builder whose primary interest is in being bailed out by fiscal regulations has been a two-edged sword. Many serious students of the building industry feel that production credit should be separated from consumer credit and that the government should slant its guarantee program toward the development of stable producers with a real interest in housing. Under present conditions, too many capable builders are quietly getting out of the industry.

Government regulations have a great influence not only on the design and construction of the house itself, but also on the design of the site plan and the layout of the community as a whole. Although one may concede the sound common sense of the present conventional standards established by the government, one may still urge that long-range public interests require greater freedom. Even in an area without other codes or controls of any sort, the builder typically finds his designs in effect dictated by FHA. Currently land is a major problem, and a new breed of speculators is entering the field, snapping up options and inflating costs. Under current rules and policies, the FHA misses an opportunity to help sound builders find land-development money, and to encourage the growth of imaginative organizations that can spread development risks over a period of years and take early losses in order to gain ultimate profits. In emphasizing the conventional soundness of each separate application, the agency may be accused of not seeing the forest for the trees.

Conclusion

A review of the complex network of building and land use controls brings out certain general points that may be made more explicit here.

Localism. The emergence of an efficient housing industry

has long been hindered by localism, but to the degree that this is understood by the public, there is evidence that it tends to meet with approval. For the most part, builders have failed to persuade citizens that there are substantial benefits in better living to be gained from the abandonment of local autonomy in controls, and they have almost completely failed to suggest satisfactory answers to such crucial local questions as: who will pay for the schools? Builders themselves rarely understand the importance of having wide market areas of uniform regulation and firm ceilings over local variation as requirements for the introduction of major innovations in materials and construction systems.

For the application of development controls in a period of high mobility and fast growth, a view larger than that of the local community is needed, and it cannot be adequately provided by court review. There seems no reason why the basic framework for building-code regulation could not be uniform throughout the state or even the entire nation, and expert review at a larger scale is needed even for local zoning and subdivision control.

Elasticity. There is a trend, on the whole desirable, in the direction of relaxing the rigid form of police power control in order to deal with the larger and more complex development projects which are becoming common. This has coincided with the emergence of trained city planning staffs, and for the larger and better-managed builders, it has offered many advantages in preparing development plans. On the other hand, the risk of arbitrary action has risen accordingly, and there are problems, of which aesthetic control is an example, which deserve much consideration if well-meaning regulation is not to cause needless interference with creative growth in the industry.

Comprehensiveness. Since the original lines between many of the controls over building and land use are fast being blurred, it is becoming clear that, whether direct or indirect, public or private, all must be considered parts of a single whole.

This may require that some separate police power tools like zoning and subdivision control be interrelated, or even combined. It surely will require a broad coordination of actions, for example, relating the extension of municipal sewers to decisions regarding tax assessment and zoning.

Implied in the comprehensive view is the idea that there should be rational objectives, and it is becoming increasingly important that development controls be the expression of a general development plan for the community. Without an approved framework of policy against which to judge specific community regulations, the courts may be expected to find them arbitrary and unreasonable. A balance must be struck not only between builder and purchaser, but also between the interests of the broad community and those of the emerging housing industry. And the nature of these interests must be frankly disclosed and fully faced. Of what use to demonstrate beyond doubt that a new product is safe and sound if the real community objective is to prohibit additional growth entirely? Conversely, if development controls are increasingly distorted to help communities avert critical problems of development cost, of what use for builders to complain, unless they are willing to face up to these critical problems?

Government Policy. Government controls, despite many advances, still are concerned primarily with conventional methods. Agencies must ask themselves whether, if the objective of their intervention is improved housing for the people, the best approach is only to assure the fiscal security of individual mortgage agreements, or whether they should not also take steps to speed the emergence of an imaginative, strong, and self-reliant housing industry.

Chapter 10

THE FUTURE BUILDERS

In this chapter, Burnham Kelly, noting a present stalemate in the housing industry, reviews the forces that appear to make major changes in housing design and production inevitable. He then suggests some courses of action that may help future builders to realize the potential benefits of an industry free to innovate in all aspects of its operations.

Present Stalemate

Earlier chapters have indicated that people are dissatisfied with the present housing industry, suspecting that they are given an inferior value for their money and a kind of design that will not fit in with the rapidly changing patterns of living in houses and in domestic communities. These are not complaints to be answered by minor adjustments, sale campaigns, and new styling. Fundamental improvements are called for, and a few merchant builders, prefabricators, and mobile home manufacturers have already demonstrated that significant steps along the way can be taken when parts of the operation no longer have to run the endless gauntlet of conventions and traditions.

Major design and production advances are in the air on all sides. New uses of materials and construction methods are being combined with improved studies of environmental needs to produce significant innovations in design of the house, of the site development, and of the production system itself. Many of the resulting new forms have had wide attention, and

348

the normal conservatism of homeowners has begun to fade, partly because of repeated experiences with the deficiencies of conventional building experienced in residential suburbs all over the nation.

Yet until the present time developments in the housing industry can hardly be called startling. Significant blocks stand in the path of all who would make major changes, blocks which are rendered doubly effective by the fact that they are interconnected, hemming in the innovator and supporting each other, so that only the most determined builders ever dare attempt to break out. Localism is the common foundation for all these blocks.

Throughout the centuries, the pattern by which houses have been designed and built has remained essentially local, though the character of construction and of building materials has undergone considerable change. Even today, when nine-tenths of the builders put up more than five houses per year and the craft builder is rapidly vanishing, a high percentage of the work is still done at the site by workmen organized along the old craft lines, and most of the building materials—though they may come from anywhere in the country—are purchased from local distributors who have to stock a large assortment for a long time and charge the builder accordingly. Decisions regarding soundness of design, construction, and marketability are made by local public officials and bankers, even though investment standards may be set in Washington. And the builders themselves, never able to predict their future, set up their organizations to cope with local variations in house design and wild fluctuations in volume of business. Organization, distribution, design, labor, controls—all aspects of the industry are admirably suited for the conventional job they have been doing. Although this picture is changing and many improvements have been made in recent years, broader and sharper changes are needed at the present time. Aggressive corporations can serve both their own and the public's interests by showing the way to sound industrialization, but it will require the coordinated attention of all elements of the industry before the web of local restraints can be swept away.

Forces for Change

A number of forces are fast developing that will bring significant changes in housing design and production. Under the impact of these forces, the industry cannot much longer continue the comfortable pretense that it remains its old, localized self. There must soon come the time when the degree and character of change have reached that subtle, indefinable point at which the strength of conventional resistance suddenly fades away and there is a "snap-over" to an entirely new industrial situation, in which stereotypes are abandoned and standards undergo rapid and radical transformation.

Demand. Among these forces for change are the extent and character of future demand for houses. Both actual and potential demand are rising steadily at present, and there seems no doubt of a swift further rise in the 1960s, starting perhaps with that convenient urban home base for the young and old adults that we have called the "minimum-involvement house," but soon swelling the market for all other housing types as well. When the demand for new dwellings runs above 1.5 million units per year, as seems entirely possible, there will be not merely an opportunity but a real need for the development of new materials and methods. The time is already short for the over-all research, planning, and organization work that will be required if the industry is to take full advantage of such a boom.

Another growing force is the tendency for house buyers to be served in larger groups, better suited to new production methods. The project approach becomes increasingly familiar —both on the outer metropolitan fringes where new highways have opened raw land areas for development and in the central city where appropriate areas have been assembled for re-development.

Builder Size. The trend towards larger-sized enterprises is clear, and definite pressures for change come with size, whether it is achieved through single integrated organizations or through the combined forces of many smaller and more specialized companies. Large orders for materials, equipment, and components mean that quantity methods may be used by basic suppliers. Programs of research may be undertaken with a reasonable expectation of paying off. Production and distribution may be so phased as to reduce the impact of such discouraging variables as weather conditions and population mobility. In turn, real advantages may be offered to building labor in the form of improved working conditions and more predictable work periods. Effective advertising and sales programs may be created, as may the service and repair forces that go with the development of an effective secondhand market.

The very speed, efficiency, and volume required of basic production operations in the future tend to encourage large organizations, as do the complex problems involved in assembling land, obtaining planning approvals, arranging for utility extensions, and carrying out site improvements. Conversely, large operators, anxious to gather and hold competent work crews, may be expected to take advantage of new materials and systems of construction in order to extend to the maximum the building year and reduce seasonal fluctuation. This implies a tendency to develop components, assemblies, and panels in advance, and to organize and mechanize site operations. In order to increase rates of production, advanced techniques are being used in financing and marketing, with the trend continuing toward acceptance corporations, package and open-end mortgages, trade-in deals, and special tax-savings arrangements.

These advantages and implications of size bring with them, however, a substantial increase in the management and overhead cost per house. It is the experience of the larger merchant builders that such costs are already a larger share of the total than the costs of the basic structure and finish on the one hand, or of the sum of its mechanical equipment and services on the other. Also required with large-scale operations is a volume of sales that is large, stable, and predictable beyond the hopes of most producers today. Although the average builder size will increase, therefore, there will remain a large number of builders in the twenty-five units per year range where complications of overhead are smaller, and they will continue to offer a valuable service.

Indeed, no particular brief should be held for size as such. No doubt it will require the cumulative concern of a number of really large organizations to effect a significant breakthrough on the tangled local front, but once this has been done, the controls and conditions will be changed for all comers. Thenceforth it will be possible for a wide range of organizations to produce efficiently, taking full advantage of industrial components, dimensional standards, and the more elastic control and finance measures that will emerge as a result of the breakthrough. In sum, the large-scale producers serve the important function of removing needless localized blocks and, in return, stand to benefit from being first in the new field. Once these blocks have been removed, the way is open for anyone to try his hand with new designs, new patterns of distribution, or new kinds of over-all production organizations.

Off-site Production. Throughout the housing industry there is a desire to avoid the inconvenience and cost inherent in site work. With the exception of the merchant builders who completely control and in effect industrialize site operations on a large scale, more and more attention is turned to the growing effectiveness and economy of off-site assembly and finishing operations.

Most builders are subject to frequent weather delays and many operations stop altogether in winter. Even where the objective of a production system is to retain a high degree of flexibility in final design by varying the site assembly of standard pieces, therefore, every effort is made to reduce the assembly operation to its simplest possible terms. At the extreme,

the makers of mobile homes have all but eliminated site operations, and this, plus the fact that the mobile home is not treated
as a piece of real estate, has almost entirely freed it from the
shackles binding the rest of the industry. Here, almost alone on
the housing front, the materials and methods of modern industry are in general use.

Skilled site labor is already scarce and is likely to become
increasingly so in the future. Off-site production should, if
union lines and policies can be worked out satisfactorily, offer
better conditions for bargaining and organization on the labor
side and for work patterns and benefits on that of management.
The building trades are old, respected, and powerful organizations, and no one expects that they will weaken and disappear,
but it is reasonable to expect that they will find ways of ad-
justing to the changing methods and conditions of housing
production. Perhaps, along the lines worked out by the unions
associated with the national highway program, several of the
building trades will combine to work out arrangements for
labor supply and processes of negotiation, taking advantage of
the opportunity to organize this major sector of the economy
as it moves toward genuine industrialization, and giving recognition to the changing work patterns that would be involved.

The Large Producers. A factor of considerable importance
in the shift from traditional localism is the growing attention
being paid to the housing field by the large producers of materials and equipment. Until recently, basic material producers
were content to sell a relatively raw material to a customer
who carried it only a step or two along the way, very seldom
concerning themselves with its ultimate incorporation in the
final house. These companies are tending to recognize that the
research and development effort required to find new and
better uses for their products is one they cannot leave to the
small fabricators and builders. On the other hand, it would not
make sense to develop a sound product and simply turn it over
to a customer to reap the rewards. Furthermore, many see
housing as an important growth area, one of the few remaining

industrial frontiers, in which the kind of organizational skill and industrial stature that they have developed can be put to profitable use. Many large materials producers are now broadening their efforts, therefore, bringing out assemblies and components that represent a real concern for the design of the final house and even exploring the fully integrated approach that lets them coordinate operations right through to the actual erection of the house. Such efforts will very soon bring about a significant change in the character of the housing industry.

Of particular interest are a number of companies not usually thought of as part of the housing industry, the appliance makers, whose influence has rapidly grown with the increasing level of mechanical services of all sorts provided in the average home. These companies have a double advantage: they serve those aspects of domestic living which are least bound by consumer conservatism and they operate in relative freedom from the localisms which encumber the regular housing industry. They have brought about major changes in housing design with minor resistance, because they concern themselves primarily with simplifying or improving household tasks and services and very little with the architectural appearance of the living areas.

The appliance manufacturers have become so active along these lines that industry spokesmen say they are selling the builders' houses for them. Indeed, some point out that if trends continue as at present, the appliance industry may soon dominate the housing industry, leaving it to the vestiges of the present industry to do a sort of exterior packaging job. For their part, appliance men know that about half of their growth items go into houses, and that well-designed houses are their best showroom. Even though the real profit in the appliance industry may come from the replacement market in 55 million existing dwelling units, the builders of new houses are at the very least a necessary evil, and the appliance industry takes good care of them with large advertising allowances and discounts. The ability of these companies to make significant innovations in design and production is clear, and they are well acquainted with the potentials of mass production. To a typical builder, 500 refrigerators may be volume, but to one of these companies it is just a drop in the bucket.

So great are the resources of many of these manufacturers that, once convinced of the long-range profitability of a new approach, they can afford to tool up for a really large-scale effort. The larger among them can even "buy in" to an emerging development field through superior ability to allocate funds to build up productive capacity and sales channels, although initial research and product development may have been done elsewhere. In the vast housing market a relatively small penetration (as little as 2 per cent) may be profitable, but those getting into large production first can dominate the field.

For several reasons, many of the large companies hesitate to attempt any broad move into the housing field at the present time. Housing production often is only a small part of their total production, and it is one for which the profit prospects are not always clear and bright. In this area, they face competition from the traditional wood technology which produces the bulk of current housing—a technology of cut-and-fit at the site and minimal investment in overhead and tools that is almost ideally adjusted to the feasts and famines of local housing demand. None of the new approaches, metals, plastics, or combinations, can get by with so little capitalization and overhead. All require large volumes of sales, continued over long periods of time, if they are to yield a decent return on investment. However, the growth prospects of the industry are great, and the rewards for effective leadership may be high. There seems little doubt that the large producers will be a major force for change.

Ways and Means

In the very broadest terms, the objective of the housing industry is to provide a better over-all living environment, and the best general means of attaining this objective is to clear the way for innovation. The potential market is so great and the present product so poor that men of high capacity would be quickly attracted to the industry if they believed that an end had come to current frustrations. This final section calls attention to some points that deserve attention from those who will be the builders of the future.

Managerial Innovation. Essential to innovation in production and design is a full understanding of the managerial framework in which the new operations will be couched. Contrary to the popular impression, the industry is rich in ideas for new materials, systems of construction, and plans. Many of the concepts which stir our imaginations today have appeared again and again in the past, in varying modulations. What has been lacking is the organization that could put these concepts into effect.

In discussing the potentialities of component construction systems, for example, a key question turns out to be: who will be the entrepreneur? Who will undertake to fill in the intervening steps between the fabricator and basic distributor on the one hand and the ultimate purchaser of the assembled house on the other? The component approach seems to call for a new kind of organization. Similarly, in the suggestion that important progress might be made if the producer could carry through all the way from the initial building-materials operations to the final house, there was implied a substantial shift from the current operating practices—a new management, able to command the resources of a large corporation but also integrated horizontally across the entire production front.

In short, one of the current needs in the housing industry is managerial innovation. This is an area in which the United States has always been strong, but somehow the housing industry has been almost bypassed. The experience of the prefabricators and the merchant builders shows how effective and how profitable it may be to view the housing production problem in management terms.

Land-development Organization. Increasingly attractive to those interested in the emerging housing industry is the creation of a land-development organization—a step taken by most of the successful big housebuilders of the 1940s and one which was discussed in Chapter 4. Many experienced men believe that, during the next decade at least, the most profitable end product of successful builder organizations will be land value appreciation, and that as a means of generating a market for any new building product, an investment in broad-based land development will yield returns well above any program of advertising and promotion among individual builders.

The process of large-scale land development may also give a better opportunity for innovation, since most of the limiting localisms can be avoided and there is reason to believe that people more readily drop their housing stereotypes when they move to a large new project.

A company interested in the housebuilding field may well consider, therefore, the use or creation of a land-development organization, either as a wholly owned subsidiary or jointly with others whose product spread in the final house would be complementary. In the first place, this forces the attention of management on the process of housebuilding as a whole, underlining the many broad implications of design. Secondly, such an organization, properly managed, should be profitable, granted enough time to gather the benefits of a planned program of purchase and development. In the third place, a land-development organization offers the means of pulling together and working with groups of local builders whose management skills leave something to be desired.

At the present time, home builders, even very successful ones, do relatively little long-range thinking. By comparison with other industry, it is rare to find a builder management in which major policies are programed in advance by a board of directors on the basis of carefully researched decisions. Far more typical is the *ad hoc* policy decision made when it can no longer be avoided by a powerful individual who is completely sure that he "knows" the industry. Tied in as final processing stages for an organization that does the long-range planning and supplies in quantity the vital development lots upon which all depend, these typical builders can supply, however, a good deal of energy, experience, and specialized skill.

One key to a successful land-development organization is a large-scale operation. The so-called volume builder typically finds land in short supply, and when he locates a tract, he finds that the landowners have figured long in advance where he will have to go and how much he will have to pay. The land developer, on the other hand, is able to buy very large land areas, well in advance of any appreciation in value, and on favorable terms. He then puts in his improvements (he may retain some utilities as an investment) and proceeds to make deals with local builders. Long before any permits are taken out, major design decisions have been made and supplies of major appliances and pieces of equipment have been ordered. It is obviously important for materials and appliance manufacturers to get in touch early with such an operation and to keep a skilled and broadly trained representative on hand throughout the design and decision period.

Integrated Subsidiary. Another way of exploring the potentials of the housing field would be to have a large company create a special subsidiary to operate all the way from land development to building. A major materials manufacturer, for example, would bring to such a combination an existing production and distribution experience and probably a close familiarity with the problems of building. The mere entrance of such an organization into the business of land assembly and community development would tend to lend the operation dignity in the public mind and would bring a range of management skills and fiscal resources not usually available. If a few major manufacturers should enter the field in this way, many more would be tempted to do so in the future, and the combined impact of a group of publicly financed and well-managed organizations operating on an integrated basis across the entire production process would be almost certain to lead to the elimination of conventional restrictions. Reliance could be placed on the competitive drive between companies and the desire to be the earliest and best in the field to put the necessary pressure on the trouble spots.

The Design Team. The process of design for an over-all production operation as complex as that of housing is obviously not one that can be isolated and assigned to men whose training and experience rarely span more than a single aspect of the operation. It becomes fairly clear that the real need is for a balanced team—representing a good cross section of experience with the whole range of housing production—where each member knows and respects the contribution that must be made by the others, much as would a group of medical specialists in group practice. Understood in this broad sense, design is an essential staff function for any future producer.

A major problem in obtaining sound over-all design is the shortage of men with the necessary education and training. The gap continues to be wide between the professional designer and the successful builder; few indeed are the men who can be said to have developed experience and skill on both sides.

Schools of architecture are hard pressed to give students a basic grasp of background and techniques while training them to perceive their environment, to understand its deficiencies, and to exercise a trained sense of responsibility for its improvement. Few can give a sense of the industry with which architects will work.

In housing work, the designer increasingly must concern himself with decisions made far up in the production channels if he is to have a broad influence over the final product; this same change is taking place in industrial work, in commercial work, and in all major building projects. Yet the student typically has little idea of emerging production techniques and little stimulus to inform himself about them.

In view of the tremendous importance of the new scale of

building and land-development operations in shaping our entire urban environment, some means must be found to build up appropriate educational resources and bring them to bear on these problems. Since many different educational fields are involved, each requiring a fair degree of sophistication, a likely initial approach might be a special forum for mutual education and policy exchange, leading to research studies that will cope with problems identified as most pressing. When the housing industry has been more truly industrialized and has become strong and stable, training a team and fitting it into the over-all operation will be easier, but the essential element must still be a fundamental concern with the design of total environment.

Consumer Education. The usual solution suggested for every design problem is consumer education; here, this may be an impractical aspiration. In some small, relatively homogeneous, and very stable countries, average levels of consumer education in design are high. This proceeds in large part from the presence of an accepted and respected elite group that serves to lead the way. In this country, we lack these benefits (and the counterbalancing disadvantages) of an elite; instead, we have developed a high degree of social mobility, a disrespect for all formal authority, and a tendency to regard the house as a symbol of our emerging status. Each buyer seeks to express in his purchase the safest common denominator of what he believes to be the standards of the group he is joining; the result is a romantic display of conservatism, kept "up to date" with gadgets.

We may hope, as writers about the automobile hope, that the decline of this product as a status symbol and its emergence as a utilitarian service will offer an opportunity for real improvement in design. The housing counterpart of the well-designed Volkswagen may be on the way soon. To illustrate the converse, it is only necessary to observe what has happened to small-boat design in the last few years, since the boat has begun to take its place as a status symbol. Perhaps the best hope for good housing will come when the implications of our nomadic family life are recognized in the over-all production process, and housing comes to be accepted by a sizable minority of families as a rental service, with all the adjustments in over-all design and production required by such a change. Two rapidly increasing groups in the population, the young and old adults, very much want such a service. If this line is followed with imagination and skill, the single-family house may lose its notoriously bad reputation as a rental property.

Government Policy. A past president of NAHB, calling for courageous leadership in the housing industry, has listed as basic needs the creation of Cabinet rank for housing, some assurance that the industry will not be used for anticyclical manipulation by economic planners, a central mortgage bank able to issue notes and debentures based on government-insured mortgages, a better FHA (renamed the Federal Mortgage Insurance Corporation to reflect its real function), improvements in trade-in financing and urban-renewal operations, and an all-out attack on costs.[1] It is interesting and significant that all but the last of these points relate directly to matters of government policy and procedure, and that even the last, upon examination, implies extensive government participation.

The importance of government intervention in this field has been underscored elsewhere in this book, and nothing indicates a diminution of its importance in the future. In fact, as is the case with many major problems of our day, the housing problem can be made manageable only when there are intelligent government programs and examples, and the cumulative effect of government policies can have a positive effect on the character and extent of private initiative and of broad innovation in the field. To complement the private industrialization of housing production, it is absolutely essential that there be coordina-

---

[1] Tom Coogan, "Today's Crises in Home Building: Halfway Measures Won't Cure Them," guest editorial in *House & Home*, vol. 15, no. 2, August, 1958, p. 130.

tion among government activities and that major policies be stable over the years.

At the present time, even units nominally part of the over-all housing agency are almost completely independent and uncoordinated, and many significant government housing operations—those of the armed services, for example—are not even nominally under the agency. Major operating bases of the industry can be upset by a single decision on the conditions or rates of mortgage insurance. If, for instance, the costs of land development were authorized for inclusion within the mortgage guarantee system, many of the advantages described earlier for land-development organizations would disappear, and any large builder could take advantage of the opportunity to plan his operations well in advance. Yet neither the government nor the industry is prepared today to make a serious analysis of the housing problem as a whole.

Such an analysis is long overdue, and it might start with the question: what is the basic objective of government activities in the housing field? *Ad hoc* programs pushed through to meet emergencies on narrow fronts tend necessarily to confuse and conflict. Broad social objectives may prove empty if they are pursued without consideration of the potentialities of design and production. In the long run, the best assurance of a high level of housing may lie in setting the conditions for the emergence of a healthy and inventive housing industry.

Rallying the Industry. A great deal of progress will be made in the next few years by large, aggressive companies that experiment with new organizations and push their way through the tangle of localized limitations that has long frustrated the housing industry. If the way is to be cleared for broad innovation, however, it is important to develop a rallying ground to which key men from all aspects of the industry will want to come, in order to build up mutual understanding and then to spark concerted action on matters of industry concern. The move in 1958 by a group of related associations and professional societies, headed by Henry Luce and ACTION, to open the way for a single set of national regulations regarding the construction of one- and two-family dwellings is a step in the right direction. We may expect a real rise in the influence and effectiveness of the industry when it is able to speak with a single, considered voice.

No existing organization is perfectly constituted to provide such a rallying ground at present. The Producers Council, which purports to bring together major producers and the design professions, has been too narrow and too conventional to take the lead in such an effort. BRAB-BRI, growing rapidly and already making a significant contribution to research and development coordination, serves the industry in many ways, but its interest has focused largely on specific technical and production problems. The Housing Center of NAHB, is helping to generate new cooperation and leadership among builders, but it does not provide a broad enough spectrum. Government agencies in general would find it very difficult to provide effective leadership. The magazines supply a useful stimulus, but they cannot be expected to convert themselves into an agency for the solution of industry problems, nor do they always have the full confidence of all concerned. Single major companies may take the lead from time to time, but for effective coordinated action, there seems no alternative to finding a new device to stimulate interest and confidence, coordinate all points of view, and seek agreement on courses of action.

Many of the considerations to be kept in mind in the development of such a device were summarized at the start of the last section of Chapter 8. Of these, the most important is that, however the initial organization may be financed and staffed, the forum must be a working tool rather than a publicity device, supported by the key elements of the industry which stand to profit most from its operation.

Conclusion

In covering the housing industry in the broadest possible way, this book has tried to show that what had long been regarded as a dismal morass is now emerging as a stimulating challenge. True, impediments to progress are more widespread and more deeply rooted than many have realized, but the basic picture is fast changing. Conventional assumptions and practices will not long survive the changes now in process throughout our society. All will applaud the emergence of a strong and stable housing industry, keyed to high standards of environmental design and dedicated to a maximum freedom of innovation. And conditions for such a development are all but ideal. But it is not reasonable to hold back and await the unequivocal demand of an aroused public. The complications are too great and the opportunities for personal exposure to the benefits of new approaches are too few. Nor can the government, assuming it could be given the appropriations, the men, and the constancy of purpose, produce by itself all the necessary conditions for change.

If the present opportunity is to be seized, the responsibility for taking the initiative rests with the designers and the producers working together with mutual respect. For the designers, the problem is a familiar one, to which a constant few have devoted creative energy for decades, usually without much basic understanding of the over-all production operations involved. For the major producers, conditions have not until recently been favorable for significant innovations, but now they have splendid opportunity to get in at the very start of an unusual growth situation. The time has come to take advantage of the situation, work out design and production plans, and lead the way to a mature housing industry in the next decade.

Appendix A
HOUSING DEMAND

This appendix, the material for which was assembled by Castle N. Day, presents a summary view of the future growth of potential and actual demand for housing and considers factors affecting the type of housing required and the available supply.

Future Demands and Requirements

The prediction of housing needs is usually made in terms of households, and for this purpose "household" is defined as a group of people occupying one dwelling unit. Obviously, the number of households formed at any given time depends not only on the size and character of the population and on the available stock of dwelling units, but also on a number of other factors such as national wealth and social attitudes. The more concrete statistics are more easily presented, however.

Table A-1 shows that three-quarters of our households are headed by husband and wife; the remaining quarter is made up either of family groups not headed by a married couple or of individuals living alone or with friends. In addition to these households, there are other family groups [1] and individuals who double

[1] In 1947, 8.7 per cent of the married couples did not have their own households; since then the proportion has steadily declined and in 1957 only 3.3 per cent were in this category. Most couples without their own households are young families living with parents. "Households and Families by Type: 1947 to 1955," U.S. Bureau of the Census, *Current Population Reports, Population Characteristics*, ser. P-20, no. 59, August 12, 1955; "Households and Families by Type: 1950 to 1957, *ibid.*, ser. P-20, no. 76, July 5, 1957.

TABLE A-1. Composition of Households in United States

Year	Total households (in thousands)	Primary families			
		Per cent households primary families	Per cent households husband-wife families	Per cent households other families	Per cent households primary individuals
1940	34,949	90.1	76.0	14.1	9.9
1947	39,107	89.4	78.3	11.1	10.6
1948	40,532	90.4	78.7	11.7	9.6
1949	42,182	90.3	78.8	11.5	9.7
1950	43,554	89.7	78.2	11.0	10.3
1951	44,656	88.6	77.0	11.6	11.4
1952	45,505	88.4	77.2	11.2	11.6
1953	46,334	87.4	76.7	10.7	12.6
1954	46,893	87.3	76.5	10.8	12.7
1955	47,788	87.3	75.9	11.4	12.7
1956	48,785	87.2	75.9	11.3	12.8
1957	49,543	87.2	76.1	11.1	12.8

Source: "Households and Families, by Type: 1950 to 1957," U.S. Bureau of the Census, *Current Population Reports, Population Characteristics*, ser. P-20, no. 76, July 5, 1957; "Households and Families by Type: 1947 to 1955," *ibid.*, ser. P-20, no. 59, August 12, 1955.

up with in-laws or acquaintances and do not form their own households. A few of these would not seek separate dwelling units under any circumstances, but many would undoubtedly prefer to have their own quarters. Some are active home seekers who consider their current status as temporary and are currently able to enter the market; they may be said to represent the *actual* demand. The rest are excluded from the market by circumstances beyond their control (primarily income limitations), but might enter the market if the circumstances should change; they may be said to represent the *potential* demand. The breakdown of these groups is shown graphically in Chart A-1.

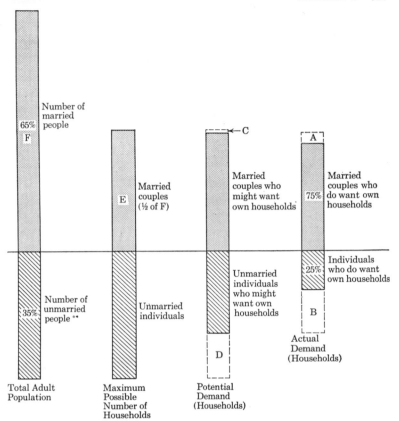

Chart **A-1.** Relation between actual and potential demand for houses:

A. Married couples not now wanting their own households. Assumed to be 5% of total married couples, these are primarily young couples living with relatives.

B. Unmarried individuals not now wanting their own households, the largest area of potential demand that might become actual demand.

C. Married couples who would never want their own households. This category is very small.

D. Unmarried individuals who would never want their own households. Assumed to be 10% of total adult population, these are primarily very young or very old individuals. (Unmarried individuals include widowed, divorced, and other individual heads of families.)

E. Total married couples. Assumed to be one-half of F.

F. Total married individuals living as married couples.

The Potential Demand. A certain number of young people of marriageable age who live at home and of older people who need constant care must be excluded even from the potential demand category. Only a rough estimate may be made of this number.[2] For convenience, Chart A-1 sets the figures at 10 per cent.

Projections of growth in the adult population may be made fairly accurately for the period up to 1970, since those who will then be fifteen years or older have already been born. (See Table A-2.) For the first time in the current century, the rate of growth of the adult population will increase.

Marriage rate directly affects potential housing demand in two conflicting ways. The potential is reduced by one when two people living in separate dwelling units get married, but increased by one when two young adults living with parents marry and move to a separate dwelling unit. Since most people who marry are in the latter category [3] the net short-range effect of an increase in the marriage rate is probably an increase in the potential.[4] The evidence is that the marriage rate has been increasing among the young adults, who make up the fastest-growing population group, and this will tend to increase potential housing demand, though at a slower *rate* than the total adult population.

Also serving to increase the potential demand is the ever-lowering death rate, which results in a greater proportion of the oldest age groups remaining together as married couples. These elderly couples are more apt to maintain their own homes than are widows and widowers.

---

[2] Assuming for the purposes of this discussion that all over the age of fourteen years are adults, we find that in 1955 about 13 per cent of the adult population were under the age of twenty-four years and unmarried. In the same year, about 1 per cent were over the age of seventy-four years and neither headed a household nor were married to a household head. Those who must be excluded from the potential demand are primarily in (though obviously only a part of) these two groups. Children under the age of fifteen years are assumed not to be possible applicants for separate dwelling units and, therefore, in no way part of the demand picture.

[3] The present median age for females is between twenty and twenty-one years.

[4] In the long run, a high rate lowers the potential by reducing the number of adults who will later leave home as single individuals.

Married couples have a strong desire to form their own households and more than 95 per cent of them do so; consequently, almost the entire number of married couples constitute both potential and actual demand for housing. By contrast, less than 20 per cent of a calculated maximum number of single-person house-

TABLE A-2. Age Distribution of Population Fifteen Years and Older: 1920–1970

	Number in age group (in thousands)							
	1920	1930	1940	1950	1955	1960	1965	1970
15–24	18,707	22,422	23,921	22,098	21,952	24,657	30,660	36,468
25–34	17,157	18,954	21,339	23,759	24,136	22,672	22,255	24,946
35–44	14,121	17,199	18,333	21,450	22,809	23,958	24,118	22,602
45–54	10,499	13,018	15,512	17,342	18,900	20,856	22,083	23,150
55–64	6,532	8,397	10,572	13,294	14,529	15,630	17,042	18,768
65 and older	4,933	6,634	9,019	12,269	14,127	15,800	17,371	18,879
Total	71,949	86,624	98,696	110,212	116,453	123,573	133,529	144,813
	Per cent distribution of population fifteen years and older							
15–24	26.0	25.9	24.2	20.1	18.9	20.0	22.9	25.2
25–34	23.8	21.9	21.6	21.6	20.7	18.3	16.7	17.2
35–44	19.6	19.9	18.6	19.5	19.6	19.4	18.1	15.6
45–54	14.6	15.0	15.7	15.7	16.2	16.9	16.5	16.0
55–64	9.1	9.7	10.7	12.1	12.5	12.5	12.8	13.0
65 and older	6.9	7.7	9.1	11.1	12.1	12.8	13.0	13.0
Number of households	24,352	29,905	34,949	42,857	47,788			
Population/ household	2.95	2.90	2.82	2.57	2.44			

Source: 1920–1950: U.S. Bureau of the Census, *Census of Population: 1950*, vol. II, *Characteristics of Population*, part 1, Table 39; 1955–1970: "Revised Projections of the Population of the United States, by Age and Sex: 1960 to 1975," U.S. Bureau of the Census, *Current Population Reports, Population Estimates*, ser. P-25, no. 123, October 20, 1955.

Estimates of the population for 1960–1970 were derived by assuming mortality and net immigration rates similar to those experienced in the last two decades.

TABLE A-3. Potential Maximum Number of Households
(in thousands) [a]

	1940	1947	1948	1949	1950	1951	1952	1953	1954	1955	1956	1957
Primary families	31,491	34,964	36,674	38,000	38,838	39,487	40,205	40,490	40,961	41,713	42,548	43,210
Subfamilies	2,062	3,123	2,681	2,530	2,402	2,227	2,061	1,968	2,107	1,969	1,823	1,802
Secondary families	675	830	606	537	465	442	373	342	241	221	295	235
Maximum primary families	34,228	38,917	38,961	41,167	41,705	42,156	42,639	42,800	43,309	43,903	44,666	45,247
Actual/Maximum	92.0	89.8	91.8	92.5	93.1	93.7	94.3	94.4	94.6	95.0	95.3	95.5
Primary individuals	3,458	4,193	4,046	4,107	4,716	5,169	5,299	5,844	5,932	6,075	6,237	6,333
Secondary individuals	5,819	4,348	4,152	4,176	4,420	4,341	4,002	4,113	3,768	3,715	3,660	3,447
Maximum primary individuals	9,277	8,491	8,198	8,283	9,136	9,510	9,301	9,957	9,700	9,790	9,897	9,780
Actual/Maximum	37.3	48.8	47.1	48.2	51.6	54.4	57.0	58.7	61.2	62.1	63.0	64.8
Total households	34,949	39,107	40,720	42,107	43,554	44,656	45,504	46,334	46,893	47,788	48,785	49,543
Maximum total	43,505	47,408	48,159	49,350	50,841	51,666	51,940	52,757	53,009	53,693	54,563	55,027
Actual/Maximum	80.3	82.5	84.1	84.9	85.7	86.4	87.6	87.9	88.5	89.0	89.4	90.0

[a] Table A-3 assumes that all family groups and all individuals living alone or with nonrelatives only are potential demanders of separate dwelling units. Therefore all units classified as subfamilies, secondary families, or secondary individuals by the Bureau of the Census publications are conceived as potentially able to form their own households. It does not allow for the splitting up of families into smaller units but assumes that adults currently living with relatives would do so under any circumstances.

An effort has been made to compute the potential maximum nonfarm households for 1950 making an allowance for single persons over eighteen years of age who are living with relatives. Economists estimated the number of children under eighteen years in normal families from frequency distributions. They were then able to compute the number of adults other than husbands, wives, or parents in families. They considered this entire group of "other relatives" as potential demanders for separate dwelling space. This group consisted of over 15 million people and represented 27.8 per cent of the total maximum number of households. (See Leo Grebler, David M. Blank, and Louis Winnick, *Capital Formation in Residential Real Estate*, Princeton University Press, Princeton, N.J., 1956, Appendix F, pp. 387–392.

Definitions

1. Primary family: the head of a household plus all other persons in the household who are related to the head.
2. Subfamily: a married couple, or a parent with one or more children, living in a household and related to, but not including, the head.
3. Secondary family: two or more related persons living in a household but not related to the head, also primary families living in quasi-households such as hotels or rooming houses.
4. Primary individual: a household head living alone or with nonrelatives.
5. Secondary individual: a person in a household or quasi-household who is not related to anyone else in the household.

Source: "Characteristics of Household, Families, and Individuals: April, 1948," U.S. Bureau of the Census, *Current Population Reports, Population Characteristics*, ser. P-20, no. 21, December 19, 1948; "Marital Status and Household Characteristics: April, 1949," *ibid.*, ser. P-20, no. 26, January 27, 1950; "Households and Families by Type: 1950 to 1956," *ibid.*, ser. P-20, no. 68, June 13, 1956; "Households and Families by Type: 1950 to 1957," *ibid.*, ser. P-20, no. 76, July 5, 1957.

holds had been formed in 1950.[5] Much of this group constitutes a potential demand which under certain conditions would enter the market. Among family groups not headed by a married couple,[6] only about 70 per cent have formed their own households. Most of the rest of these groups constitute a potential, restricted from the market mainly by low income.

The Actual Demand. Table A-3 indicates that recently the percentage of a calculated potential maximum demand which actually forms households is higher than in the past. During the first years following World War II, this probably represented the creation of new housing to fulfill an actual demand that had existed for some time, but in more recent years the housing shortage has eased and it may be concluded that there has been a shift from potential to actual. In fact, Table A-3 shows that since 1950 the number of households has grown faster than the maximum demand, for both family and individual groups. There are many possible explanations for this phenomenon, but the most tenable is the growth in personal income—about 30 per cent between 1950 and 1955. A rise in income permits young married couples to leave the homes of parents and older individuals [7] to live by themselves. Periods of high income also lead to the addition of more individual young adults to the potential and actual demand because they leave home to take high-paying jobs in other localities.

If the economy of the nation continues to prosper, the implication is that a growing percentage of the potential demand will become actual. Although the potential will probably grow at a somewhat slower rate than the total adult population, the actual will probably grow faster in the period up to 1970 than it has in the past.

[5] Leo Grebler, David M. Blank, and Louis Winnick, *Capital Formation in Residential Real Estate*, Princeton University Press, Princeton, N.J., 1956, p. 390.

[6] In the past three years there has been a rise from 2.69 to 2.83 million parent-child families. U.S. Bureau of the Census, *Current Population Reports, Population Characteristics*, ser. P-20, nos. 67, 75, May 2, 1956.

[7] In 1955, 68.4 per cent of the unrelated individuals were over forty-four years old. Fifty per cent of all unrelated individuals over thirteen years were widowed or divorced. *Ibid.*

Type of Housing Required. Table A-4 shows that the one-person household has been growing faster than any other sized group. Single persons are a large element in that part of the potential demand that is not actual demand, and if the shift from potential to actual continues, the one-person household will continue to grow in relative importance.

TABLE **A-4.** Size of Households

	Number of households (in thousands)						Per cent increase 1949–1956
	1940	1949	1950	1954	1955	1956	
One-person	2,677	3,381	3,946	5,032	5,212	5,396	59.6
Two-person	8,630	11,468	12,430	13,249	13,612	13,827	20.6
Three-person	7,796	10,168	10,011	9,776	9,725	9,936	−2.3
Four-person	6,324	8,067	7,868	8,820	9,052	9,152	13.4
Five-person	4,013	4,395	4,556	5,170	5,291	5,287	20.3
Six-person	2,360	2,310	2,295	2,521	2,568	2,624	13.6
Seven or more	3,053	2,319	2,362	2,325	2,328	2,563	10.5
Total	34,853	42,018	43,468	46,893	47,788	48,785	15.9

Per cent of total

	1940	1949	1950	1954	1955	1956	
One-person	7.7	8.0	9.1	10.7	10.9	11.1	
Two-person	24.8	27.2	28.6	28.3	28.5	28.3	
Three-person	22.4	24.1	23.0	20.8	20.4	20.4	
Four-person	18.1	19.2	18.1	18.8	18.9	18.8	
Five-person	11.5	10.4	10.5	11.0	11.1	10.8	
Six-person	6.8	5.5	5.3	5.4	5.4	5.4	
Seven or more	8.7	5.5	5.5	5.0	4.9	5.3	
Total	100.0	100.0	100.0	100.0	100.0	100.0	

Source: "Marital Status and Household Characteristics: April, 1949," U.S. Bureau of the Census, *Current Population Reports, Population Characteristics,* ser. P-20, no. 33, January 27, 1950; "Marital Status and Household Characteristics: March, 1950," ser. P-20, no. 33, February 12, 1951; "Household and Family Characteristics: April 1955 and 1954," ser. P-20, no. 67, May 2, 1956; "Household and Family Characteristics: March, 1956," ser. P-20, no. 75, June 9, 1956.

Since such households are generally made up of older individuals with less income than other household types,[8] they tend to require low-cost rental housing and to prefer it near the heart of the city. According to one authority: [9]

The very condition of prosperity which causes many families to upgrade both their housing and neighborhoods also tends to accelerate 1-person household formation, and housing which might otherwise be abandoned finds occupants.

Young, unmarried individuals are a growing element in the one-person households, and they also prefer low-rent, central housing. Thus continued economic prosperity would increase the demand for such units.

The birth rate is another factor affecting the size of dwelling unit demanded. Population experts differ as to the reasons for its recent rise after nearly 150 years of steady decline, and as to the likelihood that this represents a lasting change in human behavioral patterns. Some feel that women are simply having their children earlier than was usual and that there will be no change in the size of completed families. Yet there is some evidence that older women are having more children, too.[10] The number and ages of the children in a family largely determine the number of bedrooms, amount of living space, and relationship to community facilities demanded by the family. If what appear to be current trends continue, married couples will be demanding larger houses in child-oriented surroundings.

Migration is also a factor in dwelling type. The number of farm households has long been decreasing [11] and a net shift from farm

[8] In 1950, 78.3 per cent of the people living in one-person households were over forty-four years old; 64.1 per cent of this category were women. U.S. Bureau of the Census, *1950 Census of Housing*, vol. 11, *Non-Farm Housing Characteristics*, part 1, chap. 1, Table A-8.

[9] Louis Winnick, *American Housing and Its Use: The Demand for Shelter Space*, John Wiley & Sons, Inc., New York, 1957, p. 86.

[10] The greater increases in the birth rate have occurred in the younger age groups (i.e., mothers under thirty years). But in 1952, women between forty and forty-four years old, married and living with husband, had, per thousand, twenty-two more children under five years of age than in 1940.

[11] In 1940, the 7,074,000 farm households comprised 20.3 per cent of all households. In 1957, 5,218,000 farm households comprised 10.5 per cent of

to nonfarm units means a change in demand. Most housing industry analysts do not consider the farm population a part of the housing market, since the farmer traditionally regards his house only as part of his over-all plant, and a relatively unimportant part at that. Farmhouses are not often built by firms in the housing industry, nor are they freely available as part of the housing market. A continuing shift away from the farm probably means an increase in the demand for low-cost housing.

TABLE A-5. Population in Central Cities and Surrounding Areas

	Percentage of total population						Per cent increase in population 1940–1950
	1900	1910	1920	1930	1940	1950	
Standard-metro-politan areas	40.5	44.2	48.2	52.7	53.3	56.8	21.8
Central cities	25.1	28.3	31.5	33.5	33.0	32.8	13.9
Rings	15.4	15.9	16.7	19.2	20.4	24.0	34.7
Urban	5.5	6.8	8.2	10.5	10.7	12.0	29.2
Rural	10.0	9.0	8.5	8.7	9.7	12.0	40.8
Areas outside standard metro-politan areas	59.5	55.8	51.8	47.3	46.7	43.2	6.0
Urban	9.1	10.5	11.6	12.1	12.9	14.2	25.8
Rural	50.3	45.3	40.2	35.1	33.8	29.0	−1.6

Source: Donald J. Bogue, *Population Growth in Standard Metropolitan Areas, 1900–1950*, Housing and Home Finance Agency, Washington, D.C., 1953, p. 13.

Another form of migration is the rush to the suburbs; see Table A-5. Suburban houses are generally larger and equipped with more kinds of facilities for leisure-time activity than are city houses, and a far greater emphasis is placed on outdoor living. Demand for these houses is likely to continue to increase.

the total. U.S. Bureau of the Census, *Historical Statistics of the United States, 1789–1945*, 1949, ser. B171–181, p. 29; and "Households and Families by Type: 1950 to 1957," U.S. Bureau of the Census, *Current Population Reports, Population Characteristics*, ser. P-20, no. 76, July 5, 1957.

Since the youngest and oldest adult age groups are the most rapidly growing, there will be an increased demand for housing designed for them. Young married families have either no children or only infants, and small dwellings will both satisfy their space needs and fit their budget limitations. Similarly, retired couples do not need—and often do not desire—the space provided in today's average house. Usually they can no longer afford either to buy or to maintain such a house. Yet many of this group prefer owning their own homes to renting present-day apartments. The continued rise of real income could bring these couples into the market for small units especially suited to their needs. Many couples, on retirement, move to warmer climates (low-cost housing developments have been started in certain areas, mostly in Florida, with this market in mind). A generally favorable economy would probably accelerate the tendency of retired people to move to new localities. Depending on real-income factors, the growing number of young and old married couples can, therefore, be seen as creating a significant market for inexpensive but efficient dwelling units, a large proportion of which should be rental units. Many in these categories will not be able to afford homes of their own; others will prefer in any case to live near the center where home ownership is rare.

Median family income increased 67 per cent between 1945 and 1955. As Table A-6 indicates, most of this increase occurred in fami-

TABLE **A-6.** Percentage Distribution of Family Total Money Income

Income	1944	1945	1946	1947	1948	1949	1950	1951	1952	1953	1954	1955
$10,000 and over	1.6	1.3	...	2.5	2.5	2.3	2.8	3.1	3.5	4.6	4.9	5.3
$5,000 and over	9.9	11.9	...	16.9	18.1	17.4	19.8	24.7	27.7	32.6	32.0	35.5
Under $2,000	45.3	40.6	...	34.5	32.0	34.3	32.0	27.6	27.1	25.5	27.1	25.3

Source: "Family Income in the United States: 1955," U.S. Bureau of the Census, *Current Population Reports, Consumer Income*, ser. P-60, no. 24, April, 1957.

lies in the low- and middle-income brackets. If the growth in relative importance of the middle-income group continues, an increasing proportion of the population will be able to afford to own single-family houses, and if average income continues to rise, average selling price of the house will also rise. However, price rises may represent higher building costs almost as much as increases in accommodation or facilities. In any case, rising costs and high income and other taxes, together with changing living patterns and a shortage of servants, have made the very large house almost obsolete. The number of new houses containing ten or more rooms will certainly decrease as a percentage of total starts and may decline absolutely.[12]

The proportion of single-family houses has grown rapidly in recent decades, as noted in Chapter 1; the number of multifamily units built in the boom following World War II is about half the number built following World War I despite the fact that the total number of units of all types built following World War II was considerably higher. Nevertheless we have seen that there is evidence of an increasing market for small efficiency units for the very young and very old, and it is likely that the rate of growth in the demand for multifamily units may rise rapidly in the future, depending on the design characteristics of these units.

Other Factors Affecting Demand. Mobility of the population is likely to create a high vacancy rate and so require a greater total supply of housing to satisfy a given demand. Because most forms of housing cannot be transported, areas of emigration will show a large number of vacancies while the demand for housing in areas of immigration will generate new construction. Even if no net shift of the population occurs, differing housing requirements plus an inevitable time lag between emigration and immigration will bring about either an additional demand or a higher vacancy rate.

The population has been very mobile in the past decade (Table A-7), with approximately 20 per cent moving each year, about

[12] It is interesting to note that the increase in family income for the low- and middle-income brackets, coupled with the trend toward more modest housing for the high-income bracket, is resulting in a considerable narrowing of the range of housing characteristics—thus making the secondhand market considerably more effective.

TABLE A-7. Mobility of U.S. Civilian Population

Years	Per cent of total population moved	Per cent of total population moved within same county	Per cent of total population moved to different county	
			Inside state	Outside state
1940–1947	58.3	37.0	10.7	10.1
1947–1948	19.9	13.6	3.3	3.1
1948–1949	18.8	13.0	2.8	3.0
1949–1950	18.7	13.1	3.0	2.6
1950–1951	21.0	13.9	3.6	3.5
1951–1952	19.8	13.2	3.2	3.4
1952-1953	20.1	13.5	3.0	3.6
1953-1954	18.6	12.2	3.2	3.2
1954–1955	19.9	13.3	3.5	3.1
1955–1956	20.5	13.7	3.6	3.1

Sources: "Mobility of the Population of the United States: March, 1955, to 1956," U.S. Bureau of the Census, *Current Population Reports, Population Characteristics*, ser. P-20, no. 73, March 12, 1957; "Internal Migration in the United States: April, 1940, to April, 1947," *ibid.*, ser. P-20, no. 14, April 15, 1948.

one-third of them to a different county, and the highest rates shown by the youngest age groups.[13] There has been no increase in mobility in recent years, but as the percentage of young people in the total population increases, an upward pressure on the mobility rate can be expected. Higher incomes, particularly in the oldest age groups, may also send the rate upward. Mobility adds to the demand for housing mainly when it means an absolute fall

[13] In each year since 1950, an average of 40.1 per cent of the population between twenty and twenty-four years of age has moved. During this period, the average for the twenty-five-to-twenty-nine-year age group was 31.7 per cent; for the thirty-to-thirty-four-year age group, 24.3 per cent; for the thirty-five-to-forty-four-year age group, 17.1 per cent; for the forty-five-to-sixty-four-year age group, 11.6 per cent; and for the over-sixty-four-year age group, 9.8 per cent. U.S. Bureau of the Census, *Current Population Reports, Population Characteristics*, ser. P-20, nos. 39, 47, 49, 57, 61, 73.

in the population in a number of exporting areas. In the past, most areas characterized by large volumes of emigration have had compensatory gains from immigration from overseas, from farm areas, and from Negro areas in the South.[14] If increased migration in the future results in population declines in many areas, then the total volume of housing needed will be greater.

The number of two-house families has increased rapidly in recent years. The Census listed over a million vacant seasonal non-farm dwelling units (mainly vacation structures) in 1950, a rise of 85 per cent over 1940 and a net addition to the two-house families, even though the figure represents less than 3 per cent of the total stock and not all vacation cottages are well enough equipped to be regarded as part of the standard housing supply. This increase can be attributed to the rapid growth of income and leisure time and to greater ease of transportation. If these factors continue to operate in the future, more families will buy or rent a second dwelling unit, and the market for second homes may grow enough to raise significantly the total housing demand. However, in location, design, and construction this market is likely to remain somewhat distinct from that for standard housing.

Factors Affecting Supply. The present stock of housing will long be a primary source of the future supply. Because of the long life of residential structures, the yearly increment of new dwellings constitutes a very small percentage of the total stock. Table A-8, which presents selected characteristics of the 1950 housing stock, shows that 45.8 per cent of all dwelling units were in structures more than thirty years old. From 1940 to 1950, the median age of urban dwelling units rose from 25.4 to 28.7 years. Nevertheless, the age is still much less than in European countries, and although our construction is principally of wood, there is little danger that a significant proportion of the stock that was sound in 1950 will be physically obsolete by 1970. In 1950, however, a significant portion of it was substandard in one way or another, with more than a third classified as either dilapidated or lacking a private toilet or running water, or both. If the wages of the lowest-income groups continue to rise, a great number of these dwellings may be abandoned or condemned, and the demand for new units

[14] Grebler et al., *op. cit.,* p. 104.

TABLE A-8. Characteristics of Existing Housing Stock: 1950 (in thousands)

Condition as to private toilet, bath, and hot running water and year built	United States		Urban and rural nonfarm				Farm	
			Total		Urban	Rural nonfarm		
	Number	Per cent	Number	Per cent	(number)	(number)	Number	Per cent
Total dwelling units	45,983		39,625		29,569	10,056	6,358	
Number reporting on condition	44,502	100.0	38,368	100.0	28,763	9,605	6,135	100.0
Not dilapidated:								
Toilet, bath, hot water	28,102	63.1	26,672	69.5	22,371	4,301	1,431	23.3
Toilet, bath, no hot water	1,435	3.2	1,307	3.4	935	373	128	2.1
Running water, no toilet or bath	5,491	12.3	4,571	11.4	3,034	1,537	921	15.0
Without running water	5,133	11.5	2,673	7.0	569	2,104	2,460	40.1
Dilapidated:								
With toilet, bath, hot water	627	1.4	597	1.6	510	86	30	0.5
No hot water, toilet, or bath	3,712	8.3	2,548	6.6	1,344	1,204	1,164	19.0
Number reporting year built [a]	44,230	100.0	38,082	100.0	28,547	9,535	6,148	100.0
1945 or later	5,946	13.4	5,320	14.0	3,366	1,954	626	10.2
1940–1944	3,228	7.3	2,911	7.6	2,154	757	317	5.2
1930–1939	5,898	13.3	4,980	13.1	3,303	1,676	918	14.9
1920–1929	8,894	20.1	7,893	20.7	6,464	1,429	1,000	16.3
1919 or earlier	20,264	45.8	16,978	44.6	13,259	3,719	3,286	53.4

[a] 20 per cent sample.
Source: U.S. Bureau of the Census, *1950 Census of Housing*, vol. I, part 1, 1953, pp. 1–3 and 1–4.

will accordingly be increased. The present residents may then either create a direct market for new low-cost housing or, by constituting a trade-in market, enrich the market for higher-priced new houses. Conversely, to the degree that existing units are renovated or remodeled to provide additional units, the future demand for new units will be reduced.

Each year a certain number of units in the existing stock are torn down or destroyed. Some of these units are substandard or already abandoned, but many have previously provided adequate housing. Such demolitions reduce usable housing stock and directly or indirectly create a demand for new construction. Dwelling units also are destroyed by disasters like fires or floods or demolished to make room for new highways, buildings, or other improvements. No precise statistics are available as to how many units are lost in these ways, but one authority estimates that disasters alone take close to 40,000 units per year.[15] Expansions of highways and other public works, and increases in the volume of nonresidential construction, may mean an expanded rate of destruction in the future.

Conversion of existing structures is a means of adding to the total stock of dwelling units. Nonresidential structures may be converted to residential use, or existing dwelling units may be subdivided. Although the significance of conversions has not been accurately measured, this source of new units would appear to have been very important during the period from 1930 to 1950. Table A-9 shows that the net increase in the housing stock during those two decades was much larger than the total number of dwelling units started in the interval.[16] Most of this difference may be attributed to an extraordinary number of conversions. It has been estimated that the number of dwelling units added in this way was more than a million in the first decade and two million in the second.[17]

The need for low-cost units in the Depression and the restriction of new construction during the war years undoubtedly

---

[15] C. Everett Ashley, 3d, *How Big Is the Housing Job?* Housing and Home Finance Agency, Washington, D.C., October, 1951, pp. 10–11.

[16] A small part of the difference is caused by changes in census definitions and the addition of trailers and public housing to the total shelter supply.

[17] Grebler et al., *op. cit.*, p. 329.

stimulated the growth of conversions. Most converted units are relatively low-cost, low-quality dwellings, often in high-density and mixed-use areas. Generally speaking, therefore, if incomes continue to rise it is very unlikely that conversions will be as potent a force in the future as they have been in the twenty-year period cited.

TABLE A-9. Change in Nonfarm Housing Stock (in thousands)

	Increase in housing stock	Dwelling units started during period	Difference between increase in stock and dwelling-unit starts
1890–1900	2,271	2,941	−670
1900–1910	3,736	3,606	130
1910–1920	3,579	3,593	−14
1920–1930	6,580	7,004	−494
1930–1940	4,014	2,646	1,368
1940–1950	9,942	5,393	4,549

Source: Leo Grebler, David M. Blank, and Louis Winnick, *Capital Formation in Residential Real Estate*, Princeton University Press, Princeton, N.J., 1956, p. 86.

Since large portions of the current stock are now substandard and the conversion of existing structures into new dwelling-unit supply will probably diminish, housing demand will include not only the expected new demand, but also a considerable demand for the replacement of existing units.

Summary

The potential demand for housing will inevitably increase, though probably at a slower rate than the adult population. With prosperity, an increasing part of this potential would become actual demand, which is likely to grow faster in the near future than it has in the past. Minor additions to demand will result from increasing mobility of the population, the movement from farm to metropolis, and a trend toward two-house families. As for the present stock of housing, there will be fewer additions by conversions. Although many units will be preserved by urban renewal, as many will be destroyed in the course of programs of construction and by disasters, and there will be a considerable demand for the replacement of substandard units.

As for probable housing types, there will be a continued growth in demand for the suburban family house which is the mainstay of the current industry supplying new private houses. Because the most rapid population growth will be in the youngest and oldest groups among the adults, however, a continuing prosperity would bring a sharp rise in demand for attractive rental units in the city centers to serve individuals and for small and efficient houses to serve married couples. These are markets that should prove of great interest to the housing industry, particularly if significant improvements are made in design.

Appendix B

THE HOUSE
OF THE FUTURE

A Brief Historical Survey of Innovation in House Design

Thomas A. Edison, 1907, Poured Concrete house. Bemis, Albert Farwell, *The Evolving House,* Technology Press, M.I.T., Cambridge, Mass., 1936, vol. III, p. 411; *Cement Age,* vol. 6, pp. 268–281, March, 1908; *Scientific American,* vol. 97, p. 356, Nov. 16, 1907; vol. 101, p. 141, Aug. 28, 1909.

Grosvenor Atterbury, 1907, Precast Concrete Panel house. Bemis, *op. cit.,* p. 349; *Architectural Forum,* vol. 54, p. 365, March, 1931; *Architectural Record,* vol. 75, p. 11, January, 1934; *Architecture,* vol. 73, p. 193, April, 1936.

Suspension Steel House, 1909. Bemis, *op. cit.,* p. 541; *Engineering News Record,* vol. 104, p. 97, January 16, 1930.

Frank Lloyd Wright, 1909, Robie house. Hitchcock, Henry Russel, *In the Nature of Materials,* Duell, Sloan & Pearce, Inc., New York, 1942, plate 164; Wright, F. L., *A Testament,* Horizon Press, New York, 1957, pp. 76–79.

R. Buckminster Fuller, 1928, Dymaxion house I. Bemis, *op. cit.,* p. 401; *Architecture,* vol. 59, p. 335, June, 1929; *Architectural Forum,* vol. 51, p. 103, July, 1929; vol. 56, p. 285, March, 1932; *Architectural Record,* vol. 75, p. 9, January, 1934.

Richard J. Neutra, 1930, Diatom house. Bemis, *op. cit.,* p. 483; *Architectural Record,* vol. 75, p. 32, January, 1934.

Walter Gropius, 1930, Stuttgart Exposition house. Bemis, *op. cit.,* p. 435; *Architectural Forum,* vol. 54, p. 276, March, 1931.

Howard T. Fisher, 1932, General houses. Bemis, *op. cit.,* p. 433; *Architectural Forum,* vol. 57, pp. 65–72, July, 1932; vol. 58, p. 327, April, 1933; vol. 59, p. 52, July, 1933; *Architectural Record,* vol. 73, p. 289, April, 1933; vol. 75, p. 18, January, 1934; *Fortune,* vol. 6, p. 67, July, 1932.

Robert W. McLaughlin, 1932, American Motohomes. Bemis, *op. cit.,* p. 339; *Architectural Forum,* vol. 58, p. 327, April, 1933; vol. 60, pp. 277–282, April, 1934; vol. 62, pp. 508–511, May, 1935; vol. 63, pp. 33–35, July, 1935; *Architectural Record,* vol. 73, p. 288, April, 1933; vol. 75, p. 17, January, 1934; vol. 78, p. 117, August, 1935.

Chicago World's Fair, 1933. *American Architect,* vol. 143, pp. 22–29, July, 1933; *Architectural Forum,* vol. 59, pp. 51–62, July, 1933; vol. 60, supplement, pp. 41–98, February, 1934; vol. 62, p. 181, February, 1935; *Archi-*

tectural Record, vol. 73, pp. 342–374, May, 1933; vol. 74, p. 724, July, 1933; *Pencil Points,* vol. 14, pp. 245–251, June, 1933.

Richard J. Neutra, 1934, V. D. L. house. Bemis, *op. cit.,* p. 567; *Architectural Forum,* vol. 61, pp. 357–372, November, 1934.

Temple A. Buell, 1934, Portable house. Bemis, *op. cit.,* p. 381; *Architectural Record,* vol. 75, pp. 11–13, January, 1934.

Frederick J. Kiesler, 1934, Space house. *Architectural Forum,* vol. 60, pp. 17–22, January, 1934; *Architectural Record,* vol. 75, pp. 44–61, January, 1934.

Albert Farwell Bemis, 1936, The Cubical Modular System. Bemis, *op. cit.,* p. 71.

Corwin Willson, 1934, Mobile house. *Architectural Forum,* vol. 61, supplement, p. 34, September, 1934; vol. 66, supplement, p. 12, March, 1937; *Architectural Record,* vol. 76, p. 73, August, 1934; vol. 80, p. 64, July, 1936.

Paul Nelson, 1938, Suspended house. *Architectural Record,* vol. 84, pp. 37–41, December, 1938.

Alden B. Dow, 1940, Plastic Block house. *Architectural Forum,* vol. 80, p. 6, January, 1944; *Architectural Record,* vol. 94, p. 124, December, 1943; *California Arts & Architecture,* vol. 57, pp. 10ff., January, 1940.

R. Buckminster Fuller, 1940, Mobil Mechanical Wing. *Architectural Forum,* vol. 73, p. 273, October, 1940.

R. Buckminster Fuller, 1941, Grain Bin house. *Architectural Forum,* vol. 74, pp. 425–429, June, 1941; vol. 75, supplement, p. 22, July, 1941.

Martin Wagner, 1941, M W House. *Architectural Forum,* vol. 74, p. 87, February, 1941.

Wallace Neff, 1941, Airform house. *Architectural Forum,* vol. 75, p. 421, December, 1941; *Architectural Record,* vol. 96, pp. 81–83, July, 1944; *Architecture and Engineering,* vol. 148, pp. 20–23, January, 1942.

Frank Lloyd Wright, 1942, Berm house. *Architectural Forum,* vol. 88, p. 83, January, 1948.

Eero Saarinen, 1943, PAC house. *Architectural Forum,* vol. 79, p. 89, September, 1943.

Ralph Rapson and David Runnels, 1943, Cloth house. *Architectural Forum,* vol. 77, pp. 87–89, September, 1942; vol. 79, p. 93, September, 1943.

Walter Gropius and Conrad Wachsman, 1943, General Panel house. *Architectural Forum,* vol. 86, pp. 115–120, February, 1947; *Architectural Record,* vol. 93, pp. 50–53, April, 1943; vol. 96, p. 69, December, 1944; *Pencil Points,* vol. 24, pp. 36–47, April, 1943.

Richard J. Neutra, 1944, Four-Courter house. *Pencil Points,* vol. 25, p. 58, May, 1944.

R. Buckminster Fuller, 1945, Dymaxion house II. *Architectural Forum,* vol. 84, pp. 129–136, April, 1946; *Architectural Record,* vol. 97, p. 122, April, 1945; vol. 99, pp. 118–120, May, 1946; *Fortune,* vol. 33, pp. 166–172, April, 1946.

Ralph Rapson, 1945, Greenbelt house. *Arts and Architecture,* vol. 62, pp. 30–34, September, 1945; *Interiors,* vol. 108, pp. 116ff., September, 1948.

Carl Koch and Associates, 1949, Acorn house. *Architectural Record*, vol. 107, pp. 152ff., May, 1950.

R. Buckminster Fuller, 1949, Geodesic house. *Architectural Forum*, vol. 90, p. 16, May, 1949; *Interiors*, vol. 108, pp. 10ff., June, 1949; *Housing Mass Produced*, A. F. Bemis Foundation, M.I.T., Cambridge, Mass., 1951. (booklet.)

Charles Eames, 1949, Industrial Component house. *Architectural Forum*, vol. 93, pp. 90–96, September, 1950; *Arts and Architecture*, vol. 65, p. 40, March, 1948; vol. 67, pp. 26–39, July, 1950; *Interiors*, vol. 110, pp. 108–115, November, 1950.

Frederick J. Kiesler, 1950, Endless house. *Architectural Forum*, vol. 93, pp. 124–126, November, 1950; *Interiors*, vol. 110, pp. 122–129, November, 1950; *Time*, vol. 60, p. 62, September 15, 1952.

Eliot Noyes, 1953, Airform house. *Architectural Record*, vol. 115, p. 314, May, 1954; *House & Home*, vol. 7, p. 134, January, 1955; *Progressive Architecture*, vol. 35, pp. 116–119, June, 1954.

Eduardo Catalano, 1954, Hyperbolic Paraboloid house. *Architectural Forum*, vol. 103, pp. 170–177, November, 1955; *House & Home*, vol. 8, pp. 94–101, August, 1955.

Carl Koch and Associates, 1954, Techbuilt house. *House & Home*, vol. 5, pp. 104–117, February, 1954.

U.S. Gypsum Co., 1955, Research Village. *Architectural Record*, vol. 115, pp. 10–12, March, 1954; vol. 117, pp. 189–197, April, 1955; *House & Home*, vol. 5, p. 37, March, 1954; vol. 7, pp. 104–115, April, 1955; *Progressive Architecture*, vol. 35, pp. 9–10, March, 1954; vol. 36, pp. 127–132, May, 1955.

Richard W. Hamilton and Marvin E. Goody, 1955, Monsanto House of the Future. *Arts and Architecture*, vol. 72, pp. 20–21, November, 1955; *Architectural Record*, vol. 119, p. 205, January, 1956; vol. 120, pp. 209–210ff., August, 1956; *House & Home*, vol. 10, pp. 133–135, September, 1956; vol. 11, pp. 188ff., June, 1957; *Interiors*, vol. 116, p. 12, August, 1956; *Progressive Architecture*, vol. 36, p. 71, December, 1955; vol. 38, p. 189, July, 1957.

John MacLean Johansen, 1956, Thin-shell Concrete house. *House & Home*, vol. 10, pp. 148–149, July, 1956.

A. Quincy Jones and Frederick E. Emmons, 1956, X-100 Experimental house. *Architectural Record*, vol. 121, pp. 148–151, mid-May, 1957; *Arts and Architecture*, vol. 73, pp. 26–27, July, 1956; pp. 26–27, November, 1956; vol. 74, pp. 20–21, February, 1957.

Carl Koch and Associates, 1957, Buffalo Patio houses. *House & Home*, vol. 12, pp. 136–137, October, 1957.

George Nelson and Gordon Chadwick, 1958, Experimental Manufactured house. *Industrial Design*, vol. 5, p. 44, January, 1958.

Sources for Illustrations

1. Living areas, Eichler X-100 Steel and Plywood House, San Mateo Highlands, California; architects, Jones and Emmons; builder, Eichler Homes, Palo Alto, California; photographer, Ernest Braun.
2. Air view, Levittown, Pennsylvania; builder, Levitt and Sons, Inc., Levittown, New Jersey.
3. General Electric 1958 Kitchen Center.
4. Production line for finishing aluminum panels. National Homes Corp., Lafayette, Indiana.
5. Model home sales area; builder, John E. Long, Phoenix, Arizona; photographer, Bob Markow.
6. Panelized house assembly; architects, Walter Gropius and Conrad Wachsmann, Cambridge, Massachusetts; builder, General Panel Corporation, New York; photographer, Anna Wachsmann.
7. Installation of wall panel, Eichler X-100 House (see photograph 1).
8. Installation of extruded plastic tape; Tremco Manufacturing Co., Cleveland.
9. Model of "Endless House," 1950; architect, Frederick J. Kiesler, New York; photographer, Percy Rainford.
10. Sketch of "Space House," 1934; architect, Frederick J. Kiesler, New York.
11. Full scale model of "Space House," 1934; architect, Frederick J. Kiesler, New York.
12. Model of "Dymaxion" House, 1927; designer, R. Buckminster Fuller, Forest Hills, New York.
13. Drawing of "Geodesic Skybreak Dwelling," 1949; designer, R. Buckminster Fuller. This version developed by a group of graduate students at the Massachusetts Institute of Technology, Department of Architecture, 1952.
14. Drawing of "Berm" House, 1942; architect, Frank Lloyd Wright.
15. Unfolding of "Acorn" House, Concord, Massachusetts, 1949; architects, Carl Koch and Associates, Cambridge, Massachusetts; builder, Acorn Houses, Inc., Concord, Massachusetts; photographer, Ezra Stoller; courtesy of Ezra Stoller.
16. Designer's own house, Venice, California, 1949; designer, Charles Eames; photographer, Peter Stackpole, *Life*.
17. Concrete "bubble" house, Hobe Sound, Florida, 1953; architect, Eliot Noyes, New Canaan, Connecticut; builder, Wallace Neff Airform Construction, Los Angeles, California.
18. Model of "Wonder Home," 1954; architect, Eliot Noyes, New Canaan, Connecticut; sponsor, General Electric Co.

19. Model of "spray form" concrete house, 1956; architect, John M. Johansen, New Canaan, Connecticut; sponsor, Atlas Cement Co.

20. Molded plastic "House of the Future," 1957, Anaheim, California; architects, Hamilton and Goody, Cambridge, Massachusetts; sponsor, Monsanto Chemical Company.

21. Architect's own house, Raleigh, North Carolina, 1954; architect, Eduardo Catalano, Cambridge, Massachusetts; photographer, Ezra Stoller; courtesy of Ezra Stoller.

22. Model for house of industrially produced units, 1958; architects, George Nelson and Gordon Chadwick, New York.

23. Model of courtyard type row housing, Carlsminde, Denmark, 1955; architect, Aarne Jacobsen, Copenhagen, Denmark; photographer, Strüwing.

24. Production of building panels, Acorn Houses, Inc., Concord, Massachusetts.

25. Panel package for the construction of one house; architects, Walter Gropius and Conrad Wachsmann, Cambridge, Massachusetts; builder, General Panel Corp., New York; photographer, Anna Wachsmann.

26. Air view of merchant builder's housing, Sunnyvale, California, 1957; builder, Branden Enterprises; photographer, Pacific Air Industries.

27. Levitt House Apartments, Whitestone, New York, 1957; builder, Levitt House, Inc.; photographer, Thomas Airviews.

28. Row housing, Don Mills, Ontario, Canada; architects, Henry Fliess and James A. Murray; photographer, Max Fleet; courtesy of Max Fleet.

29. Proposed redevelopment for Cincinnati, Ohio; architects, Carl Koch and Associates, Cambridge, Massachusetts; associate architects, James Allan and Associates, Cincinnati, Ohio; builder, Webb and Knapp Development Corp., New York.

30, 31, 32. Proposed redevelopment for Buffalo–West Seneca, New York; architects, Carl Koch and Associates; builder, Webb and Knapp Communities, Inc., New York.

33. Massachusetts Institute of Technology Solar House IV, Lexington, Massachusetts, 1958; architects, Bernard P. Spring and Robert Pelletier, Cambridge, Massachusetts; sponsor, Godfrey L. Cabot Fund; builder, H. Tobiason, Arlington, Massachusetts; photographer, Bernard P. Spring.

34. Laminated wood research house, Flintridge, California; architect, John C. Lindsay, Los Angeles, California; sponsor, Rilco Laminated Products, Inc., St. Paul, Minnesota; builder, Norwood and DeLonge, San Marino, California; photographer, Robert C. Cleveland.

35. House trailer production line, Spartan Aircraft Company, Tulsa, Oklahoma; photographer, Hopkins Photography Co.; courtesy of *Trailer Travel* magazine.

36. Cutaway view of 50- by 10-foot mobile home; photographer, Ralph Crane, *Life*.

37. Trailer park; photograph courtesy of *House & Home*.

38. Family living area, House of the Future (see photograph 20).

39. Model of experimental house, roof removed; architects, Carl Koch and Associates, Cambridge, Massachusetts; sponsor, National Steel Corp.

INDEX

About the authors . . .

Burnham Kelly teaches at M.I.T., where he has divided his time between housing research (former head of the Albert Farwell Bemis Foundation) and teaching city planning. A member of several special governmental review and legislative committees, he has been a consultant on planning and administration for New England towns and cities and for U.S. agencies. He is the author of the book, *The Prefabrication of Houses.*

Castle N. Day is employed in the firm of Touche, Niven, Bailey & Smart, public accountants, in New York City. He studied economics at Williams College and is a graduate of the industrial management program at M.I.T.

Albert G. H. Dietz has been teaching since 1934 in the Department of Building Engineering and Construction at M.I.T., where he is presently a professor. He took a leave of absence in 1942 to go to the Forest Products Laboratory as Senior Engineer (Consulting). At M.I.T. he directs the Plastics Research Laboratory, the Impact Program, and the Adhesives Laboratory, and is a member of the Solar Energy Committee. He is nationally known as a consultant on lumber design, wood products, building design, and construction. He is the author of the book *Dwelling House Construction.*

John T. Dunlop taught first at Stanford University and since 1938 at Harvard University, where he is now a Professor of Economics. He was chairman of the National Joint Board for the Settlement of Jurisdictional Disputes in the building and construction industry from 1948 to 1957, vice-chairman of the Boston Regional War Labor Board, a member of the Wage Adjustment Board, which had the responsibility of stabilizing wages during World War II, a consultant to the Office of Economic Stabilization and to the National Labor Relations Board, a member of the Atomic Energy Labor Relations Panel, a member of the board of inquiry for the Bituminous Coal Industry, and a public member of the Wage Stabilization Board. His book *Collective Bargaining: Principles and Cases* appeared in 1949.

Carl Koch is a practicing architect and one of the outstanding experts in the design of small houses. Head of the firm of Carl Koch & Associates and a director of Acorn Houses and Techbuilt, Inc., he has won many awards from architectural and industrial groups for libraries and office buildings as well as small houses and has served as consultant to Lustron, National Steel, and others. He is the author of the book *At Home with Tomorrow.*

400

James A. Murray was chief of the lime and gypsum section of the National Bureau of Standards in Washington, D.C., for four years, and director of research for the Warner Company of Philadelphia for 18 years. Since 1948 he has been Associate Professor of Materials at M.I.T. As a consultant in materials construction, he has worked for Arthur D. Little, Inc., in conjunction with the government of Iraq, and for various lime and cement companies. He is the author of several technical papers, a member of the American Concrete Institute, the Building Research Institute, and the American Society for Testing Materials committees on mortars and concrete, and chairman of the ASTM committee on lime.

Hideo Sasaki taught at the University of Illinois and worked with architectural firms in site planning in Boston, Chicago, and New York. He is presently an Associate Professor of Landscape Architecture at the Harvard Graduate School of Design, where he has been teaching for the past five years. He is principal in the firm of Sasaki and Walker, landscape architects and site planners.

Bernard P. Spring worked in architectural offices in New York and as a structural designer for the U.S. Navy Department. In 1953 he was awarded a Fulbright fellowship to Helsinki, Finland, where he taught housing and design at the Royal Academy of Fine Arts before returning to teach architectural design at M.I.T., and work on research projects on the perceptual form of the city, the architectural use of plastics, and the heating of houses with solar energy.